# LATERAL LINE
# DETECTORS

# LATERAL LINE
# DETECTORS

*Proceedings of a Conference*
*held at Yeshiva University, New York*
*April 16–18, 1966*

EDITED BY

## PHYLLIS H. CAHN
*Stern College, Yeshiva University, New York*

## Indiana University Press
Bloomington      London

*The "lateral line world" has suffered a grievous loss in the sudden death of Dr. Willem van Bergeijk. His provocative brilliance sparked and challenged many of us. Future studies on lateral line function will reflect the inspiration gained from his contributions, and will serve him as a fitting memorial.*

# PREFACE

The lateral line sensory system of fishes has challenged investigators for over 100 years, but its primary function still provokes active controversy. Renewed interest in this system arose during World War II as a result of the increased development and use of sonar techniques. Since then there has been an upsurge of studies on the lateral line, and the refinements in electronics, electron microscopy, and other physical techniques now available have aided these endeavors.

Numerous functions have been attributed to the lateral line, and investigators have engaged in a semantic battle over the kinds of stimuli detected by these versatile sense cells. The major conflict has concerned the relative contribution of propagated pressure waves and hydrodynamic displacement toward the stimulation of the basic end organ. Since every pressure wave is accompanied by water displacement, the experimental separation of the two phenomena is almost impossible to achieve.

Many biologists engaged in studies of lateral line function sought the counsel of engineers and physicists who specialize in hydrodynamics and underwater acoustics. We express our gratitude to them for their help. They have led us, however, to a dilemma: We are confronted not only by our own biological problems but also by the vacillations of the theorists of underwater sound and fluid dynamics.

This impasse provided incentive for a long-needed interdisciplinary conference on lateral line detectors, where it was hoped that all the disputes would be aired. Thanks to the financial support of the National Science Foundation and to the sponsorship of Yeshiva University, this conference took place in April 1966. The Bio-Instrumentation Advisory Council of the American Institute of Biological Sciences supported the attendance of several engineers and physicists.

This was the first conference to be devoted exclusively to this sensory system. Aspects of lateral line function were considered at the Animal Orientation Conference held in 1953 (Office of Naval Research) and at the Marine Bio-Acoustics Symposia in 1963 and 1966 (Office of Naval Research), but at these meetings the lateral line was only briefly considered.

The chapters that follow reflect the principal current trends of lateral line research. The major goal of the conference was two fold:

v

to evaluate the experiments done in the past in the light of our current knowledge of underwater vibrations and, in consideration of the more sophisticated instrumentation now available for their study, to define clearly and agree on the physical characteristics of the stimuli to be used in future studies.

Organization of a conference of this scope requires motivation, encouragement, and endless cooperation and help. The prime source of inspiration that led to this symposium derived from many years of association with Dr. Charles M. Breder, Jr., Curator Emeritus of Ichthyology at the American Museum of Natural History. Much encouragement and advice were given by my friend and long-time colleague, Dr. Evelyn Shaw, Associate Curator of Animal Behavior at the American Museum of Natural History. And finally, at all the administrative and academic levels of Stern College, Yeshiva University, there prevailed an *esprit de corps* that promoted the successful achievement of the conference and this publication.

PHYLLIS H. CAHN

*Department of Biology*
*Stern College*
*Yeshiva University*
*New York, New York*

# FOREWORD

I hate to be involved in conferences and symposia. If I go, I have a feeling of guilt because I should have spent my time reading the reprints on my desk. If I do not go, I may have missed something very important. There are several good reasons for not going to a symposium:

1. Many of the discussions are out of my line of interest.

2. There is seldom time to talk to or even meet the people who work on a specific problem.

3. There is always someone who can answer and discuss almost any question. That leaves me in a difficult position, since in general I can see only a partial answer after the whole symposium is over.

4. There are some subjects which cannot be discussed in three minutes since it takes longer to define the question.

Many simple technical difficulties are also disturbing.

5. Some slides are so overcrowded with data written in small letters that they are difficult to read.

6. Many slides are presented so rapidly that I do not even remember whether a curve went up from right to left, as they usually do, or whether by chance it went down.

7. In general the chairs in the lecture room are of physiologically poor construction, in spite of the fact that human anatomy was already well described by Vesalius in his *Fabrica* in the sixteenth century.

On the other hand, there are reasons for attending a conference:

1. A well-known physicist told me, "But you have to meet the people whose work you read, because the expression on their faces may help to understand the published text better." I do not think this holds today since most of us wear masks anyhow.

2. A better reason is that a conference can give a sort of cross section of the continuous flow of research at a certain instant. It is like a flashlight picture of the development of a particular subject. It is difficult to make sure sometimes that this flash information is correct. It is always very difficult to find out what happens in a movie by looking at the still pictures in the entrance—but I am sure some movie experts do better than I do.

3. Some conferences are the meeting place of the young and the older scientists working in a common field. This can contribute very

much to producing continuity in research. If the meeting is timed correctly and the step between the two groups is not too large, it may be of utmost importance.

4. There is nothing more pleasant than to meet young scientists full of hopes, even when it is so difficult to give these young people something they can use. There is no question in my mind that the purest pleasure for a scientist is to give.

5. Sometimes we can give or take home something without knowing it, simply because the conference as a whole subconsciously breeds in us a research interest and direction, which is much more long-lasting and important than some details under discussion.

Concerning pure technical advantage, it is possible to see a large number of color slides at a meeting (and we have seen many at this conference), which could hardly be published because of the expense. And we also have a chance to see some motion pictures of experiments.

It would not be difficult to make either of these lists longer; but pros and cons compared, everyone who attended the Conference on Lateral Line Detectors will agree that it was a good idea to participate.

Already at the beginning, the discussion of Dr. Lowenstein's excellent paper brought every one *in medias res*. Immediately the question of the definition of a physical stimulus was discussed. It is a major problem for the study of any type of sensory transducer or detector in the whole field of sensory sciences. This is a well-defined borderline where the physicist meets the physiologist, and together they try to decrease the no-man's land of mutual suspicion. I think that the lateral line is an excellent subject for this endeavor. And perhaps there is a possibility of profound progress.

If we take into account that inhibition is present in the nervous system, descriptions of the nature of the stimulus become difficult, since a large part of the physically present stimuli may be discarded by the nervous system. Therefore the physical stimulus can only be determined by taking neurophysiological activity into account. We tried to use electrophysiology for this purpose, and much progress has been made in this direction. But there is still some difficulty in real cooperation between physicist and physiologist. An exchange of reprints does not seem to be enough. They should almost stand side by side at the laboratory table—or even better, should be combined in the same person. Certainly the conference proved to be a very important step in this direction.

An even more important question is the borderline between anatomy and histology, on the one hand, and functional anatomy, on the other. These seem to be almost the same as long as figures are concerned, but the way of thinking can be quite different. Functional anatomy is very close to physiology. It is really a differentiation between the tissue structures we consider important for the transmission of a stimulus and those structures which we could, in a way, consider supporting tissue. Here again I think that the lateral line has many advantages compared with the other sense organs. In many fish some of the bones are thin and soft, so that no decalcification is needed. This makes histology simple and reduces the distortion of the tissues during the process of preparing microscope slides. From the point of view of surgery, regulation of the blood flow rate is not so important a consideration as in higher vertebrates, which again simplifies the experimental conditions. Although it was not explicitly stated, my impression was that the conference pointed out this possibility very clearly, and that this was largely due to the well-organized structure of the program.

When thinking about the lateral line system in fish, I always found myself starting with a physical stimulus, then going over to physiology, from there to gross anatomy and histology, and then back to physics again, and finally trying to make both ends of this ring fit. A decade ago this looked to me like a vicious circle, but today with the help of electronmicroscopy and electrophysiology, some of the statements have become convincing, and perhaps the lateral line system will be one of the first where the transducer problem will be understood.

GEORG VON BÉKÉSY

*Laboratory of Sensory Science*
*University of Hawaii*
*Honolulu, Hawaii*

# MEMBERS OF THE CONFERENCE
# AND CONTRIBUTORS

EUGENE AGALIDES, General Dynamics Corporation, Rochester, New York

VERNON ALBERS, Ordnance Research Laboratory, Pennsylvania State University, University Station, Pennsylvania

HOWARD BALDWIN, Sensory Systems Laboratory, Tucson, Arizona

ARNOLD BANNER, Institute of Marine Science, University of Miami, Miami, Florida

BENJAMIN B. BAUER, Acoustics and Magnetics Department, CBS Laboratories, Stamford, Connecticut

GEORG VON BÉKÉSY, Laboratory of Sensory Science, University of Hawaii, Honolulu, Hawaii

MICHAEL V. L. BENNETT, Albert Einstein College of Medicine, Yeshiva University, New York, New York

WILLEM A. VAN BERGEIJK, Center for Neural Sciences, Indiana University, Bloomington, Indiana

PHYLLIS H. CAHN, Department of Biology, Stern College, Yeshiva University, New York, and Graduate Department of Marine Science, Long Island University, Greenvale, New York

HARRY CHARIPPER, Department of Biology, New York University, New York, New York

BERNARD COHEN, Mt. Sinai Hospital, New York, New York

DAVID CUSHING, Ministry of Agriculture, Fisheries, and Food, Fisheries Laboratory, Lowestoft, Suffolk, England

SVEN DIJKGRAAF, Laboratory of Comparative Physiology, University of Utrecht, Utrecht, The Netherlands

JOSEPHINE DOHERTY, National Science Foundation, Washington, D.C.

LARRY DUNN, Graduate School of Oceanography, University of Rhode Island, Kingston, Rhode Island

PER S. ENGER, Institute of Physiology, University of Oslo, Oslo, Norway

PIERCE FENHAGEN, University of Maryland, College Park, Maryland

JIM FISH, Graduate School of Oceanography, University of Rhode Island, Kingston, Rhode Island

DAN FISHER, Communications Division, Sperry Rand Corporation, Great Neck, New York

JAMES FITZGERALD, Fitzgerald and Associates, Annapolis, Maryland

ÅKE FLOCK, Sensory and Perceptual Processes Department, Bell Telephone Laboratories, Inc., Murray Hill, New Jersey

IRWIN S. FROST, Communications Division, Sperry Rand Corporation, Great Neck, New York

MASARU FUJIYA, Naikai Regional Fisheries Research Laboratory, Hiroshima, Japan

PERRY GILBERT, Department of Zoology, Cornell University, Ithaca, New York

PETER GÖRNER, Zoological Institute, Free University, Berlin, Germany

HARRY GRUNDFEST, Dept. of Neurophysiology, Columbia University, College of Physicians and Surgeons, New York, New York

SAM HA, Institute of Marine Science, University of Miami, Miami, Florida

Roy Harden-Jones, Ministry of Agriculture, Fisheries, and Food, Lowestoft Laboratories, Lowestoft, Suffolk, England

Gerard G. Harris, Sensory and Perceptual Processes Department, Bell Telephone Laboratories, Inc., Murray Hill, New Jersey

Helen Hayes, Oceanic Biology, Office of Naval Research, Department of the Navy, Washington, D.C.

Frank Hester, Fishery-Oceanography Center and Tuna Resources Laboratory, Bureau of Commercial Fisheries, La Jolla, California

Robert Iverson, Tuna Behavior Division, Bureau of Commercial Fisheries, Honolulu, Hawaii

Tamotsu Iwai, Department of Fisheries, Kyoto University, Maizuru, Japan

Kenneth John, Department of Biology, Franklin and Marshall College, Lancaster, Pennsylvania

James I. Kendall, Department of Zoology, University of Hawaii, Honolulu, Hawaii

Jan W. Kuiper, Department of Biophysics, University of Groningen, Groningen, The Netherlands

Toshiro Kuroki, Faculty of Fisheries, Hokkaido University, Hakodate, Japan

E. Rune Lindgren, Department of Engineering Science and Mechanics, University of Florida, Gainesville, Florida

Hans Lissmann, Department of Zoology, Cambridge University, Cambridge, England

Robert K. Liu, Department of Zoology, University of California, Los Angeles, California

Otto Lowenstein, Department of Zoology and Comparative Physiology, University of Birmingham, Birmingham, England

Dick Lund, Department of Vertebrate Paleontology, American Museum of Natural History, New York, New York

R. Stuart Mackay, Division of Medical Physics, University of California, Berkeley, California; and Boston University Medical School, Boston, Massachusetts

Frank Mandriota, Department of Psychology, City University of New York, New York

N. B. Marshall, Department of Ichthyology, British Museum of Natural History, London, England

Robert Mathewson, Lerner Marine Laboratory, Bimini, Bahamas

James Moulton, Department of Biology, Bowdoin College, Brunswick, Maine

Richard W. Murray, Department of Zoology and Comparative Physiology, University of Birmingham, Birmingham, England

Arthur Myrberg, Institute of Marine Science, University of Miami, Miami, Florida

Donald Nelson, Department of Biology, California State College, Long Beach, California

George Offutt, Graduate School of Oceanography, University of Rhode Island, Kingston, Rhode Island

Bori Olla, Sandy Hook Marine Laboratory, Bureau of Sport Fisheries and Wildlife, Highlands, New Jersey

Antares Parvulescu, Hudson Laboratories, Columbia University, Dobbs Ferry, New York

Arthur Popper, Department of Biology, Queens College, Flushing, New York

GEORGE RAND, Communications Division, Sperry Rand Corporation, Great Neck, New York

ROBERT RASMUSSEN, Department of Physics, Scripps Institution of Oceanography, San Diego, California

STEVE REBACH, Graduate School of Oceanography, University of Rhode Island, Kingston, Rhode Island

MOE ROSEN, U.S. Naval Ordnance Test Station, Pasadena, California

IAN RUSSELL, Department of Zoology, University of British Columbia, Vancouver, Canada

HANS SCHNEIDER, Zoophysiological Institut, University of Tübingen, Tübingen, Germany

ERICH SCHWARTZ, Zoophysiological Institut, University of Tübingen, Tübingen, Germany

EVELYN SHAW, Department of Animal Behavior, American Museum of Natural History, New York, New York

JOHN SHELBOURN, Graduate School of Oceanography, University of Rhode Island, Kingston, Rhode Island

JULIUS SIEKMANN, College of Engineering, University of Florida, Gainesville, Florida

LEO STAMLER, Consolidated Airborne Systems, New Hyde Park, New York

JOHN STEINBERG, Institute of Marine Science, University of Miami, Miami, Florida

E. E. SUCKLING, Department of Physiology, State University of New York, Downstate Medical Center, Brooklyn, New York

JOAN A. SUCKLING, Department of Biological Sciences, Hunter College of the City University of New York, New York, New York

NOBUO SUGA, Department of Neurosciences, University of California, School of Medicine, San Diego, California

THOMAS SZABO, Centre National de la Recherche Scientifique, Paris, France

WILLIAM TAVOLGA, Department of Animal Behavior, American Museum of Natural History, New York, New York

DONALD TEAS, Department of Audiology, Eye and Ear Hospital of Pittsburgh, Pittsburgh, Pennsylvania

ALBERT L. TESTER, Department of Zoology, University of Hawaii, Honolulu, Hawaii

ROBERT VALENTI, Department of Biology, New York University, New York, New York

JOHN VAN DER WALKER, Columbia Fisheries Program, Bureau of Commercial Fisheries, Portland, Oregon

WILLIAM D. VOIERS, Sperry Rand Research Center, Sudbury, Massachusetts

THEODORE J. WALKER, Department of Marine Biology, Scripps Institution of Oceanography, La Jolla, California

VLADIMIR WALTERS, Department of Zoology, University of California, Los Angeles, California

BURTON A. WEISS, Department of Psychology, University of South Florida, Tampa, Florida

GEORGE WILLIAMS, Department of Biology, State University of New York, Stony Brook, New York

HOWARD WINN, Narragansett Marine Laboratory and Graduate School of Oceanography, University of Rhode Island, Kingston, Rhode Island

# CONTENTS

# LATERAL LINE
# DETECTORS

# I HISTORICAL AND MORPHOLOGICAL ASPECTS

LATERAL LINE DETECTORS (P. Cahn, ed.), 3–12, © 1967 Indiana University Press

# 1 THE CONCEPT OF THE ACOUSTICOLATERAL SYSTEM

OTTO LOWENSTEIN

Department of Zoology and Comparative Physiology
University of Birmingham
Birmingham, England

It is both an honor and a great pleasure to give the opening address of this conference. The organizer has done well in arranging this address to be given by someone who has never worked directly on the lateral line, because there is always an obvious temptation for one more closely involved to anticipate controversy. I, on the other hand, can carry out this task with complete detachment. At the same time, my long association with studies on the vestibular end organs of the eighth nerve has prompted me to see similarities, not only in fundamental design but also in the mode of functioning. This may enable me to say things in support of useful generalizations pertaining to the interpretation of lateral line function.

It might be interesting to start by indulging in a little historical exercise. I should like to trace this line of development back to its beginning, to the concept of the close association of ear and lateral line in a common acousticolateral complex.

The man who was primarily responsible for showing the close neurological association of the lateral line organs with the ear was Dr. P. Mayser (1882), Assistant Physician at the County Psychiatric Hospital in Munich. His paper contained a critical survey of the literature, and in it he worried about the confusion in the tracing and naming of cranial nerves and their various branches. He studied the cyprinoids, and in these the eighth nerve is a mighty nerve. Its nucleus is essentially the so-called "acoustic tubercle," a swelling of the lateral wall of the fourth ventricle, which lies between the cerebellum and the confluent lobes of trigeminus and vagus, and slightly above the prominent secondary vagus-trigeminus tract. The latter forms part of the base of the medulla in this region. The tubercle consists of neurons, fiber tracts, and blood vessels. The neurons are mostly rather small, and their processes form a network. Mayser distinguished a large anterior and a smaller posterior root of the eighth nerve. On the homologization of this smaller root rests the whole concept of the acousticolateral complex.

Mayser was the first to claim that this smaller acoustical root was not, in fact, the lateralis branch of the vagus. However, the state of general confusion with respect to the designation of cranial nerves, their roots, and associated nuclei was such, and the methods available for the accurate tracing of nerve tracts so primitive, that Mayser's claims—although they may, in the long run, have proved to be correct—were not justified by weight of evidence. However prophetically true the statements made by uncannily clear-sighted workers, the evidence was often very meager indeed. In Mayser's day, the microtome had just been introduced, and carmine staining was in general used almost exclusively in conjunction with rather thick sections. For certain purposes, this is not a bad method at all, but it won't do for the minute analysis of origin and course of true fiber tracts. Whatever the evidence, and however great the uncertainty of his day, even with regard to such major nerves as the trigeminal, facial, glossopharyngeal, and, above all, the vagus, Mayser's claim about the origin of the whole of the lateralis innervation from the acoustic tubercle—irrespective of its later course, be it through the fifth, seventh, or tenth nerve—was taken seriously. This claim appeared to Mayser to support the idea that the lateral line canal system, only recently graduated from pure slime canals to the seat of well-defined sense endings, should be considered an accessory *auditory* organ. Leydig (1850) had described the lateral line sense endings much more fittingly as organs of touch. We are confronted here with one of those common cases of invasion of semantics into science. When Mayser found that the innervation of the lateral line organs stemmed from the acoustic tubercle and that the size and appearance of what he called the "broad" nerve fibers were similar in both the lateral line and the "acoustic" nerves, the acoustic (i.e., *hearing*) function of the lateral line organs was a foregone conclusion. It is remarkable that this happened in 1881, despite the fact that the discovery of the balancing function of the semicircular canals by Flourens had been published in 1842. In fact, Mayser refers to the semicircular canals as the "Bogengänge of the Gehörorgan," the "canals of the hearing organ."

Stannius, in his work on the "peripheral nervous system" (1842), described the lateral line organs of the head as innervated by "broad" fibers in the second branch of the vagus, which Mayser homologized with the posterior branch of the acoustic nerve. Both share with the anterior and main branch of the acoustic nerve the characteristic that neuron cell bodies are found in their course, a feature reported to be absent from true trigeminus pathways.

To do Mayser justice, it must be noted that at the end of this relevant section of his paper he says: "Thus, I pronounce the opinion that the mucous canals of the fishes are nothing else than an accessory hearing organ spread over the whole body surface. I am not wont to maintain that it elicits sensation of sound, but its function will be found to fall within the realm of this still imperfectly understood sense of hearing." With this formulation of Mayser nobody can quarrel, for who could have known the vicissitudes that were to stand in the way of a clear understanding of the range of function of both the labyrinth and the lateral line organs in the decades to come.

A year later, Bodenstein (1882) published a paper on the lateral line canal of *Cottus gobio.* He based his work on the findings of Leydig (1895), Schulze (1870), and Merkel (1880), and subjected the organ to a thorough scrutiny of the relationship of the canal system to the surrounding skin, of the nature of the contained fluid, the dimensions of the canals, and the relationship between canals and scales. In his description of the sense endings, he confirmed Schulze's discovery of the cupula, which he called a thin membrane, and recognized that the fixed and stained object was certain to have been thoroughly changed in extent and appearance as compared with the "fresh" state.

Bodenstein compared the lateral line end organs with the end organs of the labyrinth and made special reference to the presence of homogeneous secretions that covered the apex of the sensory hillocks in both. In this he concurred with Leydig and Schulze. Bodenstein fully accepted Mayser's definition of the lateral line organ as an accessory auditory organ, both on the basis of its innervation and on that of the striking similarity between the sensory endings.

Herrick (1897), in a paper on the cranial nerve components of teleosts, confirmed the common origin of the innervation of the lateral line organ and the labyrinth from the acoustic tubercle. He stated that "the coarse-fibered nerve of the lateral line [here he is referring to the tenth cranial nerve component] arises farther cephalad than any of the vagus roots, in connection with the eighth cranial nerve. It and its ganglion are distinct from the vagus throughout." He noted, further, that "the dorsal lateral line root [of the seventh cranial nerve] passes from the tuberculum acusticum into a distinct ganglion, thence in two branches to the supra- and infra-orbital lateral canals (ramus ophthalmicus sup. VII and ramus buccalis), and the ventral lateral line root [of the seventh cranial nerve] arises in intimate union with the dorsal root, but after its exit it remains distinct. It has a distinct ganglion and all its fibers pass into the ramus hyomandibularis VII." These statements are based on the situation analyzed by serial sections in the atherinid *Menidia*.

A further potent reason for the close relationship between the lateral line and the labyrinth was based on embryological findings. Making reference to an earlier paper by Mitrophanow (1893) based on findings in cyclostomes, elasmobranchs, teleosts, and amphibians, Wilson and Mattocks (1897) described the early states in the formation of a common rudiment (anlage) in the early salmon embryo.

About the twelfth day the embryonic shield thickens into a neural keel. Immediately at each side of this is left a comparatively thick streak of ectoderm, which extends through the anterior two-thirds of the embryo. It is the lateral sensory rudiment (anlage). Toward the end of the thirteenth day, the middle portion of the anlage begins to be invaginated to form the auditory sac. The auditory sac comes thus to lie between a preauditory and a postauditory group of cells which give rise to the infra- and supraorbital canals of the head and to the lateral line of the trunk, respectively (Wilson and Mattocks, 1897).

Ayers (1892) wrote a remarkable paper entitled "Vertebrate Cephalogenesis" that contained, besides lengthy quotations from contemporary publications, a lot of loose ad hoc speculation about auditory function. It aimed at establishing that not only the whole labyrinth, including semicircular canals and otolith organs, but also the lateral line sense organs have an acoustic function. This is the more remarkable because it was written fifty years after Flourens's discovery of the equilibrium function of the semicircular canals (1842) and shortly after Breuer's fundamental work on the canals and on the otolith organs was published (1889, 1891). Ayers made the phylogenetic prophecy that the future inner ear will not retain much else than the cochlea. The semicircular canals will disappear, the maculae of the sacculi and utriculi will gradually atrophy, and their chambers will become much modified or entirely aborted like the lagena in mammals and the "papilla abortiva (macula neglecta)." All these structures will perhaps appear fleetingly during embryological development, much to the mystification of later embryologists!

I mention Ayers's work not only as a curio but also because it has been used as evidence for an acoustic function of the lateral line organs. Ayers stated: "Every sense organ in the ear executes an auditory function, as regards essentials, in the same manner as its prototype, the lateral line sense organ; there exist between the auditory sense organs differences only in degree, not in kind, of the function observed."

For a more dispassionate review of the early literature, one should turn to Cole (1898). Here, too, Mayser's idea of the lateral line organs being accessory auditory organs was discussed, but Cole mentioned, with some undertone of regret, that Leydig, who at first thought that the lateral line was closely related to the ear, later recanted and described it as a tactile end organ of a so-called "sixth sense," which had nothing to do whatsoever with the auditory system innervated by the eighth nerve.

Schulze (1870) expressed the view that the lateral line canals were affected by water movements and low-frequency water waves. I don't want to get mixed up unduly in present-day controversy, but I should not be surprised to find in this room today some who would not quarrel with Mayser's or Leydig's or Schulze's postulate of an ancillary auditory function of the lateral line. I leave it to Dr. Dijkgraaf to sort out Schulze's water movements and low-frequency water waves.

Meanwhile, it may be amusing to have a look at the whole range of functions that at one time or other have been attributed to the lateral line. I may be wrong, but it is my belief that nobody has ever claimed a visual function for the lateral line.

There has been speculation that, in view of the similarity between the hair cells of the acousticolateral organs and the gustatory cells, the lateral line organ may be an organ of the chemical sense. Merkel (1880) rejected this in favor of a mechanical function. Hofer (1908) rejected a straightforward tactile function and denied that the lateral line responded to changes in hydrostatic pressure or to vibration. Breuer (1891) thought that the canals might record water velocity, and Lee (1894-95) claimed an equilibrium function for them, assuming that they registered relative water movements during rotational displacement of the fish body.

Finally, Hoagland (1933a, b, c, d) found in electrophysiological experiments that the lateral line sense endings responded to pressure, to ripples in the water, to irregular currents, to the active and passive movement of the trunk, to vibratory stimuli from tuning forks, and to changes in temperature between 0 and 28°C. Hoagland postulated an inhibitory effect of lateral line inflow on the responses initiated by organs in the skin and ear.

The lateral line also was considered to be the rheotactic sense organ responsible for station-keeping by fish in streams and rivers. This hypothesis was rejected on experimental grounds by Lyon (1904) and later by Dijkgraaf (1933), but has been revitalized by Harden-Jones (1962).

I have not said anything about the ampullae of Lorenzini, Savi's vesicles, and mormyromasts, all reputed to belong in the fold of the acousticolateral system. Each of these organ systems will be dealt with by people with first-hand experience from experimental studies.

Let us now consider those features of structure and function in which the vestibular sense endings and the lateral line organs resemble each other most closely: this involves the hair cell itself and the unit impulse response to adequate mechanical stimulation.

When considering the unit impulse response first, the most striking feature in the behavior of the hair cell is the existence of basic activity in the absence of overt stimulation. This activity consists of a more or less regular low-frequency impulse discharge. In vestibular endings, especially in the semicircular canals, the basic discharge frequency is of clockwork regularity, generally fluctuating not more than ±4%. These data were derived from open-loop experiments, in which any efferent innervation, if present, was not operative. The basic discharge in the lateral line endings is less regular.

When Hoagland (1933a–d) first described this as a so-called "spontaneous" discharge, he was unable to attribute a specific function to it, and he had to make an effort to convince himself that it was not an artifact. One factor that convinced him of its bona fide physiological importance was the fact that its frequency could be influenced by temperature but was inhibited by anesthetics, and that rough treatment was not its cause, for this also abolished it. The response to stimulation then consisted in a change in the frequency of this spontaneous activity. Hoagland thought that the spontaneous activity was associated with ciliary motion of the hair processes of the sensory cells. It is clear that Hoagland overestimated the frequency of the spontaneous discharge in single units, as he worked exclusively on multifiber preparations. In the end, he postulated that besides the spontaneously active units, whose activity was modified by temperature, there were others, responsible for the monitoring of pressure, that may function as proprioceptors in the control of swimming movements. No clear functional picture emerged from Hoagland's work.

Sand (1937) was the first to analyze a lateral line sense organ quantitatively, by the isolation of single units in the perfused hyomandibular canal of the ray (*Raja clavata*). Flow of perfusion fluid in two opposite directions produced increase or decrease in discharge activity according to the direction of the flow. In some cases, single receptors were excited, and in others they were inhibited, by flow in a certain direction. How well this result can be tallied with the recent ultrastructural findings with regard to the functional polarization of the hair cells in the sense endings will be dealt with by others during this symposium. The basic activity was described by Sand as a fitting condition for such two-way modulation. Sand's paper on the lateral line appeared a year after our joint publication on the activity of the horizontal semicircular canal in the dogfish, where the full functional implications of "spontaneous activity" in mechanoreceptors were set out for the first time (Lowenstein and Sand, 1936). In fact, Sand had worked on the lateral line for quite some time when we joined forces to investigate the electrophysiology of the semicircular canals. He, like Hoagland, had been rather puzzled by the spontaneous discharge, which Ross (1936) in his electrophysiological work on the eighth nerve of the frog had considered to be very probably an artifact. When finally seen in the semicircular canals of the labyrinth, the full functional meaning of the spontaneous activity fell into place. Here in the semicircular canal we found a receptor in which endolymph fluid movement in two opposite directions gave rise to a uniformly directed response, excitatory only to one and inhibitory only to the opposite stimulus. This discovery cleared up a long-debated question in labyrinth physiology: namely, whether semicircular canals are, in fact, uni- or bidirectional receptors for angular acceleration. At the same time, the spontaneous activity could, in the labyrinth, also account for the well-known tonus asymmetries and forced movements occurring after unilateral elimination of a canal. It was the obvious source of vestibular tonus.

Having learned this lesson from the labyrinth, Sand could now see the results gained in his experiments on the lateral line, and see them in their proper perspective, as reviewed in his masterful paper of 1937.

I have gone into this historical detail chiefly to illustrate the close relationship between labyrinth and lateral line, at least as far as the fundamental mechanism of mechanoelectric transduction is concerned.

Once again, much later, the labyrinth served as a guide in the interpretation of lateral line function. This was when the functional significance of the ultrastructural polarization of the hair cells was described (Lowenstein and Wersäll, 1959). The association between kinocilial orientation and excitatory-inhibitory deformation of the hair bundle could be ascertained with a high degree of confidence in the case of the semicircular canal, for which all other operative parameters were well established by previous electrophysiological work (Lowenstein, 1936; Lowenstein, Osborne, and Wersäll, 1964).

We have reached the present, and the present will be dealt with by a galaxy of experts. It will be left to them to carry forward the differential functional diagnosis with respect to the various constituents of the lateral line complex, however much the actual receptor elements, during evolution, may have become specialized and different in structure and auxiliary equipment—in some cases, beyond recognition. I am sure, however, that the concept of the acousticolateral system, though the source of many wrong generalizations, has, on the whole, been of considerable and heuristic value.

REFERENCES

Ayers, H. (1892). Vertebrate Cephalogenesis. II. A contribution to the morphology of the vertebrate ear, with a reconsideration of its functions. *J. Morphol.* 6, 1.
Bodenstein, E. (1882). Der Seitenkanal von *Cottus gobio*. Z. *Wiss. Zool.* 37, 121.
Breuer, J. (1889). Neue Versuche an den Ohrbogengängen. *Pfluegers Arch. Ges. Physiol.* 44, 135.
——— (1891). Über die Funktion der Otolithenapparate. *Pfluegers Arch. Ges. Physiol.* 48, 195.
Cole, F. J. (1898). Observations on the structure and morphology of the cranial nerves and lateral sense organs of fishes, with special reference to the genus *Gadus. Trans. Liverpool Biol. Soc.* 7, 228.
Dijkgraaf, S. (1933). Untersuchungen über die Funktion der Seitenorgane an Fischen. Z. *Vergleich. Physiol.* 20, 162.
Flourens, P. (1842). Recherches expérimentales sur les propriétés et les functions du système nerveux dans les animaux vertébrés. Paris.
Harden-Jones, F. R. (1963). The reaction of fish to moving backgrounds. *J. Exptl. Biology*, 40, 437.
Herrick, C. J. (1897). The cranial nerve components of teleosts. *Anat. Anz.* 13, 425.
Hoagland, H. (1933a). Electrical responses from the lateral line nerves of catfish. *J. Gen. Physiol.* 16, 695.
——— (1933b). Quantitative analysis of responses from lateral line nerves of fishes. II. *J. Gen. Physiol.* 16, 715.
——— (1933c). Electrical responses from lateral line nerves of fishes. III. *J. Gen. Physiol.* 17, 77.
——— (1933d). Electrical responses from the lateral line nerves of fishes. IV. The repetitive discharge. *J. Gen. Physiol.* 17, 195.
——— (1934). Electrical responses from the lateral line nerves of fishes. V. Responses in the central nervous system. *J. Gen. Physiol.* 18, 89.
Hofer, B. (1908). Studien über die Hautsinnesorgane der Fische. I. Die Funktion der Seitenorgane bei den Fischen. *Ber. Kgl. Bayer. Biol. Versuchssta. Munchen.* 1, 115.
Lee, F. S. (1894). A study of the sense of equilibrium in fishes. I. *J. Physiol.* (*London*) 15, 311.
Leydig, F. (1850). Über die Schleimkanäle der Knochenfische. *Müller's Arch. Anat. Physiol.* 170-181.
——— (1894-1895). A study of the sense of equilibrium in fishes. II. *J. Physiol.* (*London*) 17, 192.
——— (1895). Integument und Hautsinnesorgane der Knochenfische. *Zool. Jahrb. Abt. Anat. Ontog.* 8, 1.
Lowenstein, O. E., and A. Sand (1936). The activity of the horizontal semicircular canal of the dogfish, *Scyllium canicula*. *J. Exptl. Biol.* 13, 416.

————, and J. Wersäll (1959). A functional interpretation of the electron-microscopic structure of the sensory hairs in the cristae of the elasmobranch, *Raja clavata*, in terms of directional sensitivity. *Nature (London)* 184, 1807.

————, M. P. Osborne, and J. Wersäll (1964). Structure and innervation of the sensory epithelia of the labyrinth in the Thornback ray (*Raja clavata*). *Proc. Roy. Soc. (London)* B160, 1.

Lyon, E. P. (1904). On rheotropism. I. Rheotropism in fishes. *Am. J. Physiol. (London)* 12, 149.

Mayser, P. (1882). Vergleichena anatomische Studien über das Gehirn der Knochenfische mit besonderer Berücksichtigung der Cyprinoiden. *Z. Wiss. Zool.* 36, 259.

Merkel, F. (1880). Über die Endigungen der sensiblen Nerven in der Haut der Wirbelthiere. *Rostock* 25, 1.

Mitrophanow, P. (1890). Über die erste Anlage des Gehörorganes bei niederen Wirbelthieren. *Biol. Central.* 10, 190.

Ross, D. A. (1936). Electrical studies on the frog's labyrinth. *J. Physiol. (London)* 86, 117.

Sand, A. (1937). The mechanism of the lateral sense organs of fishes. *Proc. Roy. Soc. (London)* B123, 472.

Schulze, F. E. (1870). Ueber die Sinnesorgane der Seitenlinie bei Fischen und Amphibien. *Arch. Mikroskop. Anat.* 6, 62.

Stannius, H. (1842). Ueber das peripherische Nervensystem des Dorsches. *Gadus callarias. Müller's Arch. Anat. Physiol.* 338.

Wilson, H. V., and J. E. Mattocks (1897). The lateral sensory anlage in the salmon. *Anat. Anz.* 13, 658.

## COMMENTS

The major comments were concerned with the following question: Can the lateral line be considered an acoustic organ, or is it more a hydrodynamic turbulence detector?

KUIPER: I would like to remark that even if there is some physiological similarity between organs, and if there is some common innervation between them, this does not mean nor imply that the organs are the same functionally. The lateral line organ should not be considered an acoustical organ. It is much more worthwhile to think of the lateral line as a system made up of sense cells stimulated in a similar way to those in the semicircular canals and cochlea, but to leave the similarity at this point.

LOWENSTEIN: This kind of a discussion can involve us in the dangerous circular argument about what is an acoustic organ. The celebrated answer is "an acoustic organ is an organ that serves hearing, and hearing is the perception of mechanical events by an acoustic organ."

KUIPER: When a biologist looks up the definition of sound in a physics book, he may find sound defined as "those waveforms which are detected by the ear." This leads to the same argument: "What is an ear?" I personally define sound as consisting of compression waves. Compression waves are waveforms transported through material over a long distance. This distance is much longer than the length of the lateral line.

SUCKLING: It appears that our idea of hearing is something that belongs to humans. The lateral line may detect vibrations, water movement, or a combination of these by a totally different mechanism than what we suppose. In fact, there exists the possibility that the lateral line may perceive the entire spectrum from the tactile sense to hearing.

LOWENSTEIN: We cannot say that hearing is a definition just for humans. We know that fish hear, and that fish have pitch discrimination over quite a considerable range of the auditory spectrum. Fish disappoint us, however, in the ability to accurately localize the origin of the sound. Fish have extremely poor sound localization, for the simple reason that they are to all intents and purposes transparent to sound. [This statement requires clarification, since not all parts of a fish permit sound to pass through unchanged.]

TAVOLGA: In relation to our definition of hearing, it is necessary to consider whether we are talking about the transducer component or about the entire sense organ. It is also important to remember that when we're talking about hearing we are talking about either a psychological or a perceptual problem.

LATERAL LINE DETECTORS (P. Cahn, ed.), 13–25, © 1967 Indiana University Press

# 2 HISTORY, HISTOLOGICAL METHODS, AND DETAILS OF THE STRUCTURE OF THE LATERAL LINE OF THE WALLEYE SURFPERCH †

THEODORE J. WALKER

Department of Marine Biology
Scripps Institution of Oceanography
La Jolla, California

## HISTORY

The following information represents an extremely interesting and little-known fragment of lateral line history.

The lateral line of fish was first described by Stenonis (1664), although it had been known in its gross features to the ancients. To it was ascribed the function of producing slime. Credit for the discovery that the lateral line is truly a sensory organ should go to Jacobson (1813), who concluded on the basis of structure that it resembles organs of touch. He theorized that the hairlike extensions of the sensory cells which he described were actuated by the flow of water past them. Knox (1825), aware of Jacobson's paper, designated this organ as a sixth sense designed to inform the fish about the motion of the water around it. He concluded from the location of the afferent fiber nucleus, as well as from the structure, that the organ has a closer relationship to the organs of hearing than to touch. These two pioneer works, although offering little in the way of precise illustrations to support their arguments, penetrated surprisingly deep into the problem. Leydig (1850 and subsequently), who published voluminously on the histological features, has been credited in the literature with assigning to

† This paper was not presented at the conference, but it represents part of a study carried out by the author some years ago and supported by the Office of Naval Research. Dr. Cahn had the opportunity to read this previously unpublished manuscript and felt that the valuable techniques and ideas contained in this work should be made available to others. With the author's permission, therefore, the manuscript was shortened and revised by Dr. Cahn for inclusion in this volume.

the lateral line a sensory function. Schulze (1870) described the cupula and postulated that this is a displacement mechanism, and that the failure of earlier anatomists to find it was probably due to its fragility and to its being washed out of the canals during preparation. He showed the existence of the lateral line system in amphibia, and it is to him we owe the term "Seitenorgane." Malbranc (1874) concluded from the orientation of units within the housing that the lateral line could not have a gustatory function. Because of the remarkable similarity of the pit and trench organs of the lateral line to the taste buds, which are likewise widely distributed over the heads of fish, it was not until Nagel's (1894) extensive and masterful monograph on taste buds that the anatomical differences were well defined. Neurologists later (Herrick, 1903) corroborated the differentiation by locating the brain centers responsible for each system. Dercum (1879) postulated that the fluid in the canal may be moved by the motion of the water over the external pores. Merkel (1880) described, instead of delicate hairs, stiff short cell processes projecting up into the canal. He considered these to be levers which are actuated by the flow of fluid within the canal. During the latter part of the 19th century, many papers appeared on the morphological differences of the system in different species.

## HISTOLOGICAL METHODS

The task of preparing histological material of the lateral line system, free of spatial distortions and artifacts, proved difficult. Many methods were investigated by systematically varying techniques, ingredients, and concentrations, with the result that ultimately more than 3,000 procedures were evaluated. These efforts led to a procedure that involved double fixation and double embedding, which gave sections as thin as 3 to 4 microns, free of artifacts.† In such an involved and complicated procedure, the superiority of one ingredient or step over another may have been slight, but cumulatively the combined advantages made the difference between a good preparation and a preparation that was useless.

To preserve the geometry of the lateral line system, either the whole fish was fixed or individual scales were processed; but in the latter case, precise alignment of the scales for sectioning was difficult, and frequently the neuromasts were damaged by scale removal. The following procedure was used:

† A method of bulk nerve staining using thionin, and followed by sectioning, gave very good resolution of the lateral line nerve endings.

1. Pith or anesthetize fish (curare, urethane, or ice water).
2. Immerse fish in first fixative for 5 min. This solution consisted of 450 parts of acetone, 100 parts of 10% formalin, and 100 parts of glacial acetic acid.
3. Hold fish by dorsal fin and remove from fixative.
   a. Inject fixative subdermally at 3 to 5 injection sites, at 3 scale rows below the lateral line scale row. This will permit the tissue beneath the lateral line scales to be irrigated.
   b. Remove every third lateral line scale, taking care not to derange the other scales. This manipulation permitted the fixative ready access to the interior of the intervening sections of the canal.
   c. Hold the fish vertically, and cut it in half longitudinally, being careful to prevent scuffing of the epidermis. Remove the viscera, and return the two halves of the fish to the fixative, scales up, for 30 to 60 min.
4. Transfer the fish to the second fixative, which includes the decalcifying agent and contains the following components: solution (1) consists of 90 cc 10% formalin and 10 cc glacial acetic acid; solution (2) consists of 90 cc 10% Lugol's solution and 10 cc glacial acetic acid. The two solutions are mixed together. The fish are left in the decalcifying fixative for about 24 hr.
5. Bleach in 9% hydrogen peroxide solution (technical grade) with ultraviolet illumination, for 30 min. This intensifies nerve staining, but diminishes the intensity of other cellular details of the neuromasts. It is best to divide the material into two batches, one of which is bleached and the other not.
6. Immerse in the following staining solution for 24 hr: 0.1% thionin (100 cc), glacial acetic acid (10 cc), and chloral hydrate (2 g).
7. Wash tissue for 30 min.
8. Strip away the musculature, leaving the skin intact. Cut out strips of the lateral line region, about 5 scale rows wide by 10 scales long, using an iris scissors. Tie the strips lightly to glass slides, epidermis up. The slides can then be manipulated in regular staining dishes.
9. Wash for about 4 hr.
10. Dehydrate in tertiary butyl alcohol (TBA) as follows:
    a. 50% TBA for 1 hr.
    b. 100% TBA for 1 hr.
    c. 100% TBA (new solution) for another hour.
11. Place in oven at 45°C for 1 hr.
12. Infiltrate with Stedman's ester wax (Stedman, 1947) as follows:
    a. $\frac{3}{4}$ TBA to $\frac{1}{4}$ ester wax for 1 hr.

     *b.* ½ TBA to ½ ester wax for 1 hr.

     *c.* ¼ TBA to ¾ ester wax for 1 hr.

     *d.* Pure ester wax for 12 hr.

13. Place the tissue in the oven at 56°C. Replace the ester wax with Waterman's paraffin mixture (Waterman, 1939), and allow it to stand for 1 hr.

14. Remove the tissue from the slides and embed at 10°C.

15. Cut tissue in a room kept at 12°C. Spread and mount ribbons on albuminized slides, heated to a temperature of 52°C. Dewax dried slides with toluene at 56°C, transfer to clean toluene, and apply the coverslip for permanent mounting with Fisher's Permount.

## THE LATERAL LINE OF THE WALLEYE SURFPERCH

The walleye surfperch *Hyperprosopon argenteum* Gibbons was chosen for this study because of its availability, and because its scales do not require extensive decalcification. These fish were secured by angling (with Paulus lure) from the Scripps pier, just beyond the surf. The fish were released without handling into a plastic bucket for transportation to the holding tanks, which were supplied with running seawater. The fish proved very hardy when fed three to five times a day on naturally occurring foods obtainable from the pile community. It was noted that this species does best in holding tanks when there are at least two dozen specimens. Smaller schools manifested considerable nervousness in confinement.

The lateral line system of this fish is typical of that found in most fishes. It consists of a number of regions of sensory epithelium, the neuromasts, which may be flush on the surface, on slight eminences, at the bottom of open pits or canals, or in tunnels that open to the surface only at intervals. Figure 1 shows the location of the major portion of the lateral line system on the left side of this fish. It shows the lateral line proper, extending from a point near the operculum to the base of the tail. Most of the head canal system can also be seen, except for the tunnels on the roof of the skull and on the underside of the lower jaw.

The present study concerns the lateral line proper. The walleye surfperch also has a sparse array of small surface neuromasts associated with the lateral line but unobservable without extensive preparation. These were not examined in this report.

The lateral line proper is a continuous tunnel from its connection with the head system to the base of the tail. Generally lying above the midline in the surfperch, it arches upward in the region of the anterior

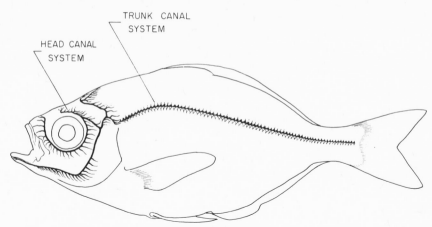

HEAD CANAL
SYSTEM

TRUNK CANAL
SYSTEM

Fig. 1. Lateral line system of the walleye surfperch (natural size).

edge of the dorsal fin and curves down gradually in the region of the caudal peduncle.

The continuous tunnel of the trunk canal consists of a series of fundamentally identical units, each associated with a single scale, as shown diagramatically in Fig. 2. In this illustration, three adjoining lateral line scales are split longitudinally to show the location of the neuromasts, and the general features of the housing. The diagram is oriented so that the exterior surface of each scale faces the right and the buried surface faces the left. The anteriormost scale (A) overlies the next posterior scale (B), which in turn rests on the scale posterior to that (C), and so on. The tunnel also runs in a diagonal direction through the scale, to the outer surface for about 400 to 1000 $\mu$. Thus the diagonal section of the tunnel is continuous with the longitudinal section. To provide space for this part of the tunnel, not only is the lateral line scale thicker than the adjacent scales, but also its two surfaces are arched out (Fig. 3). Each lateral line scale overlaps the next sufficiently to cover the anterior opening of this diagonal part of the tunnel (the suprascalar pore). Similarly, the succeeding and partially covered lateral line scale extends forward at least to the point where the diagonal part of the tunnel of the preceding scale opens (the infrascalar pore).

The scales of the adjoining scale rows separate the lateral line scales by a shimming process (Fig. 3). This produces a space, lined by epithelium, which is fused to the lining of the diagonally directed part of the tunnel, as well as to the edges of the shim scales. This results in a flattened horn-shaped section of the tunnel, which opens posteri-

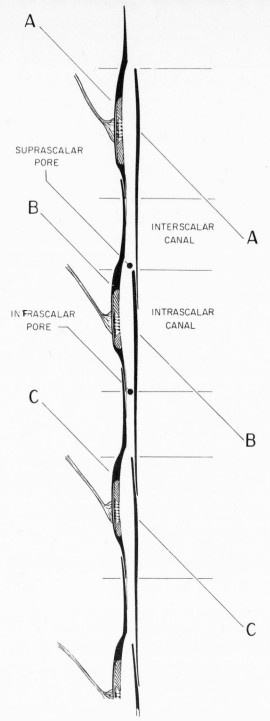

A

SUPRASCALAR
PORE

B

INTERSCALAR
CANAL

A

INFRASCALAR
PORE

INTRASCALAR
CANAL

C

B

C

FIG. 2. Longitudinal schematic of the trunk lateral line. External surface of scales is on the right; neuromasts with nerves are on the left.

18

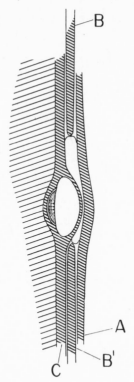

Fɪɢ. 3. Cross-section schematic of the trunk lateral line. The uppermost scale (A) overlaps the scale beneath (C) to produce the vestibule. The ends of the adjacent shim scales (B and B′) lie between the two lateral line scales.

orly along the edge of the overhang. Although this epidermal lining is thin, it too is rigidly backed to the scales, and its shape is constant because of the shimming arrangement. This rigid arrangement of the epidermal lining prevents the overhanging scale from pressing down on the arched ceiling of the diagonal part of the tunnel. The external pore is partially occluded by this arch. The arch is generally in close proximity to the ventral shim scale, and it creates a narrow vestibule between itself and the dorsal shim scale.

The neuromast occupies a depression in the inner wall of the intra-scalar canal. It looks somewhat like a thick saucer, turned up around the edges. Approximately circular, it varies in diameter from 100 to 250 $\mu$ and in thickness from 30 to 50 $\mu$. A peripheral and central zone of the neuromast can be clearly distinguished in vertical section.

The peripheral zone of the neuromast consists of a single layer of columnar cells, which constitute 70 to 90% of the total volume of the

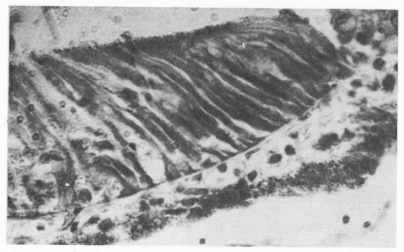

FIG. 4. Peripheral zone of the neuromast. Lumen of the tunnel is above; capillary supply is below the basement membrane.

neuromast (Fig. 4). No innervation to the cells of the peripheral zone has been observed. These peripheral zone cells represent the so-called "supporting cells" (Dijkgraaf, 1963), and they show little in the way of cytoplasmic differentiation. The upper portions of the supporting

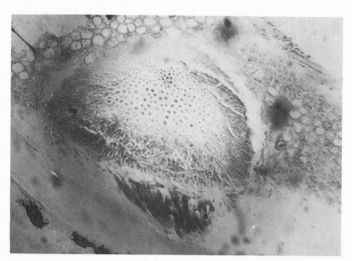

FIG. 5. Tangential section through the neuromast. The section shows the lightly stained central zone, partially ringed by the peripheral zone. Plexus and lateral line nerve branchlet are at the bottom; swollen mucus cells of the canal lining and the partially exposed tunnel appear at upper left.

cells are so closely adfixed as to be almost indistinguishable from one another. Basally these cells have the shape of a capital "L," and they are attached to the basement membrane. The cells are expanded slightly above the bases to accommodate the nuclei. In general, the supporting cells are similar to those described in the neuromasts of other fishes (Cordier, 1964).

The central zone of the neuromast is partially overlaid by the peripheral zone (Fig. 5), so that it is shaped like a truncated cone. These cells in the central zone represent the sensory or hair cells (Dijkgraaf, 1963). Sometimes two layers of hair cells can be seen in the central zone.

The basement level of the central zone is filled largely with nerve fibers (Fig. 6). The nerve fibers branch out and thread their way upward.

Figures 7, 8, and 9 show thionin-stained cross sections through the central zone. A double layer of hair cells can be seen in Fig. 7. Figures 8 and 9 show the comparatively dense inclusions in the more basal regions of the hair cells.

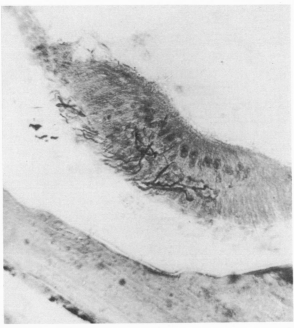

Fig. 6. Cross section of the neuromast showing the plexus differentiated with Bodian's protargol preparation and counterstained with eosin. Canal lumen is at the upper right; scale recess is at the bottom. The space between is due to shrinkage.

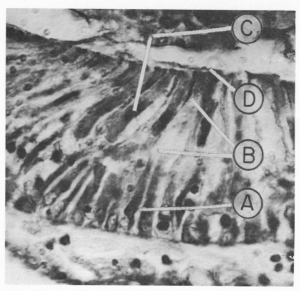

Fig. 7. Cross section of the central zone of a neuromast. Capillary and plexus are at the bottom. A and C represent a double layer of sensory cells; B appears as a clear region, relatively free of stained inclusions. This clear region terminates apically in a darker stained region, near the surface membrane (D).

Great effort was made to demonstrate the neuromast cupula, but without success. In most preparations, the neuromast surface was cluttered with debris, and this debris sometimes resembled a shrunken cupula. It is the opinion of this author that this debris represents a leakage of cell material into the lumen and is not a true cupula. Fixatives that contained osmic or picric acid, or phenols, seemed to cause the release of neuromast secretions that collected in the lumen, where the cupula is usually located. In many preparations where this "cupula" was seen, extensive voids were found in the cells of the neuromast, in both the sensory and supporting cells.

## THEORETICAL CONSIDERATIONS

It is the opinion of this author that the design of the housing of the lateral line system suggests that pressure signals, at least at low frequencies, could be transmitted without distortion or delay. The pressure fluctuations generated by the fish's own propulsive movements, as well as the pressure changes produced by hydrodynamic activity in the medium, may be sensed by the lateral line neuromasts. It is difficult to believe, from the varying dimensions, irregular shapes, and sinuous

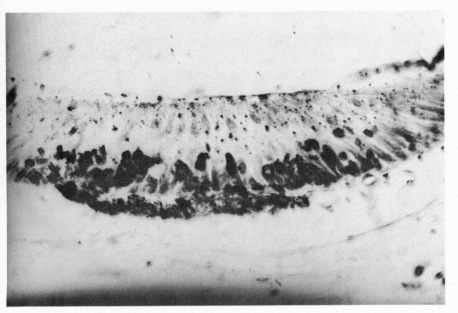

Fig. 8. Cross section of a neuromast. Thionin differentiation, showing nerve plexus at the bottom.

Fig. 9. High-power view of Fig. 8. Thionin differentiation of plexus showing intense surface staining. (Arrows point to inclusions in the sense cells.)

course of the lateral line canals, that the direction and velocity of water motion outside the fish is related in a systematic way to the direction and velocity of water motion at each neuromast. Of course, we now know from the ultrastructural and electrophysiological studies of Wersäll et al. (1965) and others that the neuromast hair cells are directionally polarized. We also know, from the work of Harris and van Bergeijk (1962), who used the microphonic potential as an indicator of neuromast sensitivity, that the lateral line hair cells are displacement detectors. Much additional work is needed on a large variety of different species, and on both head and trunk lateral line organs, before we can fully rule out pressure or displacement phenomena.

REFERENCES

Cordier, R. (1964). Sensory cells, in *The Cell: Biochemistry, Physiology, and Morphology*, Vol. VI. (J. Brachet and A. Mirsky, eds.), Academic Press, New York, Chap. 5.

Dercum, F. (1879). The lateral sensory apparatus of fishes. *Proc. Acad. Nat. Sci. Phila.* 152.

Dijkgraaf, S. (1963). The function and significance of the lateral line organs. *Biol. Rev. Cambridge Phil. Soc.* 38, 51.

Flock, A., and J. Wersäll (1962). A study of the orientation of the sensory hairs of the receptor cells in the lateral line organ of fish, with special reference to the function of the receptors. *J. Cell. Biol.* 15, 19-27.

Harris, G., and W. A. van Bergeijk (1962). Evidence that the lateral line organ responds to near-field displacements of sound sources in water. *J. Acoust. Soc. Am.* 34, 1831.

Herrick, C. J. (1903). On the morphological and physiological classification of the cutaneous sense organs of fishes. *Am. Naturalist* 37, 313.

Jacobson, L. (1813). Extrait d'un memoire sur une organe de sens dans les raies et les squales. *Nouv. Bul. Sci. Soc. Philomotique Paris* 3, 332.

Knox, R. (1825). On the theory of the 6th sense in fishes. *Edinburgh J. Sci.* 2, 12.

Leydig, F. (1850). Über die Schleimkanale der Knochenfische. *Arch. Anat. Physiol. Wiss. Med.* 170.

———— (1868). Über Organe eines sechsten Sinnes. *Nov. Acta Acad. Cae. Leopold Carol. Germ. Nat. Curios.* 34, 1.

Malbranc, M. (1874). Von Seitenlinie und ihren Sinnesorganen bei Amphibien. *Z. Wiss. Zool.* 26, 24-82.

Merkel, F. (1880). *Über die Endigungen der Sensiblen Nerven in der Haut der Wirbelthiere.* Verlag der Stiller'schen Hof-und Universitats-Buchhandlung, Rostock.

Nagel, W. A. (1894). Vergleichende Physiologie und Anatomie Untersuchungen über der Geruchs und Geschmacksinn und ihre Organe. *Bibliotech. Zool. Stuttgart* 7, 1-207.

Schulze, F. E. (1870). Über die Sinnesorgane der Seitenlinie bei Fischen und Amphibien. *Arch. Mikroskop. Anat.* 6, 62.

Stedman, H. F. (1947). Ester wax: A new embedding medium. *Quart. J. Microscop. Sci.* 88, 123.

Stenonis, N. (1664) from M. R. Wright (1951). The lateral line system of sense organs. *Quart. Rev. Biol.* 26, 264.

Waterman, H. C. (1939). The preparation of hardened embedding paraffins having low melting points. *Stain Tech.* 14, 55.

Wersäll, J., A. Flock, and Per-G. Lundquist (1965). Structural basis for directional sensitivity in cochlear and vestibular sensory receptors. *Cold Spring Harbor Symp. Quant. Biol.* 30, 115.

# 3 STRUCTURE AND DEVELOPMENT OF LATERAL LINE CUPULAE IN TELEOST LARVAE †

Tamotsu Iwai

Department of Fisheries
Kyoto University
Maizuru, Japan

There is a considerable literature dealing with the structure and function of the canal organs of fishes, and the results have been reviewed comprehensively by Dijkgraaf (1963). More recently, with the aid of the electron microscope, additional light has been shed on functional aspects of canal organs (Flock and Wersäll, 1962; Hama, 1965; Flock, 1965). However, scant attention has been given to the detailed structure and ecological significance of the naked neuromasts arranged on the body surface of larval fishes. There is little adequate information on the ultrastructure of the naked neuromasts, except for the description by Trujillo-Cenóz (1961). It would seem appropriate, therefore, to study the ultrastructure of naked neuromasts of larval fishes so as to compare them with the closely related canal organs.

Reports on the primary element of naked neuromasts, the projecting cupulae, were sparse until the past ten years. Cupulae in larvae are difficult to observe because of their transparency and fragility. Most of the earlier investigations were concerned only with the neuromasts. Naked neuromasts on the sides of the body of newly hatched larvae were briefly described as sensory papillae in *Sardinia pilchardus* (Cunningham, 1894; Lebour, 1921) and in *Clupea sprattus* (Lebour, 1921), but no description of the cupulae was given. In the last decade, intensive studies were carried out on cupulae attached to the apical edges of neuromasts of teleost larvae. Notable among these investigations are descriptions and reviews by Thomopoulos (1957), Disler (1960), and Cahn and Shaw (1962) for many teleost larvae having

† I am grateful to Dr. K. Matsubara of Kyoto University, Dr. Phyllis H. Cahn of Yeshiva University, and Dr. George A. Moore, Professor Emeritus, Oklahoma State University, for helpful suggestions and stimulating discussions.

rodlike cupulae. Cahn and Shaw (1965) quantitatively analyzed the relationships between lateral line cupulae and the rheotactic orientation of *Menidia* larvae.

Knowing when cupulae appear may help to analyze the behavior of larval fishes. The period of the first appearance of cupulae is still uncertain in many fishes. Thus it is necessary to acquire much more detailed knowledge of the exact manner of origin and the subsequent development of the cupulae as well as the neuromasts.

This report is not intended as a complete review of the subject of lateral line mechanoreceptors in embryos and larvae of teleosts, but it is intended to present available examples of the ultrastructure of naked neuromasts and the formation of cupulae.

NAKED NEUROMASTS AND CUPULAE

Many teleost larvae possess transparent cupulae that extend out from the naked neuromasts (Table 1). When the larvae are positioned with the dorsal surface uppermost, jellylike cupulae are seen on both sides along the body surface. The cupulae project perpendicular to the body axis under relatively static conditions, when the fish are more or less stationary. When the cupulae are subjected to water flow, they are moved back and forth. The cupulae along the lateral line of the trunk and tail are usually located in the vicinity of the myotomes. In addition to these body cupulae, similar cupulae are seen in the head, in supraorbital, infraorbital, postorbital, occipital, and pre-operculo-mandibular regions (Fig. 1). The head cupulae are usually difficult to observe in live larvae, unless they happen to project from the lateral surface of the head. Each cephalic neuromast shows a bilateral distribution, and arrays of neuromasts cover the whole surface of the head. According to van Bergeijk (1964), the combination of such serial neuromasts is precise and regularly distributed in three dimensions, and it contributes to the ability of the fish to localize a source of turbulence.

Papillary naked neuromasts lie in the epidermal layer, not in dermal canals or pits, and rise apically beyond the level of the surrounding epidermal surface. Many naked neuromasts appear ultimately to become enclosed in the skin and scales as the fishes grow (Lowenstein, 1957). In *Menidia beryllina,* and in *M. menidia* 9 to 12 mm long, Cahn et al. (1965) described the formation of grooves and canals that contained neuromasts, after the naked neuromasts had formed. A similar pattern seems to occur in larvae of *Oryzias latipes* 11 to 13 mm long.

The principal part of the neuromast is the patch of sensory cells couched among the supporting cells. Distally the neuromast is covered

TABLE 1. SUMMARY OF SOME OF THE LITERATURE DEALING WITH
THE CUPULAE OF TELEOST LARVAE [a]

Cypriniformes:
  Cyprinidae
    *Gnathopogon caerulescens*      Nakamura (1949)
    *Rutilus rutilus*      Vasnetsov (1948); Disler (1960)
    *Leuciscus schmidti*      Disler (1960)
    *Leucaspius delineatus*      Disler (1960)
    *Tribolodon hakonensis*      Iwai (unpublished data)
    *Zacco platypus*      Iwai (unpublished data)
    *Ischikauia steenackeri*      Nakamura (1950)
    *Gobio gobio*      Suworow (1959)
    *Schizothorax pseudaksaiensis*      Disler (1960)
    *Diptychus maculatus*      Disler (1960)
    *Diptychus dybowski*      Disler (1960)
    *Abramis brama*      Disler (1960)
    *Carassius carassius*      Disler (1960)
    *Carassius auratus*      Iwai (1965)
    *Cyprinus carpio*      Hikita (1956); Iwai (unpublished data)
  Cobitidae
    *Nemachilus (Deuterophysa)*      Nikolsky (1963)
  Characidae
    *Astyanax mexicanus*      John (unpublished data)
Anguilliformes:
  Muraenidae
    *Muraena helena*      Thomopoulos (1957)
  Nettastomidae
    *Nettastoma melanurum*      Thomopoulos (1957)
  Ophichthidae
    *Coecula coeca*      Thomopoulos (1957)
    *Coecula imberbis*      Thomopoulos (1957)
    *Ophichthys remicaudus*      Thomopoulos (1957)
Cyprinodontiformes:
  Cyprinodontidae
    *Fundulus heteroclitus*      Cahn and Shaw (1963)
    *Oryzias latipes*      Iwai (1964)
Perciformes:
  Atherinidae
    *Menidia beryllina*      Cahn and Shaw (1962)
    *Menidia menidia*      Cahn and Shaw (1962)
  Sparidae
    *Crystovomer major*      Yamashita (1960)
    *Pagellus acarne*      Thomopoulos (1957)
  Maenidae
    *Smaris insidiator*      Thomopoulos (1957)
  Blenniidae
    *Blennius yatabei*      Iwai (1963b)
  Ammodytidae
    *Ammodytes personatus*      Senta (1965)
  Ophidiidae
    *Ophidion barbatus*      Thomopoulos (1957)
  Gobiidae
    *Tridentiger trigonocephalus*      Iwai (1963a)
    *Bathygobius fuscus*      Dôtu (1955a)
    *Acentrogobius masago*      Dôtu (1958)
    *Aboma lactipes*      Dôtu (1955b)
    *Chaenogobius castaneus*      Dôtu (1955b)
    *Chasmichthys gulosus*      Dôtu (1955b)
    *Eutaeniichthys gilli*      Dôtu (1955b)
    *Luciogobius saikaiensis*      Dôtu and Mito (1958)
Pleuronectiformes:
  Pleuronectidae
    *Limanda limanda*      Soin (1964)
  Soleidae
    *Solea lascaris*      Thomopoulos (1957)

[a] System of classification used is that of Berg, L. S., 1940.

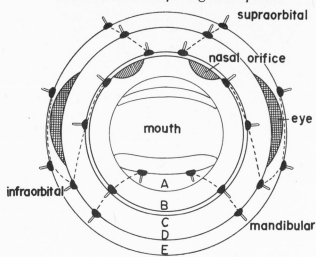

Fɪɢ. 1. Anterior view of arrangement of naked neuromasts in head of goldfish larva. Cross sections are made at levels (A) immediately before the olfactory cavity, (B) olfactory cavity, (C) immediately before the eye, (D) immediately behind the lens, and (E) midway between the eye and auditory vesicle.

by the flexible jellylike cupula. Bundles of nerve fibers supply basal portions of the neuromast.

Van Bergeijk and Alexander (1962) found a strip arrangement of sensory cells in an oval patch of supporting cells in the canal organs of adult *Fundulus heteroclitus*. Dijkgraaf (1963) mentioned the same pattern of sensory cells in free neuromasts of the clawed toad *Xenopus laevis*. In many naked neuromasts of teleost larvae, sensory cells are grouped in an oval patch surrounded by supporting cells. Vertically, the apical edges of the sensory cells are exposed to the surface, and their basal ends are located in the elaborate bed of supporting cells, not on the basement membrane (Fig. 2).

NAKED NEUROMASTS IN 1-DAY LARVAE OF *ORYZIAS LATIPES*

If we take as an example a 4.5-mm larva (Fig. 7), the sensory cells, pearlike in shape, are located in the central portion of the organ and are completely surrounded by supporting cells. The apical edge of the sensory cell is flat and is provided with so-called "sensory hairs" that consist of a kinocilium and 30 to 40 stereocilia (Figs. 3 and 4). The kinocilium is about 0.25 $\mu$ in diameter and is located at one end of the bundle of stereocilia; it is characterized by having the ubiquitous "9 + 2" pattern of fibers (Fig. 4). The stereocilia are about 0.12 $\mu$ in

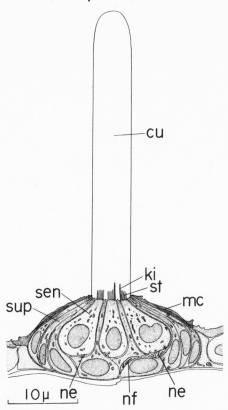

Fig. 2. Schematic drawing of section of naked neuromast in pre-operculo-mandibular series. The cupula outline is based on phase-contrast microscope observation. cu, cupula; ki, kinocilium; mc, mantle cell; ne, nerve ending; nf, nerve fiber; sen, sensory cell; st, stereocilium; sup, supporting cell.

diameter and have a cytoplasmic core that contains a filamentous element by which each stereocilium extends into the cuticular plate of the sensory cells. The cuticular plate is developed along the apical edge of the sensory cell. Immediately below the cuticular plate, the fine filaments run along the long axis of the cell. Well-developed mitochondria are distributed in the supranuclear portion. The roughly oval nucleus lies near the center, a little toward the base of the sensory cell. Occasionally, the nuclear envelope is deeply infolded.

There are prominent nerve endings on the basal surface of the sensory cells. The nerve endings are spherical or ellipsoidal, and fit into a concave sensory cell membrane. The nerve cytoplasm contains a cluster of small mitochondria, with only a few vesicles (Fig. 5). In

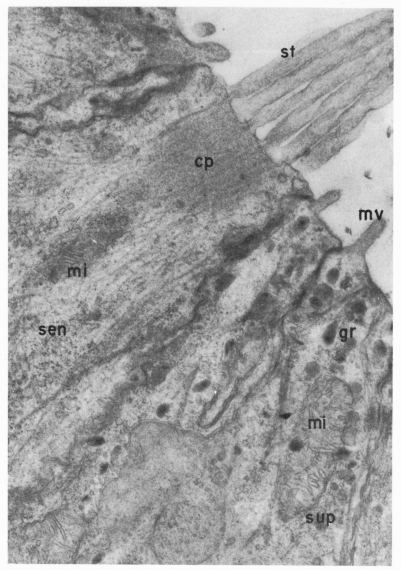

Fig. 3. Electron micrograph of longitudinal section through apical region of sensory cell and supporting cells of naked neuromast (×40,000). cp, cuticular plate; gr, granule; mi, mitochondria; mv, microvillus; sen, sensory cell; st, stereocilium; sup, supporting cell.

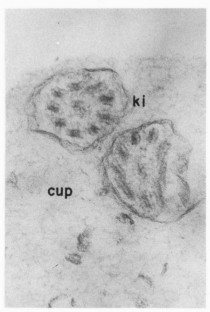

F<small>IG</small>. 4. Electron micrograph of cross section of two kinocilia (ki) in cupula (cup). Note the fine fibrous network in cupula (×100,000).

close association with these nerve endings, spherical bodies of homogeneous density, 0.4 to 0.5 $\mu$ in diameter, occur in the cytoplasm of the sensory cell (Fig. 5). The spherical bodies are surrounded by small vesicles and are referable to synaptic bars. These nerve endings resemble the afferent nerve endings. From the nerve endings, unmyelinated fibers rise and penetrate between the supporting cells. These run toward the basal edge of the neuromast.

The supporting cells are pillar-shaped, with a basal bulge, and are located around and among the sensory cells. Those arranged near the peripheral portion of the neuromast extend beyond the basal ends of the sensory cells and curve around the outer margins of the neuromast, encircling the bases of the sensory cells (Fig. 2). The central supporting cells do not end at the level of the base of the sensory cells, but extend upward as slender processes to the apical edge of the organ, so that they surround closely the lateral surface of the sensory cells. The cell membranes between the supporting cells are highly tortuous, exhibiting distinct interdigitations with the adjoining cells. Many desmosomes are also present on the contact surface of the supporting cells.

This evidence of a tight connection between the supporting cells indicates the elaborate sustentacular structure for the sensory cells. The microvilli, about 0.1 $\mu$ in diameter, protrude from the apical surface of the supporting cell. In general appearance they resemble the stereocilia found in the sensory cells, though they are rather short as compared with the latter. Well-developed Golgi apparatus and mitochondria are scattered in the cytoplasm of the supporting cells. The Golgi apparatus is usually oriented in relation to the long axis of the cell in the supranuclear portion. Some endoplasmic reticula that run along the long axis of the cell are found in the cytoplasm of the peripheral supporting cells. The nucleus lies at the base. The most striking feature in the supporting cells is the fact that a number of dense granules, about 0.06 to 0.1 $\mu$ in diameter, are found in the distal portion of the cytoplasm (Fig. 3). Judging from the evidence mentioned above, it is plausible that the supporting cells contribute not only to the embracement of the sensory cells but also to a secretory function, perhaps the secretion of the cupular component.

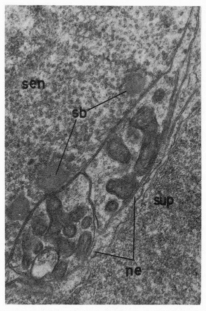

Fig. 5. Electron micrograph showing synaptic region at base of sensory cell (×17,000). ne, nerve endings; sb, synaptic bars; sen, sensory cell; sup, supporting cell.

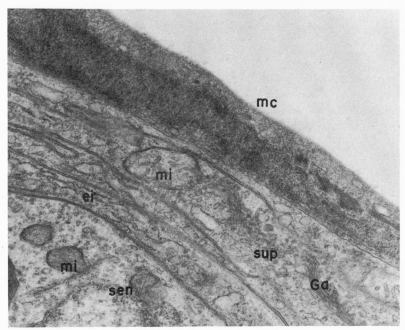

Fig. 6. Electron micrograph of longitudinal section through peripheral region of neuromast (×9,000). er, endoplasmic reticulum; Ga, Golgi apparatus; mc, mantle cell; mi, mitochondria; sen, sensory cell; sup, supporting cell.

The laterodistal surface of the neuromast is covered by a thin layer of mantle cells. The mantle cells are very thin, about 0.8 to 1 $\mu$ thick, and contain dense cytoplasm with a few mitochondria (Fig. 6). The centrally located nucleus is slender. These laminar mantle cells are well defined with dense cytoplasm, but a secretory function is dubious. They may serve as the outer sheath of the neuromast.

A rodlike cupula, 40 to 50 $\mu$ in length and 5 to 7 $\mu$ in diameter, is attached to the apical edge of the neuromast. The cupula is composed of a jellylike substance, secreted from the apical edges of the supporting cells. When fixed cupulae are examined, they may be shrunken, and the detailed structure cannot be estimated reliably from such preparations. But as shown in Fig. 4, there is a fine fibrous network within the cupula. This may serve as a sustentacular element in the cupula. Basally, the cupula embraces the kinocilia and stereocilia of the sensory cells. This forms a conduction chain for the stimuli from the cupula to the sensory cells.

## COMPARISON OF NAKED NEUROMASTS WITH CANAL ORGANS

From the foregoing description it is clear that the ultrastructural elements of naked neuromasts are virtually the same as those of the canal organs of adult fishes, though the former are relatively smaller and are composed of fewer cells as compared with the latter. Most investigators agree that the sensory cells of the lateral line organs are apically provided with hair bundles, each consisting of some stereocilia and a peripherally located kinocilium (Trujillo-Cenóz, 1961; Flock and Wersäll, 1962; Flock, 1965; Hama, 1965). The topographic distribution of the kinocilia in the neuromast has been considered by Flock and Wersäll (1962) and Flock (1965) as an important feature in relation to the bidirectionality of the lateral line organs. According to their work on *Lota vulgaris,* kinocilia are arranged alternately, on opposite sides, from hair bundle to adjacent hair bundle—i.e., craniad in one hair bundle and caudad in the adjacent hair bundle. In the absence of sections to indicate adequately the topographic distribution of kinocilia in the naked neuromasts of *Oryzias* larvae, I can present only a guess concerning this problem. But they may appear to show the alternating pattern of distribution, because in many sections contiguously arranged kinocilia were recognized.

The ultrastructure of the supporting cells suggests both a sustentacular and a secretory function. Flock (1965), Hama (1965), and Petraitis (1966) demonstrated the close contact between the supporting cells and sensory cells, as well as the tortuous boundaries between the supporting cells. Görner (1963) divided the supporting cells of *Xenopus* neuromasts into two groups, central supporting cells and peripheral mantle cells, and surmised that the cupular substance is mainly secreted from the mantle cells. Basing their investigation on the secretory features of supporting cells, Hama (1965) and Petraitis (1966) presented the opinion that the supporting cells play a dual role, the secretory function of the cupular substance and the nutritive function for the sensory cells. Insofar as was observed, the naked neuromasts of *Oryzias* larvae were provided with supporting cells similar to those in the canal organs. The endoplasmic reticulum is not as well developed as in the canal organs described by Hama (1965) for *Rhynchocymba* and by Petraitis (1966) for *Fundulus.* On the other hand, many granules are evident in the apical portion of the supporting cells of naked neuromasts, which are seen in the electron micrograph of the neuromast of *Cnesterodon* larvae presented by Trujillo-Cenóz (1961). It is probable that these cells contribute to the secretion of the cupula.

The cupula is said to be a homogeneous jellylike substance. Thomopoulos (1957) determined that the jelly consists of acid mucopolysaccharides, but Satô (1962) demonstrated neutral polysaccharides in the cupulae. Pronounced longitudinal striations have been observed in the cupulae of both naked neuromasts and canal organs (Denny, 1937; Jielof et al., 1952; Satô, 1962; van Bergeijk and Alexander, 1962; Iwai, 1963a,b, 1964; Flock, 1965). These striations may correspond with the sensory hair bundles. However, there remains the question as to whether these striations are real or are shrinkage artifacts occurring in the cupulae, especially in exposed cupulae. The cross striations have also been described in cupulae of canal organs (Jielof et al., 1952; Denny, 1937; van Bergeijk and Alexander, 1962; Flock, 1965; Petraitis, 1966). Van Bergeijk and Alexander (1962) called these shrinkage artifacts, and Petraitis (1966) suggested they were growth rings of the cupula.

It is a common observation that cupulae are very fragile and easily broken by mechanical contact. The tear is usually very sharp and irregular. In this connection, the fine fibrous network in the cupula of naked neuromasts is interesting. Satô (1962) also stated that numerous fine threads are present in the cupula of the pit organ of the goby. Recently, Flock (1965) found a network of fibrils in the cupula of a canal organ and concluded that the cupular material is arranged in a honeycomb pattern. Such evidence may offer a basis for inference that the cupula is supported by sustentacular elements.

In estimating the sensitivity of naked neuromasts in larvae, the state of innervation of the neuromasts is a first consideration. There appears to be a very limited amount of information available concerning the innervation indicative of the sensory function of naked neuromasts. Trujillo-Cenóz (1961) distinguished calyx-type and knob-like nerve endings in naked neuromasts. The nerve endings have been identified on the basal surfaces of the sensory cells in naked neuromasts of 1-day-old *Oryzias* larvae. The nerve endings found in *Oryzias* larvae resemble the afferent nerve endings described by Lowenstein and Osborne (1964), Hama (1965), and Flock (1965), for they have few vesicles or granules in the cytoplasm, but there are associated synaptic bars in the sensory cells. Another type of nerve ending, the efferent nerve ending, was of uncertain identification in the naked neuromast of 1-day larvae of *Oryzias,* so that the function of these neuromasts is still dubious. Working with the organ of corti in mice, Kikuchi and Hilding (1965) found that the efferent innervation becomes evident on the eleventh day after birth, whereas afferent nerve endings and fibers can be identified at birth. According to Shaw (1960, 1961), schooling behavior of

*Menidia* becomes evident in fry over 12 mm in length. Cahn et al. (1965) reported for *Menidia* larvae that neuromasts do not become innervated until the fry grow to 9 to 12 mm, and that maturation of the lateral line coincides with the onset of schooling behavior. Both afferent and efferent nerve endings may probably be formed at this stage.

Some investigators have noted the influence of the nerve upon the maintenance of differentiation of epidermal sense organs in fishes. Brockelbank (1925) recognized that, after removal of the lateral line nerve, epidermal epithelial cells are organized into lateral line sense organs under the influence of the regenerating nerve. Bailey (1937), in an experimental study of the lateral line organs of fishes, confirmed that the regeneration of the lateral line sense organs depends upon the lateral line nerve. Parker (1922), May (1925), and Torrey (1940) postulated that neurohumoral substances play an important role in maintenance and regeneration of the sensory organs. Bailey (1937) mentioned that such chemical hypotheses may apply to the origin of the sense organs in embryos. It is quite possible that nerves induce the formation of sense organs from epithelial cells in teleost embryos or larvae. Farbman (1965) found that, in association with the underlying nerve process, clusters of vesicles appear in the epithelial cells that differentiate into the taste bud cells in rat embryos. Further electron microscope examination would contribute to revealing the exact manner of development of nerve endings and the formation of naked neuromasts, as well as their relationships.

DEVELOPMENT OF CUPULAE

The cupulae of naked neuromasts have been recognized in many diverse species and families of teleosts. Table 1 is a summary of some of the literature that describes the cupulae of teleost larvae. In some species, cupulae have been observed in the head and body of newly hatched larvae. It has become obvious in the past few years that the cupula is a product derived from the supporting cells of the neuromast. It is difficult, however, to determine whether or not cupulae first appear in prehatching embryos, because the transparent cupula may not be discernible through the dense egg membrane, and also because it is of a fragile structure, it is destroyed by histological fixatives.

Thomopoulos (1957) illustrated the cupulae in prehatching embryos of *Muraena helena*. Iwai (1963a) showed cupulae moving in prehatching live embryos of the goby, *Tridentiger trigonocephalus* (Fig. 8). In the embryos of this goby, the cupulae first appear as slender bars at

A

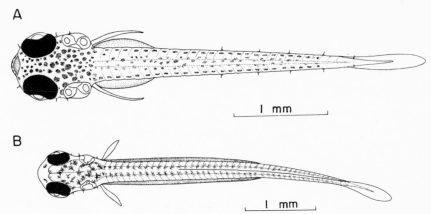

I mm

B

I mm

FIG. 7. Dorsal views of 1-day larva of *Oryzias latipes* (A) and 4-day larva of *Tribolodon hakonensis* (B), showing cupulae extending out from naked neuromasts.

the retinal pigment stage, and fully formed cupulae are visible before hatching and in all subsequent stages of larval development. In many marine teleosts, newly hatched larvae are generally provided with well-organized cupulae (Thomopoulos, 1957; Cahn and Shaw, 1962; Iwai, 1963a,b). On the contrary, Iwai (1965) was unable to detect the cupulae in embryos of the goldfish, where they did not appear until after hatching. In newly hatched larvae of *O. latipes*, the cupulae may be seen as a papillary bud on top of the naked neuromasts, and they enlarge rapidly within 24 hr after hatching (Iwai, 1964). Vasnetsov (1948) indicated the appearance of cupulae in 5-mm larvae of *Rutilus rutilus*. In the Japanese dace, *Tribolodon hakonensis*, the cupulae are not yet

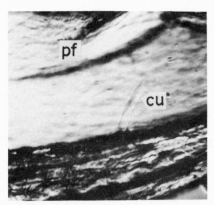

FIG. 8. Cupula in prehatching embryos of goby, *Tridentiger trigonocephalus* (×200). cu, cupula; pf, pectoral fin.

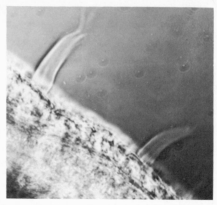

FIG. 9. Cupulae located in occipital region of 5-day larva of *Tribolodon hakonensis* (×450).

developed at hatching, but they become visible in 10-mm larvae, about 4 days after hatching (Figs. 7 and 9). Evidently, there are species differences in the period of initial formation of cupulae. In general, it appears that the pelagic larvae have flexible cupulae in earlier stages as compared with freshwater fish larvae. According to my preliminary observations, many pelagic larvae with fully formed cupulae tend to exhibit darting and swimming movements immediately after hatching, whereas newly hatched larvae of many freshwater fishes, lacking exposed cupulae, remain on the bottom of the aquaria while they have a prominent yolk sac. Cupulae may function as the first element in the mechanoreception of larvae, responding to minute change in water flow. The lateral line may therefore play an important role in locomotor and rheotactic behavior of these larvae.

SUMMARY

Electron microscope observations on the neuromasts of 1-day larvae of *O. latipes* have revealed the presence of all principal elements. The sensory cells, pearlike in shape, are couched among the supporting cells. The apical edge of the sensory cell is flat and is characterized by the presence of sensory hairs that consist of a single kinocilium and 30 to 40 stereocilia. The afferent-type nerve endings are located in the basal surface of the sensory cell. Each sensory cell is completely surrounded by supporting cells, which are tightly bound to each other and to the sensory cells. Secretory features are evident in the apical portion of the supporting cell. Probably the cupula is a product derived from the supporting cells. The laminar mantle cells with electron dense cytoplasm cover the lateral surface of the naked neuromast. A rodlike cupula, 40 to 50 $\mu$ in length, is attached to the apical edge of the neuromast. The cupula, transparent and very fragile, is often destroyed by mechanical handling. There is a fine fibrous network within the jellylike cupula. Basally, the cupula embraces the bundles of kinocilia and stereocilia.

There are species differences in the period of initial formation of cupulae. For example, in the embryos of the goby, *Tridentiger trigonocephalus*, bending cupulae can be observed in prehatching stages. In larvae of many marine teleosts, at least at hatching, naked lateral line cupulae bend sensitively in response to water flow. In some freshwater teleosts, on the other hand, the formation of cupulae is delayed, and fully formed cupulae become visible after hatching. In the Japanese dace, *Tribolodon hakonensis*, flexible cupulae are not recognizable for several days after hatching, up to the 10-mm stage. In general, it appears that the pelagic larvae have more slender cupulae in earlier stages than do the other larvae.

To provide background for studies of the function of naked neuromasts in teleost larvae, much more detailed studies are needed on the ultrastructure of innervation and the sensory physiology and behavior of larvae.

REFERENCES

Bailey, S. W. (1937). An experimental study of the origin of lateral-line structures in embryonic and adult teleosts. *J. Exptl. Zool.* 76, 187-233.

Berg, L. S. (1940). Classification of fishes both recent and fossil. Reprint 1947. Edwards Bros., Ann Arbor, Mich.

Bergeijk, W. A. van (1964). Directional and nondirectional hearing in fish. In *Marine Bio-Acoustics* (W. N. Tavolga, ed.). Pergamon Press, Oxford, pp. 281-299.

———— and S. Alexander (1962). Lateral line canal organs on the head of *Fundulus heteroclitus. J. Morphol.* 110, 333-346.

Brockelbank, M. C. (1925). Degeneration and regeneration of the lateral-line organs in *Ameiurus nebulosus* (Les.). *J. Exptl. Zool.* 42, 293-305.

Cahn, P. H., and E. Shaw (1962). The first demonstration of lateral line cupulae in the Mugiliformes. *Copeia* 1, 109-114.

———— and E. Shaw (1963). Lateral line activity in rheotactic orientation of schooling fishes. *Am. Zool.* 3, 168.

———— and E. Shaw (1965). A method for studying lateral line cupular bending in juvenile fishes. *Bull. Marine Sci.* 15, 1060-1071.

————, E. H. Atz, and E. Shaw (1965). Lateral line nerve differentiation correlated with schooling in the marine fish, *Menidia. Am. Zool.* 5, 142.

Cunningham, J. T. (1894). The life-history of the pilchard. *J. Marine Biol. Assoc. U.K.* 3, 148-153.

Denny, M. (1937). The lateral line system of the teleost, *Fundulus heteroclitus*. *J. Comp. Neurol.* 68, 49-65.

Dijkgraaf, S. (1963). The functioning and significance of the lateral-line organs. *Biol. Rev.* 38, 51-105.

Disler, N. N. (1960). Lateral Line Sense Organs and Their Role in the Behavior of Fishes. Institute of Animal Morphology, Academy of Sciences, U.S.S.R., 309 pp.

Dôtu, Y. (1955a). Life history of a goby, *Gobius poecilichthys* Jordan et Snyder. *Sci. Bull. Fac. Agr. Kyushu Univ.* 15, 77-86 (in Japanese with English summary).

———— (1955b). On the life history of a gobioid fish, *Eutaeniichthys gilli* Jordan et Snyder. *Bull. Biogeogr. Soc. Japan* 16-19, 338-344 (in Japanese with English summary).

———— (1958). The life history of the gobioid fish, *Acentrogobius masago* (Tomiyama). *Sci. Bull. Fac. Agr. Kyushu Univ.* 16, 359-370 (in Japanese with English summary).

———— and S. Mito (1958). The bionomics and life history of the gobioid fish, *Luciogobius saikaiensis* Dôtu. *Sci. Bull. Fac. Agr. Kyushu Univ.* 16, 419-426.

Farbman, A. I. (1965). Electron microscope study of the developing taste bud in rat fungiform papilla. *Develop. Biol.* 11, 110-135.

Flock, A. (1965). Electron microscopic and electrophysiological studies on the lateral line canal organ. *Acta Oto-Laryngol. Suppl.* 199, 1-90.

———— and J. Wersäll (1962). A study of the orientation of the sensory hairs of the receptor cells in the lateral line organ of fish, with special reference to the function of the receptors. *J. Cell Biol.* 15, 19-27.

Görner, P. (1963). Untersuchungen zur Morphologie und Elektrophysiologie des Seitenlinienorgans vom Krallenfrosch (*Xenopus laevis* Daudin). *Z. Vergleich. Physiol.* 47, 316-338.

Hama, K. (1965). Some observations on the fine structure of the lateral line organ of the Japanese sea eel *Lyncozymba nystromi*. *J. Cell Biol.* 24, 193-210.

Hikita, T. (1956). On the anatomy and development of carp in Hokkaido. *Sci. Rept. Hokkaido Fish Hatchery* 11, 65-95 (in Japanese).

Iwai, T. (1963a). Development of lateral-line cupulae in the gobioid fish, *Tridentiger trigonocephalus* (Gill). *Bull. Misaki Marine Biol. Inst. Kyoto Univ.* 4, 1-20.

———— (1963b). Sensory cupulae found in newly hatched larvae of *Blennius yatabei* Jordan et Snyder. *Bull. Japan. Soc. Sci. Fisheries* 29, 503-506.

———— (1964). Development of cupulae in free neuromasts of the Japanese Medaka, *Oryzias latipes* (Temminck et Schlegel). *Bull. Misaki Marine Biol. Inst. Kyoto Univ.* 5, 31-37.

———— (1965). Notes on the cupulae of free neuromasts in larvae of the goldfish. *Copeia* 3, 379.

Jielof, R., A. Spoor, and H. de Vries (1952). The microphonic activity of the lateral line. *J. Physiol.* (*London*) 116, 137-157.

Kikuchi, K., and D. Hilding (1965). The development of the organ of corti in the mouse. *Acta Oto-Laryngol.* 60, 207-222.

Lebour, M. V. (1921). The larval and post-larval stages of the pilchard, sprat and herring from Plymouth district. *J. Marine Biol. Assoc. U.K.* 12, 427-458.

Lowenstein, O. E. (1957). The acoustico-lateralis system, in *The Physiology of Fishes*, Vol. 2 (M. Brown, ed.). Academic Press, New York, pp. 155-186.

———— and M. P. Osborne (1964). Ultrastructure of the sensory hair cells in the labyrinth of the ammocoetes larva of the lamprey, *Lampetra fluviatilis*. *Nature* 204, 197-198.

May, R. M. (1925). The relation of nerves to degenerating and regenerating taste buds. *J. Exptl. Zool.* 42, 371-410.

Nakamura, M. (1949). The life history of a cyprinid fish, *Gnathopogon elongatus caerulescens* (Sauvage) in Lake Biwa. *Bull. Japan. Soc. Sci. Fisheries* 15, 88-96.

———— (1950). The life history of a cyprinid fish, *Ischikauia steenackeri* (Sauvage) in Lake Biwa. *Bull. Japan. Soc. Sci. Fisheries* 15, 833-840.

Nikolsky, G. V. (1963). *The Ecology of Fishes* (translated by L. Birkett). Academic Press, New York, 352 pp.

Parker, G. H. (1922). *Smell, Taste, and Allied Senses in the Vertebrates*. Lippincott, Philadelphia, 192 pp.

Petraitis, R. (1966). Fine structure of supporting cells in the lateral line canalorgan of *Fundulus*. *J. Morphol.* 118, 367-378.

Satô, M. (1962). Studies on the pit organs of fishes. V. The structure and polysaccharide histochemistry of the cupula of the pit organ. *Annot. Zool. Japon.* 35, 80-88.

Senta, T. (1965). The buoyancy of sand-eel eggs and their distribution in the Seto Inland Sea. *Bull. Japan. Soc. Sci. Fisheries* 31, 511-516.

Shaw, E. (1960). The development of schooling behavior in fishes. *Physiol. Zool.* 33, 79-86.

———— (1961). The development of schooling behavior in fishes. II. *Physiol. Zool.* 34, 263-272.

Soin, S. G. (1964). Propagation and development of the White Sea dab *Limanda limanda* L. *Vopr. Ikhtiol.* 4, 495-511 (in Russian).

Suworow, J. K. (1959). *Allgemeine Fischkunde* (translated by H. W. Hattop). *Deutsch. Verlag Wiss.*, Berlin, 581 pp.

Thomopoulos, A. (1957). Sur la ligne laterale des téléostéens. II. La cupule et les neuromastes chez des embryons et des larves planctoniques d'espèces marines. *Bull. Soc. Zool. France* 82, 437-442.

Torrey, T. W. (1940). The influence of nerve fibers upon taste buds during embryonic development. *Proc. Natl. Acad. Sci. U.S.* 26, 627-634.

Trujillo-Cenóz, O. (1961). Electron microscope observations on chemo- and mechano-receptor cells of fishes. *Z. Zellforsch.* 54, 654-676.

Vasnetsov, V. V. (1948). Morphological characteristics which determine the feeding of the bream, roach and carp in all stages of development. Academy of Sciences, U.S.S.R. (after Nikolsky, 1963).

Yamashita, K. (1960). Madai shigyo no kôdô ni kansuru kôsatsu (observations on the behavior of larvae of the Japanese porgy). *Sogo Kaiyo Kagaku* (*Marine Sci.*) 2, 201-208 (in Japanese).

## DISCUSSION

WALKER: Your paper leads me to recall how important it is to study the behavior of larval fishes, as related to the dramatic changes that occur in the development of the lateral line system. Considering the size of the larvae and their somewhat feeble swimming efforts, and the problems they have in avoiding their being eaten, behavioral dependence on the lateral line system may be more significant than when they become larger, more "sophisticated" animals.

TESTER: When the larvae grow up, do they retain any of the naked neuromasts?

IWAI: Yes, they do retain some of the naked neuromasts.

FLOCK: Were you able to see any efferent nerve endings?

IWAI: No, only afferents were seen.

CAHN: In regard to the length of the cupulae described by Dr. Iwai, it must be kept in mind that he was studying newly hatched fry. As the young fish mature, the cupulae of both naked neuromasts and canal organs in many teleosts appear to become proportionately shorter and less flexible.

MARSHALL: I'm very glad that more information is now available on the shapes of the fish cupluae, especially in the larvae. Are the larval cupulae of importance in reactions to a turbulent medium? A small, 5-mm larva being swept about by turbulence might "like" to find, by the use of its neuromasts, some undisturbed water.

# 4 TRUNK LATERAL LINE NERVES: SOME ANATOMICAL ASPECTS †

JOAN A. SUCKLING

Department of Biological Sciences
Hunter College of the City University of New York
New York

For more than a hundred years the lateral line system has intrigued many researchers working in a number of different fields. The early workers were interested in its anatomical aspects; but, later, experimentation in behavior and physiology followed. At this time, it is clear that more complete knowledge of the neuroanatomy may affect both the theories and the types of experiments performed on this system. Many of the early workers—such as Allis (1903), Cole (1898), and Herrick (1899), to name a few—were more interested in the lateral line canals of the head than in those of the trunk, and this emphasis has continued to the present time. Stannius (1849) has left the most complete record of the trunk lateral line nerves for several different species.

In our studies we have more or less confined ourselves to the trunk portion of the lateral line system, and our interest in the neuroanatomy stems from some ambiguous results from neurophysiological experiments. This stimulated us to examine the nerve network lying between the neuromasts in the lateral line scales and the junction of the lateralis nerve with the vagus before it passes through the skull. Almost all the dissections were done on live or freshly killed fish, with the aid of a dissecting microscope.

## SCALE ARRANGEMENT

Goodrich's (1909) illustration of the lateral line scales shows clearly the individual neuromast in the lateral line canal, with the nerve twigs

† This work was supported in part by the Office of Naval Research, the American Museum of Natural History, Downstate Medical Center of the State University of New York, and the Bureau of Commercial Fisheries U.S. Fish and Wildlife Service.

Fig. 1. Series of lateral line scales from the trunk region of *Spondyliosoma cantharus*. ep, epithelium; c, canal; n, nerve twig to individual neuromast; dn, dorsal nerve.

passing from the lateral line nerve between the scales to the neuromasts. It is suggested that there may be some modification of this arrangement in various other species. In *Spondyliosoma cantharus*, a species of sea bream, the neuromast lies within the scale, and the nerve twig passes through the scale to join the dorsal ramus of the lateral line nerve. Removing the individual scale severs the nerve twig from the end organ.

Figure 1 illustrates the lateral line scales, neuromasts, and the nerve twigs and their relationship to the dorsal nerve. Figure 2 represents a series of scales just posterior to the pectoral girdle in the skipjack tuna. These are large, heavy armorlike scales with an anterior-posterior dimension of about 1 cm and a scale lateral line canal of about 0.7 cm. The neuromasts are very large, being of the order of 700 to 800 $\mu$. On

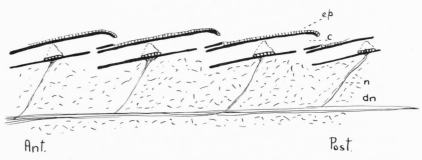

Fig. 2. Series of lateral line scales immediately posterior to the pectoral girdle in *Katsuwonus pelamis* (skipjack tuna). In individual scales the canal may be 0.7 cm in length and the neuromast 700 to 800 $\mu$. ep, epithelium; c, canal; n, nerve twig to neuromast; dn, dorsal nerve.

FIG. 3. Skipjack tuna (*K. pelamis*). Cross section of a lateral line scale taken from the edge of the corselet region, showing the typical neuromast within the scale. (The cupula has probably been destroyed during preparation of the material; there are blood cells and other debris within the canal.) c, lateral line canal.

the undersurface of each scale is a very small foramen, which lies close to the anterior opening of the next posterior scale. The size of the lateral line scales, their canals, and the neuromasts diminishes considerably caudad. In the largest anterior scales, there does not appear to be a continuous uniform lateral line canal of the type described by Goodrich for the perch. A cross section of a skipjack lateral line scale, from the edge of the corselet region, is shown in Fig. 3. This illustrates a scale with the typical neuromast present within the canal. There are blood cells and some debris in the canal, but no sign of a cupula, which was presumably destroyed in the preparation of the material. Unfortunately, attempts to section the largest scales were completely unsuccessful, so that a complete series of trunk lateral line scales is not available at present. Figure 4 shows a scale in the caudal peduncle region, where there is a very heavily cornified flange on either side of the tail. Both the size of the canal and the amount of neural tissue present are considerably reduced from that seen in Fig. 3. (Both sections are of the same magnification.)

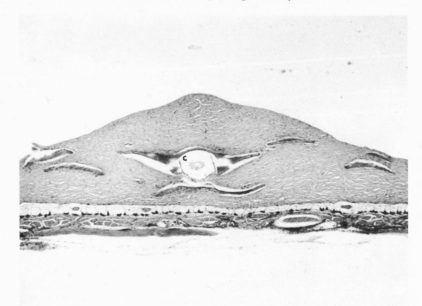

Fig. 4. Skipjack tuna (*K. pelamis*). Cross section of the lateral line in the region of the caudal peduncle, showing the heavily cornified flange. c, lateral line canal.

NEURAL PATHWAYS

Between the neuromasts on the surface of the fish's trunk and the point where the lateralis nerve becomes part of the vagus, there appears to be a number of different neural pathways or patterns that nerves may follow. The simplest appears in the carp and others (Allis, 1888-1889), where each nerve twig from an individual neuromast passes directly to the lateralis nerve. Another type is seen in *Fundulus heteroclitus*, where the lateral line nerve forms two rami, each of which has its own row of end organs, as discussed by Denny (1937-1938). A more complicated nerve pattern appears to be very common among teleosts. Variations on this pattern have been seen in over twenty different species of fish from twelve different families commonly caught in the vicinity of Bimini, Banyuls-sur-mer, Honolulu, and New York (see Table 1).

In this neural pattern the lateralis branch of the vagus may be quite superficial or may lie deeply along the horizontal septum. In skipjack tuna it may be as much as 1 cm below the surface. In addition to this nerve, there is always a dorsal ramus that is quite superficial and associated with the position of the lateral line scales. Passing from this

TABLE 1[a]

| Species | Location | Complete dissection | Partial dissection | Physio-logical evidence |
|---|---|---|---|---|
| *Simple lateralis nerve pattern; no dorsal branch* | | | | |
| Order Elopiformes, Family Elopidae: | | | | |
| *Albula vulpes* (Linnaeus) | Bimini | | 2 | – |
| Order Cypriniformes, Suborder Cyprinoidei, Family Cyprinidae: | | | | |
| *Cyprinus carpio* (Linnaeus) | New York | | 12 | – |
| *Dorsal nerve present with commissures passing to lateralis nerve* | | | | |
| Order Gadiformes, Family Merlucciidae: | | | | |
| *Merluccius bilinearis* (Mitchell) | New York | | 6 | – |
| Order Beryciformes, Family Holocentridae: | | | | |
| *Holocentrus ascensionis* (Osbeck) | Bimini | | 6 | 3 |
| Order Perciformes, Suborder Percoidei: | | | | |
| Family Serranidae: | | | | |
| *Epinephelus striatus* (Bloch) | Bimini | | 5 | 4 |
| *Epinephelus guttatus* (Linnaeus) | Bimini | | 5 | 3 |
| *Cephalopholis fulva* (Linnaeus) | Bimini | | 2 | – |
| *Serranus cabrilla* (Linnaeus) | Banyuls-sur-mer | | 5 | 1 |
| *Morone punctata* (Bloch) | Banyuls-sur-mer | | 1 | – |
| Family Branchiostegidae: | | | | |
| *Malacanthus plumieri* (Bloch) | Bimini | | 1 | – |
| Family Emmelichthyidae: | | | | |
| *Maena smaris* (Linnaeus) | Banyuls-sur-mer | 1 | 3 | 1 |
| Family Lutjanidae: | | | | |
| *Lutjanus griseus* (Linnaeus) | Bimini | | 5 | 3 |
| *Lutjanus apodus* (Walbaum) | Bimini | | 5 | 3 |
| Family Pomadasyidae: | | | | |
| *Haemulon sciurus* (Shaw) | Bimini | | 1 | – |
| Family Sparidae: | | | | |
| *Puntazzo puntazzo* (Cetti) | Banyuls-sur-mer | | 1 | 1 |
| *Pagellus mormyrus* (Linnaeus) | Banyuls-sur-mer | | 1 | 1 |
| *Pagellus erythrinus* (Linnaeus) | Banyuls-sur-mer | | 2 | 1 |
| *Spondyliosoma cantharus* (Linnaeus) | Banyuls-sur-mer | 1 | 9 | 6 |
| *Diplodus annularis* (Linnaeus) | Banyuls-sur-mer | 1 | 7 | 5 |
| *Diplodus vulgaris* (Geofr. St. Hilaire) | Banyuls-sur-mer | 1 | 4 | 4 |
| Family Chaetodontidae: | | | | |
| *Pomacanthus paru* (Bloch) | Bimini | | 2 | 1 |
| Family Cichlidae: | | | | |
| *Tilapia macrochir* | New York | | 6 | 4 |
| Suborder Labroidei: | | | | |
| Family Labridae: | | | | |
| *Tautoga onitis* (Linnaeus) | New York | | 6 | 6 |
| *Tautogolabrus adspersus* (Walbaum) | New York | | 3 | |
| Suborder Scomroidei: | | | | |
| Family Scombridae: | | | | |
| *Katsuwonus pelamis* (Linnaeus) | Hawaii | 1 | 34 | 20 |
| *Euthynnus affinis* (Cantor) | Hawaii | | 2 | – |
| *Thunnus albacares* (Bonnaterre) | Hawaii | | 2 | – |

[a] Classification essentially based on P. H. Greenwood, D. E. Rosen, S. H. Weitzman, and G. S. Myers, Phyletic studies of teleostean fishes, with a provisional classification of living forms, *Bull. Am. Museum Nat. Hist.* 131, art. 4, 1966, New York.

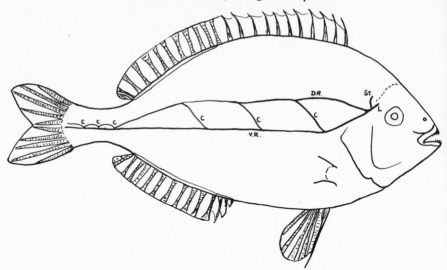

FIG. 5. *S. cantharus* illustrates the nerve network of the trunk lateral line nerve. The individual nerve twigs from the neuromasts join and become part of the dorsal nerve shown in Fig. 1. c, commissure; l, lateralis nerve; DR, dorsal ramus; VR, ventral ramus.

superficial dorsal ramus are a number of commissures which join the lateralis nerve. There may be as few as two, as Stannius demonstrated for the cod (1849); six, as seen in Fig. 5 for *Spondyliosoma cantharus;* ten, in some other marine teleosts; and up to thirty or more in skipjack

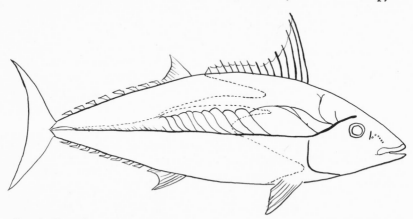

FIG. 6. Skipjack tuna illustrating trunk lateral line innervation (dashed line indicates edge of the corselet and lateral line scales in the posterior trunk and caudal region). Note numerous commissures between the dorsal nerve or ramus and the lateralis nerve, which is related to the position of the horizontal septum.

tuna, as illustrated in Fig. 6. Loops in the dorsal ramus are very common, and there may be more than one along its length. The commissures are not segmentally arranged; therefore they are easily distinguished from the spinal nerves. In *S. cantharus* the dorsal nerve appears continuous and unbroken, so that a question arises regarding the individual efferent and afferent fibers and their possible pathways between the neuromasts of the lateral line and the point where the lateralis nerve becomes part of the vagus. Some fibers obviously travel for only a short distance before passing by a commissure to the lateralis nerve, whereas others probably are part of the dorsal nerve for varying distances before crossing by a commissure to the more ventral nerve. The dorsal ramus in the pectoral region may be comparable in size to the lateral line nerve in this region, and both nerves have large and small fibers. The individual neuromasts are larger than the more posterior ones. The most anterior nerve twigs were estimated to be approximately 300 $\mu$ in skipjack tuna, and they reflect the large size of the sensory receptors in the more anterior part of the trunk.

Preliminary histological studies on the lateralis nerve of *Katsuwonus pelamis* and *Tautogolabrus adspersus* suggest that there are both large and small fibers present. The number appears to be of the order of 1000 fibers in the lateralis nerve, before it becomes part of the vagus.

## REFERENCES

Allis, E. P., Jr. (1888-1889). The anatomy and development of the lateral line system in *Amia calva*. *J. Morphol.* 2, 463-566.

———— (1903). The skull and the cranial and first spinal muscles and nerves in *Scomber scomber*. *J. Morphol.* 18, 45-328.

Cole, F. J. (1898). Observations on the structure and morphology of the cranial nerves and lateral sense organs of fishes with special reference to the genus *Gadus*. *Trans. Linn. London Ser.* 2, Vol. 7, Pt. 5, 115-221.

Denny, M. (1937-1938). The lateral line system of the teleost *Fundulus heteroclitus*. *J. Comp. Neurol.* 68, 49-65.

Goodrich, E. S. (1909). *A Treatise on Zoology*. Part IX. *Vertebrata Craniata, Cyclostomes and Fishes*. A. & C. Black, London.

Herrick, C. J. (1899). The cranial and first spinal nerves of *Menidia*, a contribution upon the nerve components of bony fishes. *J. Comp. Neurol.* 9, 153-455.

Stannius, H. (1849). *Das peripherische Nervensysteme der Fische*. Rostock.

## COMMENTS

WALKER: The distribution of the lateral line nerves as demonstrated here brings up the very important and embarrassing problem of how to extirpate the total system. I should like to stress that the lateral line nerves also innervate many tiny surface neuromasts from the very same twigs which supply the canal neuromasts. Many of the surface neuromasts can only be seen after special staining, and their nerve branchlets are no more than 1 or 2 mm in length, often passing for their full length within the armor of the scale. How can one determine differences in function of the two types of neuromasts by cutting lateral line nerves?

LUND: Were you able to find the lateral line nerve extending posterior to the caudal peduncle?

SUCKLING: No. As far as we could observe, while viewing through a binocular microscope, the nerve gets very fine as one proceeds caudally. In the region of the tail, we could no longer see the nerve.

CHARIPPER: Do you have any information on the lateral line organs in the head of the fishes you studied?

SUCKLING: No, we were more interested in the trunk structure, that is, in the small interconnections from scale to scale.

# 5 INNERVATION OF FREE AND CANAL NEUROMASTS IN THE SHARKS *CARCHARHINUS MENISORRAH* AND *SPHYRNA LEWINI* †

ALBERT L. TESTER AND JAMES I. KENDALL

Department of Zoology
University of Hawaii
Honolulu, Hawaii

Tester and Nelson (1967) reported recently on the identification, distribution, morphology. and histology of so-called "pit organs" in shark species of the families Squalidae, Orectolobidae, Triakidae, Carcharhinidae, and Sphyrnidae.

In the species they examined, each pit organ is associated with a pair of modified scales (two or more pairs in *Squalus*) partially protecting it from water currents flowing along the surface of the body. Usually, the anterior scale of the pair is only slightly modified as compared with the normal scale, whereas the posterior scale is strongly modified, with a raised crest on the crown. If care is taken to distinguish these modified scales from those associated with other structures such as openings to sensory canal tubules and openings to ampullae of Lorenzini, they serve to mark the location of the pit organs.

As reported by Johnson (1917) and Norris and Hughes (1920) for *Squalus acanthias* and *Mustelus canis,* and later by Budker (1938) for other species, there is a pair of pit organs in front of each endolymphatic pore, a mandibular row back of the lower jaw, and an umbilical row between the pectoral fins. These authors also found a lateral row in some species (accessory neuromasts of Johnson, 1917) on the body dorsal to the lateral sensory canal, and a dorsolateral (or parasagittal) row extending from the head either to the first dorsal fin (as in S. *acanthias,* Fig. 1A) or along the entire length of the body (as in *M.*

† Contribution No. 269, Hawaii Institute of Marine Biology, University of Hawaii. We are indebted to the Office of Naval Research for financial support of this study.

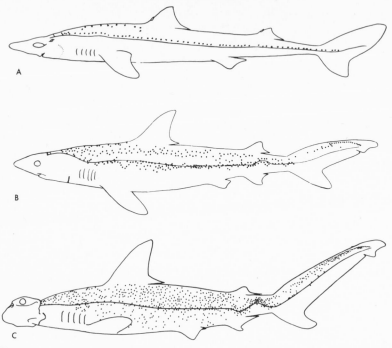

Fɪɢ. 1. Pit-organ distribution (each pit organ is represented by a dot) in (A) *S. acanthias* (79 cm), (B) *C. menisorrah* (56 cm), and (C) *S. lewini* (61 cm).

*canis*). Tester and Nelson (1967) showed, however, that in other species (e.g., *Carcharhinus menisorrah*, Fig. 1B) the pit organs extend in two diffuse bands along the dorsolateral surface of the body, with a row reaching the tip of the caudal fin. They showed that in still other species, pit organs are scattered along the dorsolateral surface of the body in an apparently random arrangement, sometimes (as in *Sphyrna lewini*, Fig. 1C) extending well below the lateral sensory canal. However, even when widely scattered, the pit organs are spaced discretely, and at times they seem to be lined up in short rows that run perpendicular or at an oblique angle to the longitudinal axis of the shark.

Pit organs (Pl. I-1) are budlike structures arising from the epidermal epithelium between the bases of modified scales (Budker, 1938, 1958; Tester and Nelson, 1967). They consist of (1) pear-shaped sensory cells extending about halfway between the proximal membrane and the distal surface, with sensory hairs; (2) elongated supporting cells extending the entire height of the organ, enveloping the sensory cells at their periphery and probably extending between them; and (3) a delicate tonguelike cupula resting on the distal surface of the sensory cells and enveloping the projecting sensory hairs. The cupulae, seen by Tester and Nelson only in a few sections of S. *lewini*, seemed to be applied (or attached?) to the posterior tip of the anterior scale crown and to the anterior edge of the posterior scale crown. These authors are uncertain whether the cupula is a gelatinous tongue with definite form as in larval teleost fishes (Cahn and Shaw, 1962; Branson and Moore, 1962; Iwai, 1963, 1964) or whether it is a mucous covering without definite form. Despite this uncertainty, they conclude that the pit organs are free neuromasts, as stated by Johnson (1917), rather than external taste buds, as suggested by Budker (1938, 1958).

The present paper is concerned with innervation of the free and canal neuromasts in advanced embryo and juvenile sharks. It is hoped that the information presented here, although not yet complete, will be of value in designing electrophysiological and behavioral experiments aimed at clarifying the function of the lateral line sensory system in sharks, and particularly in determining the respective parts played by free and canal neuromasts in their presumed function of mediating water displacements and providing information on the location of prey in the near field (Dijkgraaf, 1963).

MATERIALS AND METHODS

The material for dissection and microtechnique consisted primarily of several formalin-preserved, advanced *C. menisorrah* embryos (30 to 33 cm total length, taken from a 168-cm female, Johnson Island, Pacific Ocean, 1965); one *C. menisorrah* juvenile (ca. 100 cm, Johnson Island, 1965); and several freshly caught juvenile S. *lewini* (50 to 60 cm, Kaneohe Bay, Oahu, 1965). In addition, the ramus lateralis (X) was traced in *Negaprion brevirostris* (74 cm, Bimini, Bahamas, 1964) and in *Ginglymostoma cirratum* (127 cm, Bimini, Bahamas, 1964). Also, the ramus mandibularis (VII) was traced in *C. melanopterus* (heads from small juveniles, Christmas Island, Pacific Ocean, 1963).

In tracing the paths of the major nerves, as dissection proceeded, the formalin-preserved tissues were flooded with a saturated solution of Oil Red O (C.I. 26125) in 99% isopropyl alcohol, washed briefly with 60% isopropyl alcohol, and then washed with tap water. This stained the nerves, particularly the finer branches, a brighter red color than the muscle or connective tissue. The larger nerves stained only after their connective tissue sheath was cut or teased apart to allow the dye to penetrate. Dissection continued until the nerves could no longer be seen, and the staining process was repeated. Some preparations were immersed in Oil Red O for one to several hours and were then de-

PLATE I. (1) Longitudinal section through pit organ of juvenile *S. lewini* (Bouin's, hematoxylin-triosin) showing shallow sensory cells and elongate supporting cells. The pit organ lies between an anterior (left) and a posterior (right) modified scale. (2) Section along mandibular row of pit organs in juvenile *C. menisorrah* (silver-impregnated, toluidine blue) showing nerves entering pit organs. (3) Tangential section through dermis posterior to gill slits in embryo *C. menisorrah* (silver-impregnated) showing two subramuli innervating canal neuromasts and a pit-organ nerve trunk arising from subramulus (near center) and dividing into two pit-organ nerves, one proceeding posterodorsally and the other looping over the canal and proceeding posteroventrally. Branched spinal nerves in background. (4) Tangential section through dermis in midbody region of embryo *C. menisorrah* (silver-impregnated) showing subramuli innervating canal neuromasts and three pit-organ nerves (arising from subramuli, but connections not shown) looping over the canal to proceed posteroventrally in the dermis. The third loop has a branch that proceeds posterodorsally. Branched spinal nerves in background. (5) Whole mount of stripped dermis of juvenile *S. lewini* from anterior part of body (decalcified, bleached, silver-impregnated) showing pit-organ nerve following a straight course and arborizing within pit organ near right-hand side. Spinal nerve network in background. (6) Cross section of caudal peduncle of embryo *C. menisorrah* (silver-impregnated) showing nerve plexus of lateral sensory canal and innervation of a pit organ (enlarged in Pl. II-1) lying above the canal.

PLATE II. (1) Cross section of caudal peduncle of embryo *C. menisorrah* (silver-impregnated) showing fibers of a pit-organ nerve entering a pit organ. (2) Cross section of caudal peduncle of embryo *C. menisorrah* (silver-impregnated, gold-toned) showing pit-organ nerve fibers dividing into fibrils and fibrillae within the pit organ. The sensory cells cannot be seen. (3) Cross section of caudal peduncle of embryo *C. menisorrah* (silver-impregnated, gold-toned) showing the lateral sensory canal nerve plexus, fibrils and fibrillae. The sensory cells cannot be seen. (4) Longitudinal section of caudal peduncle of embryo *C. menisorrah* (silver-impregnated, gold-toned) showing the heavy nerve plexus below the basement membrane, fibrils penetrating the membrane and dividing into fibrillae within the neuromast. The sensory cells cannot be seen. (5) Cross section of caudal peduncle of juvenile *S. lewini* (formalin, decalcified, silver-impregnated, toluidine blue, 10-$\mu$ paraffin section, oil immersion) showing a neuromast of the lateral sensory canal, sensory cells, and presumed sensory hairs. (6) Tangential section of dermis of embryo *C. menisorrah* (silver-impregnated) showing the coiled ending of a fine branch of a spinal nerve within a "terminal corpuscle."

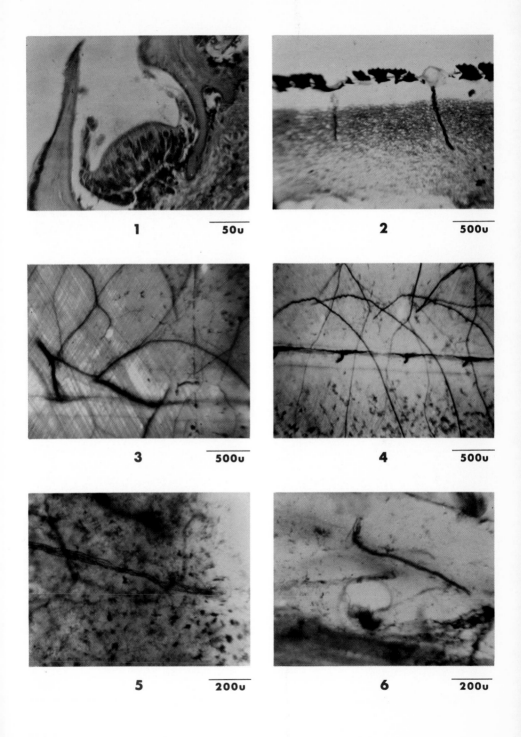

1                    50u

2                    500u

3                    500u

4                    500u

5                    200u

6                    200u

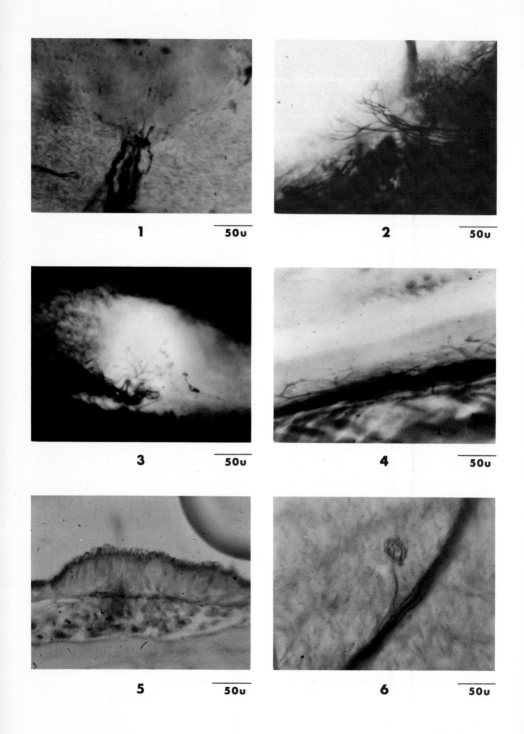

1                    50u          2                    50u

3                    50u          4                    50u

5                    50u          6                    50u

stained and washed as above before dissection, with similar differential staining results. Very little success was achieved with Williams's (1943) method (maceration and clearing in KOH, immersion in Sihler's solutions, and clearing in glycerine) when applied to either whole embryos or parts of juvenile sharks.

Details of free and canal neuromast innervation were determined by cutting thick (50 $\mu$ or more) frozen sections at various angles to the surface of the body with a sliding microtome. Some skin preparations were stripped from the body with the aid of a razor blade or scalpel. In some cases, frozen sections and freehand preparations were stained in Oil Red O, cleared in glycerine, and mounted in glycerine jelly. The myelinated nerves were well differentiated by the stain. In other cases, frozen sections and freehand preparations were impregnated with silver after the method of Gilbert (1965), dehydrated in 99% isopropyl alcohol, cleared in xylol, and mounted in synthetic resin (Permount). Some silver-impregnated sections were gold-toned. Considerable variation in the success of silver impregnation was encountered, particularly in those preparations which previously had been bleached to remove melanin pigment and then decalcified (or just decalcified), both to soften the scales and to prevent silver uptake in them.

RESULTS

As found by Norris and Hughes (1920) in *S. acanthias* and *M. canis*, the mandibular row of pit organs in *C. menisorrah*, *C. melanopterus*, and *S. lewini* is innervated for the most part by branches of a long, slender nerve arising from the posterior division of the ramus mandibularis externus (VII) (Fig. 2). This nerve, lying superficially in the subcutaneous connective tissue, parallels the course of the mandibular row but remains anterior to it on the side of the head and distal to it on the ventral surface of the head. Its ramuli, sometimes branched, run posteriorly in the connective tissue before entering the dermis to innervate individual pit organs (Pl. I-2). This slender nerve does not innervate the entire row. The first few pit organs, those anterior to the first gill slit, are supplied by branches arising directly from the main trunk of the posterior division of the ramus mandibularis externus (VII).

As nearly as can be determined, all remaining pit organs of the body are innervated by branches of the vagus (X), although there is some question as to whether the ramus supratemporalis (IX) participates in innervating a few in the dorsocephalic region (Budker, 1938, citing Hawkes, 1906, for *Chlamydoselachus*, and Ewart and Cole, 1895, for

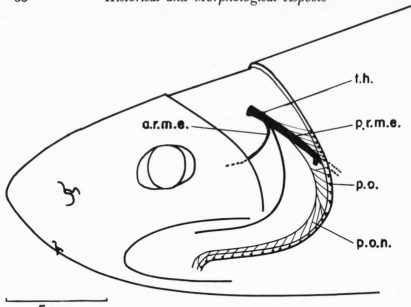

5 cm.

FIG. 2. Innervation of the mandibular row of pit organs by the facial nerve
(VII) in a juvenile *C. melanopterus*. a.r.m.e., anterior division of ramus mandibularis externus; p.o., pit organ; p.o.n., pit-organ nerve; p.r.m.e., posterior division
of ramus mandibularis externus; t.h., truncus hyomandibularis.

*Laemargus*). However, Norris and Hughes (1920) state categorically
that no pit organs are connected with the ninth nerve, even though the
ramus supratemporalis (IX) sends three ramuli to canal neuromasts
in the anterior part of the lateral sensory canal.

In the sharks we have examined, we have not yet managed to trace
satisfactorily the ramus supratemporalis (X), which in *S. acanthias*
innervates the neuromasts of the commissural canal and the pair of pit
organs situated just anterior to the endolymphatic duct; nor have we
been able to trace the ramus dorsalis (X), which in *S. acanthias* innervates a few anterior neuromasts of the lateral sensory canal and a row
of dorsolateral pit organs extending from above the gills to the first
dorsal fin. Because the species with which we have worked lack a
definite dorsolateral row, there is some question as to whether the
ramus dorsalis (X) exists as a separate nerve or whether it is represented by anterior ramuli of the ramus lateralis (X). Also we have not
yet attempted to trace the innervation of the umbilical row of pit organs, which in *S. acanthias* is supplied by a branch of the ramus post-
trematic of the fourth branchial nerve (X-3). To date we have directed

our attention to tracing the ramus lateralis (X) and its ramuli, which innervate most of the lateral sensory canal and the pit organs scattered over the dorsolateral surface of the body.

The ramus lateralis (X), or lateral line nerve, is a large nerve emerging from the posterior border of the lateral line ganglion and passing first laterally and then medially in an arc above the gill chambers. It then follows the vertebral column along the body, lying adjacent to the centra and just above the transverse septum between the dorsal and ventral muscle masses (Fig. 3). Below the notch in the caudal peduncle it veers rather abruptly toward the dermis. Along the caudal fin it lies within the transverse septum, adjacent to the dermis but medial to the lateral vein and dorsal to the lateral sensory canal. The path of the ramus lateralis (X) is similar in juvenile *S. lewini* and embryo *C. menisorrah*. In contrast, in juvenile *N. brevirostris* and *G. cirratum*, the ramus lateralis veers abruptly toward the dermis in the caudal peduncle, starting at the base of the second dorsal fin. This may be an ontogenetic change which may also take place in larger specimens of *S. lewini* and *C. menisorrah*. The diameter of the ramus lateralis, about 2 to 3 mm at its origin in a 60-cm specimen, progressively decreases from the head to the tip of the caudal fin.

Starting near the lateral line ganglion, branches or ramuli are given off segmentally from the ramus lateralis (X). Anterior to the caudal peduncle, each ramulus emerges from a slight swelling of the ramus lateralis opposite each vertebra and proceeds posteriorly at an acute angle, at first nearly paralleling the ramus (Fig. 4). The ramulus then proceeds posterodorsally, without branching, within the connective tissue sheath between the myomeres until it reaches the subcutaneous connective tissue in the vicinity of the lateral vein. Here, each ramulus divides into three or more branches or subramuli. Each subramulus then proceeds dorsally to enter the dermis at the level of the lateral sensory canal and to innervate the canal neuromasts that lie on its medial wall (Pl. I-3). It may be noted that spinal nerves, emerging from each vertebra, pass above and below the ramus lateralis at the origin of each ramulus and follow a similar course. These may be distinguished from the ramuli by their origin, by the greater angle at which they emerge, and by their branching into the musculature.

In juvenile *S. lewini*, the subramuli entering the lateral sensory canal anterior to the caudal peduncle are about 85 μ in diameter (in silver-impregnated preparations), and are spaced about 1 mm from each other. A subramulus enters the medial wall of the canal opposite each canal tubule and sends fibers along the canal wall both anteriorly and posteriorly to interdigitate with those of adjacent subramuli, forming

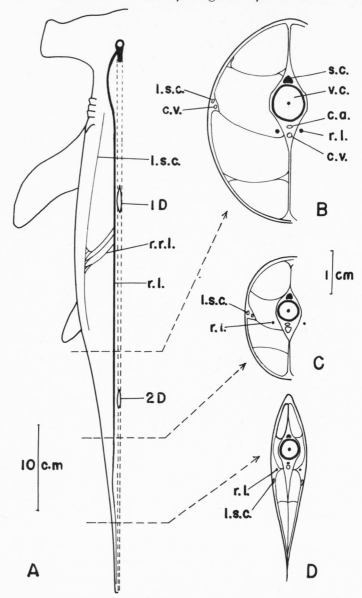

Fig. 3. Diagram of path of ramus lateralis (X) in *S. lewini*. (A) Dorsal view.
(B) Cross section anterior to second dorsal fin. (C) Cross section through caudal
peduncle. (D) Cross section through caudal fin. 1D, first dorsal fin; 2D, second
dorsal fin; c.a., caudal artery; c.v., caudal vein; l.s.c., lateral sensory canal; r.l.,
ramus lateralis; r.r.l., ramulus of ramus lateralis; s.c., spinal cord; v.c., vertebral
column.

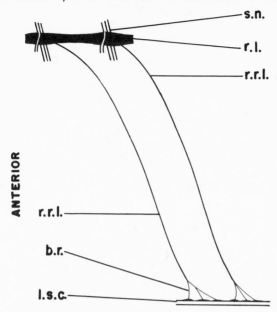

Fɪɢ. 4. Dorsal view of ramus lateralis, its ramuli and subramuli (not drawn to scale). b.r., subramulus; l.s.c., lateral sensory canal; r.l., ramus lateralis; r.r.l., ramulus of ramus lateralis; s.n., spinal nerve.

a continuous nerve plexus. From this plexus, individual fibers enter three aggregations of cells lying within the canal on its medial wall. Each aggregation, separated by a slight depression in the sensory epithelium, is a neuromast consisting of sensory cells surrounded by supporting cells. Each neuromast is about 300 $\mu$ in length and about 85 $\mu$ in width. The middle neuromast appears to be innervated by fibers from both an anterior and a posterior subramulus.

Canal innervation is similar in embryo *C. menisorrah* to that just described for *S. lewini*. Although the subramuli are more slender (about 45 $\mu$ in diameter), they also are spaced about 1 mm from each other and enter the canal opposite a canal tubule. There are also three neuromasts in the sensory epithelium between two subramuli. The arrangement differs from that reported by Johnson (1917) for *M. canis*. On the anterior part of the body of this species, the ramuli apparently enter the canal opposite each canal tubule without branching into subramuli, and there are about 16 neuromasts in the sensory epithelium between two adjacent ramuli.

On the caudal peduncle and anterior part of the caudal fin of *S. lewini* and *C. menisorrah*, as the ramus lateralis moves closer to the dermis, the ramuli become progressively shorter and divide into two subramuli only (at least in S. *lewini*) before entering the canal. Farther posterior, where the ramus lateralis lies close to the lateral vein and dorsal to the canal, the ramuli are short and do not branch before entering the canal. They are about 70 μ in diameter in S. *lewini* and about 27 μ in diameter in C. *menisorrah*. In both species they are spaced about 2 to 3 mm from one another, but the spacing rapidly decreases at the caudal end. There is a pronounced thinning of the nerve plexus of the canal between adjacent ramuli, but we have been unable to determine how many neuromasts occur.

Pit organ innervation along the body is similar in S. *lewini* and C. *menisorrah* (Fig. 5A). Nerve branches, consisting usually of 10 to 15 fibers, arise from the subramuli and proceed through the subcutaneous connective tissue to enter the dermis immediately dorsal to the lateral sensory canal. On entering the dermis, they divide into 2 or 3 subbranches, each usually of 5 (more rarely of 3, 4, or 6) fibers, 1 or 2 of which are sometimes more slender than the rest. These are the pit organ nerves. A 5-fiber nerve measures 25 to 30 μ in diameter in juvenile S. *lewini*, and 15 to 20 μ in diameter in embryo C. *menisorrah* silver-impregnated preparations. When two subbranches occur, one proceeds posterodorsally between the compact and vascular layers of the dermis, without further branching, to innervate a single pit organ lying dorsal to the canal; the other loops posterodorsally over the canal and then proceeds posteroventrally between the two dermal layers, without branching, to innervate a single pit organ lying either directly over or ventral to the canal. When three subbranches occur, two proceed dorsally and one ventrally as just described. Thus the pit organ nerves form a dorsal and a ventral series, each consisting of unbranched nerves of uniform diameter that follow a parallel course (Pl. I-4). However, single or paired dorsal pit organs are linked to single ventral pit organs by a common nerve trunk arising from a subramulus.

On the caudal fin of S. *lewini*, after the ramus lateralis takes up a position adjacent to the lateral vein in the subcutaneous connective tissue, individual pit organ nerves arise from the ramus lateralis directly, rather than from its ramuli (Fig. 5B). When pit organs occur both dorsal and ventral to the canal, as is the case along the anterior part of the caudal fin, individual pit organ nerves arise from either the dorsal or the ventral surface of the ramus lateralis. They then proceed between the two dermal layers, running directly to the respective dorsal or ventral pit organ. Toward the end of the caudal fin, the nerves arise only from the dorsal surface of the ramus to innervate individual pit organs of the row along the dorsolateral surface of the fin (Fig.

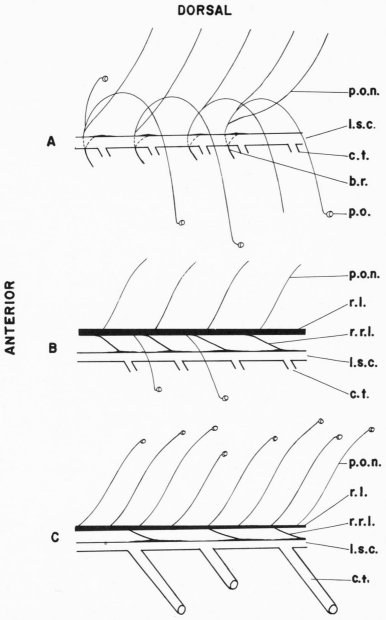

FIG. 5. Diagrams of lateral sensory canal and pit-organ innervation. (A) Anterior to caudal peduncle. (B) Anterior part of caudal fin. (C) Posterior part of caudal fin. b.r., subramulus; c.t., canal tubule; l.s.c., lateral sensory canal; p.o., pit organ; p.o.n., pit organ nerve; r.l., ramus lateralis; r.r.l., ramulus of ramus lateralis.

5C). The pit organ nerves of the caudal fin, as of the body, consist usually of 5 fibers. Occasionally a thicker nerve arises from the dorsal surface of the ramus to divide near its base into two nerves, which then follow the usual parallel course to innervate adjacent pit organs. The ramus lateralis appears to terminate abruptly, giving off two finer nerves (3 or 4 fibers) to innervate the two terminal pit organs of the caudal fin.

The arrangement of pit organ nerves on the caudal fin of embryo *C. menisorrah* is similar to that of juvenile *S. lewini*, except that on the posterior part of the fin the nerves innervating the dorsal row of pit organs arise either from the ventral side of the ramus lateralis or from the ventrally directed ramulus. They loop ventrally before proceeding posterodorsally to the dorsal row of pit organs. Some of the thicker nerves divide into two or three branches near their bases before proceeding in a parallel course to adjacent pit organs.

The pit organ nerves are characterized by their uniform size, number of fibers, straight path, parallel arrangement, and lack of branching (Pl. I-5). They may be distinguished readily from spinal nerves, which also occur in the dermis but which branch, anastomose, and decrease progressively in size. Some of the spinal nerves of the dermis appear to end in fibrillae in the vascular layer, often adjacent to melanophores which they may innervate. Often fine branches of spinal nerves end in a complex coil within oval-shaped corpuscular bodies in the connective tissue, particularly on or near the walls of blood vessels (Pl. II-6). Similar "terminal corpuscles" with coiled nerve endings have been described by Wunderer (1908) in the connective tissue of the fins of elasmobranchs. Their function has been investigated by Lowenstein (1956), with the conclusion that they are primarily pressure receptors but may also serve as second-order proprioceptors. Bone (1964) reports that they occur also in the edges of myosepta, just under the skin.

The termination of the pit organ nerves is seen best in silver-impregnated frozen sections of embryo *C. menisorrah*. On reaching a position below the pit organ, the nerve veers sharply toward it through the vascular layer of the dermis (Pl. I-6). Just before reaching the neuromast the fibers start to spread, lose their myelin sheath, and branch below the basement membrane of the neuromast (the "plexus sousgemmal" of Budker, 1938) (Pl. II-1). From the plexus, fine fibrils penetrate the basement membrane and arborize into fibrillae ending about halfway through the epithelium, presumably at or near the bases of the sensory cells (Pl. II-2). The intimate relationship of the free endings to the sensory cells cannot be seen. The fibrils occasionally show varicosities (triangular-shaped swellings) where they branch, and the fibrillae occasionally have end knobs. However, both may be artifacts of the silver-impregnation technique. In caudal pit organs still undergoing development, the plexus is poorly developed and the fibrils seem to end before penetrating the basement membrane.

Innervation of the canal neuromasts is essentially similar to that of the pit organs. The fibers comprising the much more extensive nerve plexus derived from the ramuli or subramuli lose their myelin sheath and divide into fibrils in the connective tissue below the basement membrane (Pl. II-3; Pl. II-4). The fibrils then penetrate the membrane and arborize into fibrillae as described for the pit organs. The individual fibrillae appear to terminate in free nerve endings among the sensory cells. Varicosities at fibril branches and small end knobs on the fibrillae are seen occasionally. The pattern of innervation of the canal neuromasts is similar to that described for *M. canis* by Johnson (1917).

The silver-impregnated sections of *S. lewini* and *C. menisorrah* show a brushlike fringe (about 3 $\mu$ in height) at the distal surface of the sensory cells of both canal and free neuromasts (Pl. II-5). The fringe may consist of sensory hairs, or it may be formed of the protruding ends of sensory cells. The interpretation is uncertain at present.

DISCUSSION

From studies of morphology and histology, Tester and Nelson (1967) conclude that the pit organs of sharks are free neuromasts, as assumed by Norris and Hughes (1920), rather than external taste buds, as suggested by Budker (1938, 1958). The present study of innervation of pit organs of *C. menisorrah* and *S. lewini* supports this conclusion, as do the earlier studies of *M. canis* and *S. acanthias* by Johnson (1917) and Norris and Hughes (1920). On the dorsolateral surface of the body and caudal fin, where the majority of the pit organs occur, their innervation is intimately associated with that of the canal neuromasts. Both are supplied by branches arising from the ramus lateralis (X).

Tester and Nelson (1967) note that in species such as *C. menisorrah* and *S. lewini* the pit organs of the dorsolateral surface of the body seem occasionally to be lined up in short rows running perpendicular or at an oblique angle to the longitudinal axis of the body. We have not found a common nerve paralleling and innervating these short rows. Rather, each pit organ is innervated by its own nerve, which may run for a considerable distance (one to several centimeters) in the dermis. However, sometimes two or three pit organs—one or two dorsal and one ventral to the lateral sensory canal—are linked by a common nerve trunk arising from a subramulus. If the pit organs, like other free neuromasts, are assumed to be mechanoreceptors mediating water displacement, this arrangement should provide information simultaneously on displacements at two or three different levels in the same vertical plane. At the same time, because of the discrete spacing of pairs or groups in a series of vertical planes along the body, information should also be transmitted to the central nervous system on displacements along the longitudinal axis of the body. This "programming" system, along with that of the canal neuromasts, may provide part of the mechanism for locating a source of water displacement in the near field, as suggested by Dijkgraaf (1963).

The present study is incomplete. The nerve supply of the umbilical row of pit organs and of the most anterior pit organs on the head, known for S. *acanthias*, should be determined for other species. In addition, much more extensive histological work is needed to determine the orientation of the sensory cells and cupulae of pit organs with respect to the body axis, for their orientation governs directional response (Dijkgraaf, 1963). Electron microscopy should be employed to reveal the details of sensory cell innervation and to investigate the intimate structure of the sensory hairs, several of which may be associated with one sensory cell.

This study is aimed at providing information on innervation as a guide to electrophysiological and behavioral experiments. It is obvious that electrophysiological experiments on *in situ* or excised preparations of pit organs will be difficult because of the problem of microdissection through the hard scales and into the tough dermis, because of the small size of the pit organ nerves, and because of the difficulty of isolating pit organ nerves from the confusing network of spinal nerves closely associated with them in the dermis. However, the task is not impossible, particularly in sharks such as S. *acanthias,* in which the pit organs of the lateral row are relatively large and easy to locate and in which the scales are more widely spaced than in other species. Equally delicate operations have been performed, e.g., by Lowenstein (1956), on terminal corpuscles in the connective tissue at the base of the fins in *Scyliorhinus canicula.*

It will be difficult also to differentially occlude canal and free neuromasts for behavioral experiments. Severing the lateral line nerve will occlude both systems caudad to the operation. Elimination of canal neuromasts by injecting drugs or other substances into the canal is one possibility, provided the escape of the substance through the canal tubules can be blocked. The elimination of free neuromasts can be accomplished fairly readily by direct application of drugs or other substances to the pit organs, particularly in those species such as S. *acanthias* in which the pit organs are large, few in number, and lined up in rows. It would be difficult to accomplish in species such as S. *lewini,* in which the lateral pit organs are numerous and scattered, without also occluding the sensory elements of the spinal nerves in the dermis and thus complicating the interpretation of the results. Despite these difficulties, such experiments should be tried, for they are essential to providing definitive information on the respective functions of free and canal neuromasts.

REFERENCES

Bone, Q. (1964). Patterns of muscular innervation in the lower chordates. *Intern. Rev. Neurobiol.* 6, 99-147.

Branson, B. A., and G. A. Moore (1962). The lateralis components of the acustico-lateralis system in the sunfish family Centrarchidae. *Copeia* 1, 1-108.

Budker, P. (1938). Les cryptes sensorielles et les denticules cutanés des plagiostomes. *Ann. Inst. Oceanog.* 18, 207-288.

————— (1958). Les organes sensoriels cutanés des sélaciens, in *Traité de Zoologie,* 15(2). Library de l'Academie de Médicine. Masson, Paris, pp. 1033-1062.

Cahn, P. H., and E. Shaw (1962). The first demonstration of lateral line cupulae in the Mugiliformes. *Copeia* 1, 109-114.

Dijkgraaf, S. (1963). The functioning and significance of the lateral line organs. *Biol. Rev.* 38, 51-105.

Ewart, J. C., and F. J. Cole (1895). On the dorsal branches of the cranial and spinal nerves of Elasmobranchs. *Proc. Roy. Soc. Edinburgh* 20, 475-480.

Gilbert, B. (1965). Triple silver impregnation for selective staining of avian nerves. *Stain Technol.* 40, 301-304.

Hawkes, O. A. (1906). The cranial and spinal nerves of *Chlamydoselachus anguineus* Gar. *Proc. Zool. Soc. London* 2, 959-990 (cited by Budker, 1938).

Iwai, T. (1963). Development of lateral-line cupulae in the gobioid fish, *Tridentiger trigonocephalus* (Gill). *Misaki Marine Biol. Inst. Kyoto Univ. Bull.* 4, 1-20.

————— (1964). Development of cupulae in free neuromasts of the Japanese mendaka *Oryzias latipes* (Temminck et Schlegel). *Misaki Marine Biol. Inst. Kyoto Univ. Bull.* 5, 31-37.

Johnson, S. E. (1917). Structure and development of the sense organs of the lateral canal system of selachians (*Mustelus canis* and *Squalus acanthias*). *J. Comp. Neurol.* 28(1), 1-74.

Lowenstein, O. E. (1956). Pressure receptors in the fins of the dogfish *Scylliorhinus canicula. J. Exptl. Biol.* 33(2), 417-421.

Norris, H. W., and S. P. Hughes (1920). The cranial, occipital and anterior spinal nerves of the dogfish (*Squalus acanthias*). *J. Comp. Neurol.* 31, 293-402.

Tester, A. L., and G. J. Nelson (1967). Free neuromasts (pit organs) in sharks, in *Sharks, Skates and Rays.* Johns Hopkins Press, Baltimore, pp. 503-531.

Williams, T. W. (1943). A technique for the gross differential staining of peripheral nerves in cleared vertebrate tissue. *Anat. Rec.* 86, 189-194.

Wunderer, H. (1908). Über Terminalkörperchen der Anamnien. *Arch. mikroskop. Anat.* 71, 504-569.

## COMMENTS

FLOCK: I think it is a very interesting, admirable, and important work. I noticed that you mentioned that in a shark neuromast there is a long axis and a short axis, and this could be seen in the outline of the sensory cell. If you look at the canal organs in other fishes, and in the free neuromasts in the toad, you always have a rather oval crypt, and it's always along the long axis that the directional displacement is able to cause excitation. Therefore we have here a means to provide directional information. We would assume that the toad or the fish would line up so that these organs would give the animal important directional information. This would permit the animal to pick up the significant vertorial or hydrodynamic displacement. It therefore would be very interesting to study the orientation of the neuromasts in the lateral line scales along the body of fishes.

TESTER: This has been done to a small extent. It deserves a much more thorough study, but we find differences such as you have indicated. In the canals the axis is longitudinal; whereas, at least in those free neuromasts we have studied in tangential section, the sensory cells are definitely arranged vertically. I would like to do more work on this problem, to trace them all over the body and try to get their exact orientation with regard to the body axis, because I feel as you do that this is extremely important.

SCHWARTZ: I have made some observations on the arrangement of neuromasts on the body of the topminnow, and it was found that there were three lines of naked neuromasts arranged in clusters. The neuromasts in one line were arranged mostly parallel. In another line, the neuromasts showed an alternating orientation—one was perpendicular to the longitudinal axis, and the other was parallel.

MOULTON: In your behavioral studies, is there any correlation between the distribution of these neuromasts and the swimming behavior or other overt behavior that would permit some kind of a correlation in the distribution of turbulence receptors, or something of that kind?

TESTER: I have hunted for some general relationship between differences in shark behavior and the change in pattern of distribution of pit organs from the simple arrangement in *Squalus* to the complex pattern in *Sphyrna*. I've been unable to find anything in the literature that would indicate that the sharks with the greater number of neuromasts behave differently in some way from the others. However, this doesn't mean that the literature is accurate or complete in this regard. Last year I started out to do some conditioned-response experiments, and I found that sharks can be conditioned to respond to a current impinged on their bodies. When they're crosswise to the current, they respond better than when they're longitudinal to the current. I thought that all I had to do was to occlude one of the sensory systems and find out whether the free neuromasts or the canal neuromasts were responsible for this response. At that point, of course, I ran into difficulty. I didn't know enough about the morphology or the innervation to approach this problem intelligently, so I went back to the microscope and the microtome to learn more about these aspects. I think that this must be done before we can ever hope to understand thoroughly the parts played by the respective sensory organs.

# II BEHAVIORAL AND ELECTROPHYSIOLOGICAL STUDIES OF LATERAL LINE FUNCTION

LATERAL LINE DETECTORS (P. Cahn, ed.), 73–81, © 1967 Indiana University Press

# 6 INTRODUCTORY COMMENTS ON LATERAL LINE FUNCTION

WILLEM A. VAN BERGEIJK

Center for Neural Sciences
Indiana University
Bloomington, Indiana

I should like to confine my introductory remarks largely to a brief review of the work that Harris and I did on the peripheral organ (Harris and van Bergeijk, 1962). Since this is only one organ out of several hundred distributed over the fish, we cannot say very much about what the fish perceives from what the organ appears to respond to. But at least, I think, we can make some statements about the class of stimuli that a fish *could* perceive, for anything that does not excite the peripheral organ cannot be perceived, of course.

There has long existed a controversy about what the proper stimulus to the lateral line really is. Some people have argued that it is *sound*, and they have very good evidence for their view. Others have said that it is *not* sound, but water currents or motions; and they, too, can adduce excellent evidence in their favor. Now, something must be wrong here, because a statement and its negation cannot both be true. Thus Harris and I started to look into this problem, some years ago, and began by considering what a real sound source actually produces in the way of radiated energy. We soon found out, as was well known, that a source produces displacements of the water around it, as well as pressure waves. If you consider "sound" to be only pressure waves, you have only half the story. If one is close to the source, in its *near field*, he encounters displacements much larger than those which result from compression.

Thus, if one were observing a fish close to a source of sound (in the near field, that is), one could conclude correctly that the fish responded to sound, whereas actually it responds to the displacements. Both views are valid: water motion and sound in this case are two different descriptions of the same phenomenon, namely, near-field displacements of a sound source in water. It could be incorrect, however, to conclude that the fish responded to a pressure wave.

We considered several simple sound sources in our work, but I will discuss only the one that is directly relevant here. Figure 1 is an idealized dipole, or first-moment, source: a sphere which vibrates along one axis. It has a radius $A$, and moves with an amplitude $\Delta$, where $\Delta$ is supposed to be very small compared with $A$. Now we look at some distance, $r$, from the center of the ball, and consider the displacement of the water there. The *magnitude* of deflection is the interesting point here. It is proportional to the volume of the source $(A^3)$ and inversely proportional to the *cube* of distance $(1/r^3)$. At any one point in this field, one can break down the actual motion, $d$, which may have an angle with respect to the axis of motion of the source. This is done into two component vectors—one parallel to the radius of the ball, one perpendicular to it. As indicated in Fig. 1, $d_r$ and $d_\theta$ simply designate the radial and angular vector breakdown. This is a near-field displacement. It is not an elastic phenomenon; if the ball moves in one direction, the water must flow around it because water is not very compressible. The motion of the ball will also generate a pressure field, of course, because it has a certain velocity. The pressure field really consists of two types of pressures: the far-field pressure, and the near-field pressure associated with the near-field motions. The first decays as $1/r$, the latter as $1/r^2$.

This gives us a way of telling whether the lateral line is responding to the near-field displacement or to the near-field pressure. In the first case, we should observe a $1/r^3$ decay in response; in the second case, a $1/r^2$ fall-off. If the experiment were done in the far field, both the displacement and pressure would have a $1/r$ fall-off. Thus, by working in

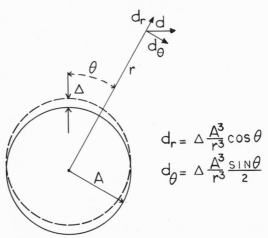

$$d_r = \Delta \frac{A^3}{r^3} \cos\theta$$

$$d_\theta = \Delta \frac{A^3}{r^3} \frac{\sin\theta}{2}$$

Fig. 1. Fields around a vibrating sphere (see text for explanation).

Fig. 2. Experimental setup with killifish (*Fundulus heteroclitus*) in holder. Electrode (slightly retouched for clarity) enters nasal canal organ; a 1-cm-diameter plastic sphere serves as stimulus.

the near field, a measurement of fall-off rate can distinguish between pressure sensitivity and displacement sensitivity.

The experiment we performed to decide between these alternatives consisted of recording the microphonic potentials from the canal organs on the head of the killifish (*Fundulus heteroclitus*), while a dipole source was moved with respect to the fish. Figure 2 shows a killifish in a holder of foam rubber and Plexiglas. The nasal organ of the head was studied with an electrode, which can be seen going into the canal. A dipole source was located in front of the fish.

If the fish responds to a near-field motion (as we keep the ball vibrating), and we progressively move the ball farther away, we may expect that the microphonic potential recorded will go down as the cube of the distance. If the fish is responsive to the pressure field, the potential should go down as the square of the distance. In other words, if we plot this on a log-log plot, we should find that responses to the near-field displacements give us a slope of −3; from the near-field pressure a slope of −2 is expected.

The results are shown in Fig. 3. Our prediction of a slope of −2 or

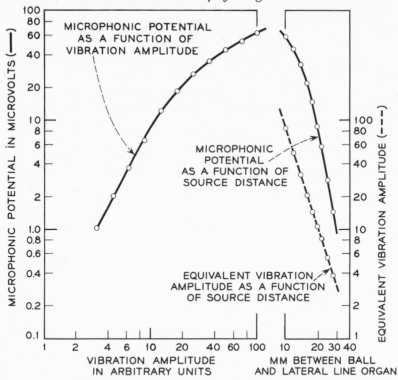

Fɪɢ. 3. Results of the near-field experiment (see text for explanation).

−3 would hold only if the organ had a linear response (i.e., an increase of a factor *n* in the stimulus results in an increase of response by a factor *n* also), or if we knew its actual response curve, so that we could use it for calibration. The left-hand side of Fig. 3 shows such a response curve. The ball is kept at a constant distance from the fish, the frequency of vibration is kept constant, but the amplitude of vibration is changed, as shown on the abscissa in log units. On the left ordinate is plotted the microphonic amplitude, also in log units. The resulting curve ("microphonic potential as a function of vibration amplitude") is not linear, but saturates at higher levels.

We are now ready to measure the response of the organ as a function of distance from the source. Keeping amplitude and frequency constant, we take readings with the ball at different distances from the organ. The right-hand side of Fig. 3 shows the result, with log distance plotted on the abscissa. For the raw data, the left-hand ordinate is appropriate, and the curve labeled "microphonic potential as a function of source distance" describes the result of the experiment. Since the left-hand curve tells us how much displacement corresponds to what size of microphonic potential, we can use it to calculate the equivalent vibration amplitude (at the organ) as a function of source distance. This is the dashed curve, which refers to the right-hand ordinate. The units on this ordinate are arbitrary.

The slope of the curve is exactly −3.0; thus we conclude that it is indeed the near-field motions of a sound source which excite the lateral line organ. We cannot say anything about the forcing term (displacement, velocity, or acceleration), however, without further experimentation. By measuring the phase of the response with respect to the phase of the water displacement, we demonstrated that the canal organ of the killifish, at least, is a displacement detector. But this does not mean that every lateral line organ is displacement-sensitive; it depends on surrounding and associated structures. Just as a galvanometer (which is a current-sensitive device) can be used to measure potential in a series configuration, so the hair cells of the lateral line can be used to measure velocity, for instance, or pressure.

In the toad *Xenopus*, as a case in point, the organs (which are free-standing on the surface of the skin) are sensitive to the *velocity* of water motion. (Görner, 1963; Harris and Milne, 1966). Harris and Milne point out (*op. cit.*, p. 40) that the elliptical cross section of the flag-shaped cupula is responsible for this effect, since motion in the major axis of the ellipse (which is the direction of sensitivity of the hair cells) is proportional to fluid drag, and therefore to velocity.

In the killifish the canal organ is surrounded by a considerable mass of mucus present in the canal, and the resonant frequency of the structure indicates that it is the mass of the canal, and not only the cupula, which is the determining mass (Harris and van Bergeijk, 1962). The structure of the canal organ thus leads us to generalize that the hair cells proper, the actual transducers of motion to neural activity, are *displacement detectors:* they respond to *displacement* of the cupula. Flock (1965) also showed this. The cupula's displacement, in turn, is proportional to some *function* of displacement: velocity (which is a differential function of displacement) in the case of *Xenopus;* or displacement itself (though filtered through the resonance of the system) in the case of the killifish. In the related systems of the inner ear it is well known that the displacement of the cupula in the semicircular canal is proportional to acceleration (a double differential function of simple displacement), while in the cochlea the displacement is proportional to the sound pressure (an integral function of displacement).

The apparent sensitivity and function of an organ as a whole depend on the geometry and nature of the structures associated with the hair-cell transducers, in much the same way as in electronic equipment such disparate operations as digital counting and television broadcasting are accomplished by means of various components embedded in particular circuit configurations with vacuum tubes or transistors (which, per se, are amplifiers). For instance, a hearing organ that is sensitive to pressure waves needs, in addition to the hair cells, an air bubble that transforms pressure into displacements (van Bergeijk, 1966, 1967).

The sensitivity of the lateral line *organ*, however, is only one aspect of the problem of lateral line function. As I noted earlier, the capabilities of the organ only define the general class of stimuli to which the fish can, potentially, respond. And that appears to be—as Dijkgraaf correctly inferred more than 30 years ago (Dijkgraaf, 1934)—water motions, pure and simple. What Harris and I have contributed here is the realization that "sound" under certain circumstances (viz., in the near field), is also water motion, and as such is indistinguishable from other motions by a lateral line organ. For the lateral line *system*, however, with its hundreds of organs spread over the body, there may be a distinction between water motions attributable to a near-field source and motions of different origin, such as the current of a river, or the motions generated by the fish's own swimming movements. Dijkgraaf (1934) demonstrated that laminar water flow (i.e., river current) does not excite the lateral line system, but there appears to be no evidence on the question of lateralis involvement in the perception of the animal's own swimming motions. Extirpation of part or all of the lateral line does not appear to affect the animal's swimming ability,† so that one can at least postulate that the lateral line is not involved in the proprioceptive control of swimming. On the other hand, there is ample evidence that the lateral line system is instrumental (and, in fact, essential) for the detection of near-field sources. Dijkgraaf (1963) and van Bergeijk (1967) have reviewed the evidence critically.

There is at present no evidence about the mechanisms by which a fish is able to differentiate between water motions due to near-field sources and those due to water flow, although evidently the peripheral single neuromast is excited equally well by either. I should like to suggest that the difference lies in the *curvature* of the stimulus field and that, for the fish to perceive an external object, there must exist a

---

† Dijkgraaf (1934) does not state explicitly that lateralis extirpation has no effect on swimming ability, nor does anyone else, so far as I can ascertain. If there had been an effect, however, it surely would have been noted, because it would raise grave doubts about the validity of the experimental results.

*stimulus gradient* over the animal's body. This would result in some organs of the lateralis system being excited more than others. In the near field of a moving object there is indeed a strong intensity gradient (inverse cube of distance, see Fig. 1), and differential stimulation of peripheral neuromasts will thus be obtained. In a laminar-flow channel, on the other hand, all neuromasts will be stimulated about equally, and the fish evidently does not perceive a source. A laminar-flow channel, of course, has an infinite radius of curvature, whereas an object in the near field has a finite, and presumably small, radius. An experimental question that evidently has not been asked is: What is the minimum field curvature and attenuation rate† that allows a fish to perceive an object, and how do field curvature, size of animal and object, and accuracy of localization interrelate? Clearly, an object large compared with the fish under consideration has a rather large radius of curvature; but the fish may be close enough to it to experience a high field-attenuation rate. Accuracy of source localization would tend to become poorer as field-curvature radius increases and as field-attenuation rate decreases.

Questions such as these are no longer amenable to solution with physiological techniques, at least not with *present* techniques. Only careful behavioral studies can give satisfactory answers to these problems. The physiological work, however, performs an essential function: it delineates the class of stimuli and the relevant stimulus parameters to which the peripheral neuromast is sensitive, thus allowing the behaviorist to choose his stimulus parameters with some sophistication.

REFERENCES

Bergeijk, W. A. van (1966). Evolution of the sense of hearing in vertebrates. *Am. Zoologist* 6, 371-377.
——— (1967). The evolution of vertebrate hearing. *Contrib. Sens. Physiol.* 2, 1-49.
Dijkgraaf, S. (1934). Untersuchungen über die Funktion der Seitenorganen an Fischen. *Z. Vergleich. Physiol.* 20, 162-214.
——— (1963). The functioning and significance of the lateral line organs. *Biol. Rev.* 38, 51-105.
Flock, A. (1965). Electron microscopic and electrophysiological studies on the lateral line canal organ. *Acta Oto-Laryngol. Suppl.* 199.
Görner, P. (1963). Untersuchungen zur Morphologie und Elektrophysiologie des Seitenlinienorgans vom Krallenfrosch (*Xenopus laevis* Daudin). *Z. Vergleich. Physiol.* 47, 316-338.

† Attenuation *rate* (in dB/cm) is independent of the nature of the source; it is dependent only on the properties of the decibel. A little calculation shows it to be a simple inverse function ($1/r$) of distance from the source.

Harris, G. G., and D. C. Milne (1966). Input-output characteristics of the lateral-line sense organs of *Xenopus laevis*. *J. Acoust. Soc. Am.* 40, 32-42.

——— and W. A. van Bergeijk (1962). Evidence that the lateral-line organ responds to near-field displacements of sound sources in water. *J. Acoust. Soc. Am.* 34, 1831-1841.

COMMENTS

SUCKLING: How would you accomplish the cutting of the lateral line nerves?

VAN BERGEIJK: There are several ways of doing this, and Dr. Dijkgraaf can tell you more about this than I can. It is possible to cut the nerves so that you effectively eliminate the lateral line system. People have done it painstakingly and have drawn out every one of them. One is never really quite sure whether they're all gone, but you can be fairly sure. One would expect, in any case, that even if there's a little bit left, you'd have a considerable decrease in the response.

SUCKLING: With regard to this cutting of nerves, I must draw attention to the slides that my wife showed, where there is present this ventral nerve component of the lateral line. The dorsal nerve of the lateral line runs along just underneath the canal. If this dorsal component is cut, the commissure may also become involved, but the ventral nerve of the lateral line may be left untouched.

WALKER: Dr. van Bergeijk commented that it is important to consider behavioral observations to confirm our conclusions of lateral line function. We are, however, apt to err by considering behavior only as it is manifested by the animal in the laboratory. We must not lose sight of the fact that we are, under these conditions, dealing with a captive fish, in a virtually turbulence-free medium. Such an environment is one that is or may be totally lacking in directive and meaningful stimuli. In laboratory investigations, one often selects species restricted to those which flourish under laboratory treatment, or those which are extraordinarily tough.

Extirpation and nerve recordings are useful tools, but not the final answer. Animals function by relying on a variety of sensory stimuli. I believe that the normal responses of the animal result from using all its senses. We all know about how an animal can compensate for lack of an organ system. It would be nice if we could manipulate stimuli effective for the lateral line, without altering stimuli for related sensory systems and without introducing extraneous secondary cues. This is difficult to accomplish. Dijkgraaf's studies, which have been a cornerstone of lateral line function, need only to be extended to a greater variety of fishes and under a greater variety of physical conditions in order not to be regarded merely as a special case.

MACKAY: I'd like to ask the following: If you fix sort of a random place in this overall distribution around the little vibrating ball, will you have cyclic pressure changes and cyclic displacements if you're in close enough?

It's sort of unfortunate to bring in equations, but it's as though there are two terms added together, and most of the energy is in the component that is falling off with the cube, when in close. When far away, most of the energy is then falling off with the square. In this case, isn't the result of your experiment sort of inevitable, that you get operation of the cube law if your test object is in close? I think that this argument is a little misleading, in that part of the result you observed is not attributable to the lateral line but to the fact that the fish was in close with respect to the wavelength of the source.

van Bergeijk: Yes, it might be. I'd like to let Harris answer that.

Harris: I think that it is important to keep in mind that in these experiments we were trying to establish the proper stimulus for the lateral line organ. Does the lateral line respond to pressure like a pressure hydrophone, or does it respond to a vector function such as displacement or velocity? In this context the advantage that the near field possesses is that pressure and displacement are different functions of distance, whereas in the far field they are not different functions of distance. By using the near field, we hoped to be able to distinguish between a pressure detector and a displacement detector. The measurements showed an inverse cubic relationship, which is how displacement should vary. A hydrophone showed an inverse square relationship with distance, which is what a pressure receptor should show.

LATERAL LINE DETECTORS (P. Cahn, ed.), 83–95, © 1967 Indiana University Press

# 7 BIOLOGICAL SIGNIFICANCE OF THE LATERAL LINE ORGANS

SVEN DIJKGRAAF

Laboratory of Comparative Physiology
University of Utrecht
Utrecht, The Netherlands

The lateral line organs are extremely sensitive to minute water displacements. In several mechanoreceptors, such as the semicircular canals or the mammalian ear, there are complicated structures intended to focus selected mechanical forces on the sense cells involved and to screen them from inadequate stimuli. In the lateral line organs, however, and particularly in most superficial neuromasts with their freely protruding cupulae (Fig. 1), screening structures are hardly developed; and as a consequence, nearly all water displacements will affect and stimulate the sense organs, irrespective of their origin and causation.

It is obvious that in the absence of a selecting mechanism at the periphery the integrative centers in the brain will have the task of trying to discriminate between irrelevant stimuli and stimuli which indicate biologically relevant events. Therefore, behavioral experiments in which the integrative action of the brain can become manifest are needed if we wish to determine the use that fishes and amphibians make of their lateral line organs.

Some water displacements occurring in nature and affecting the lateral line will be briefly considered in order to see to what extent they represent biologically relevant stimuli.

First of all, there are the water displacements caused by any object or animal moving under water (Fig. 2). Both fishes and amphibians have quite generally been found to be sensitive to the motions of other animals at short distance. Prey, enemies, and sexual partners are perceived and localized in this way through the lateral lines on the basis of local water displacements. In their sexual display, many fishes show a phase in which the partners stimulate each other mutually by pushing movements thereby creating small flows of water against their

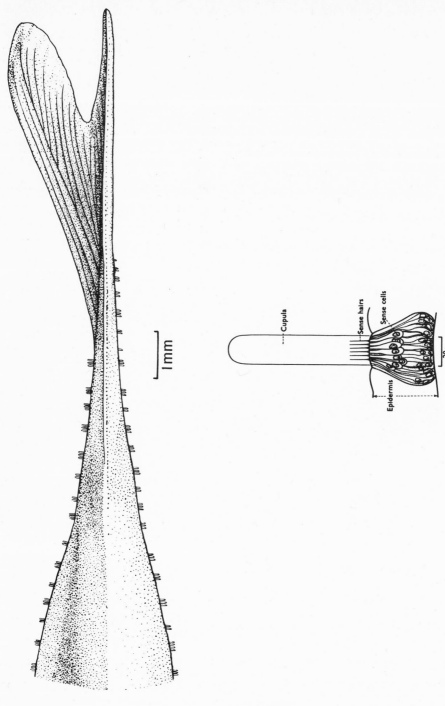

Labels on lower diagram: Cupula · Sense hairs · Sense cells · Epidermis · 20μ

FIG. 1. Tail end of a minnow (*Phoxinus phoxinus*) as seen from above, with protruding cupulae of free neuromasts in correct size relation. (Below) Diagrammatic section through one free neuromast.

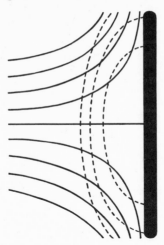

Fig. 2. Motion of water particles (solid lines) and area of increased pressure (dashed lines) in front of a stationary obstacle (disc, shown in section as a black bar) in a stream. Similar phenomena occur when an object moves through standing water.

companions (Fig. 3). Even when both animals are blinded, one can observe this behavior.

To what extent the lateral line organs are also used in the maintenance of contact between members of a fish school is not yet quite clear. In general, blinding causes dispersion of the school, but Moulton (1960) observed that a blinded specimen of *Anchoviella* immediately joined a school of normal fish and followed its veering motion when

Fig. 3. Mutual stimulation of fishes by means of water flows caused by waving motions of body and tail fin [from Tinbergen, 1951].

the school was startled by a hand movement near the aquarium. Evidently, things may be different with different species.

In behavioral experiments, both a water flow that hits the fish locally and the near approach of moving objects may release clear and oriented reactions in blinded fishes and amphibians. These reactions are mostly either flight or approach and snapping, dependent on the size of the object, its type of motion, and the mood and previous experience of the animal. Local elimination of the lateral line organs by nerve section causes a local loss of sensitivity to the stimuli involved.

In contrast with these clear and unequivocal results there is much contradiction and uncertainty as to the part played by the lateral line in behavioral reactions to specific vibratory stimuli. In about half of the related papers, the negative conclusion is drawn that the lateral line organs are not involved; in the remaining half, the authors arrive at the opposite conclusion.

The diversity of results is, in the main, caused by the great variety of stimuli used in these experiments. They vary from application of a vibrating rod in direct contact with a single sense organ to vibration of the whole aquarium by a low-frequency tuning fork or a cord attached to its wall.

In general, positive evidence seems confined to arrangements in which local stimulation of the lateral line system predominated, whereas a more or less overall vibratory stimulation, such as that with tuning forks, has usually yielded negative conclusions. As an example of this latter category, the well-known experiments of Von Frisch and Stetter (1932) with the minnow may be mentioned.

In these sound-conditioning experiments, labyrinth receptors were clearly involved. After removal of both labyrinths, however, reactions still occurred in the low-frequency range, i.e., below 100 to 150 cps. But further elimination of the lateral lines did not abolish these reactions. Evidently another receptor participated in the perception of low-frequency vibrations, presumably the cutaneous or tactile sense.

Still, one cannot conclude from these experiments that the lateral lines did not participate at all (van Bergeijk, 1963), because the authors failed to determine intensity thresholds before and after lateral line elimination.

It does not seem useful to go into much further detail with regard to papers of this kind because they all have some imperfections. One should not forget that stimuli which do not occur at all in nature cannot have any biological significance. Of course, there are also natural vibratory stimuli, such as a wriggling worm or a flapping fishtail, and nobody doubts that they represent biologically adequate stimuli to the

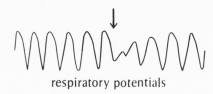

respiratory potentials

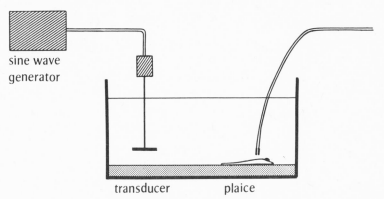

FIG. 4. Reaction of plaice (inhibition of respiratory movements) on stimulation with low-frequency sound. (Arrow indicates onset of sound stimulation.)

lateral line, if applied at sufficiently close range. We do not yet know exactly the thresholds in terms of size, distance, and frequency of the stimulating objects as determined on the basis of behavioral experiments.

In my laboratory a series of determinations. of this kind, with flatfish, were started recently. To determine the effect of vibratory stimuli, the respiratory rhythm was recorded electrically, using spread muscle potentials (Fig. 4). The breathing of the resting fish in a quiet environment, partly buried under the sand, is extremely regular. Every vibratory stimulus causes an immediate transient interruption of the rhythm.

The distance between the vertically vibrating disc, which had a diameter of 6 cm, and the center of the fish was about 20 cm. With a frequency of 5 cps, the threshold displacement of the disc was determined to be about 10 $\mu$ and the horizontal displacement of the water along the center of the fish's body at about 0.05 $\mu$.

Cutting the lateral line nerves at the upper side of the trunk (three nerves) close behind the head caused *no change* of the threshold. Although this experiment is not quite conclusive it seems that another receptor was involved in the perception of these vibrations.

Regnart (1928) performed similar experiments with whiting, in the frequency range 3 to 30 cps. He observed oriented reactions to the vibrating disc, at frequencies below 10 cps. After the whole lateral line system was put out of function, reactions still occurred, but these were no longer oriented. The amplitude of the disc, however, was very large in this case—about 5 mm. Moreover, not only the lateral line nerves were cut but also the nerves supplying the general cutaneous senses of the head.

More quantitative experiments with threshold determinations in terms of water displacement and velocity, as well as proper elimination techniques, are needed in order to arrive at a better understanding of the part played by the lateral line in the causation of behavioral responses of fishes to sound.

Some fishes with particularly sensitive lateral line organs can even feel *motionless* obstacles they are approaching at short range. If, for example, a blinded codfish gliding smoothly through the water of a big tank happens to approach a fixed vertical strip of glass (Fig. 5), the obstacle is perceived and avoided at a distance of a few centimeters. Evidently, the usual water displacement pattern around the moving fish undergoes a change on close approach of the obstacle, and this unexpected change of flow acts as a stimulus to the animal.

It does not seem correct to speak of reflection of a water wave and the like in this case, because the fish simply pushes the water in front of his head. A moving quantity of water (i.e., a water flow) is not *re*flected on collision with a solid obstacle but is *de*flected along its surface.

Apart from water displacements caused by moving animals, there

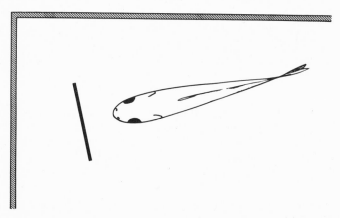

Fig. 5. Detection of a stationary obstacle at a distance by an approaching blinded codfish (*Gadus morhua*).

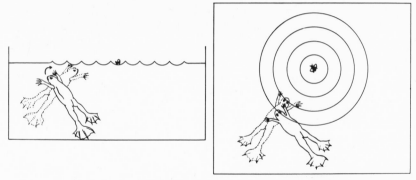

Fɪɢ. 6. Localization of a struggling insect by a blinded *Xenopus laevis* on the basis of surface waves, as seen from the side (left) and from above (right).

are only two kinds of water movement which occur in nature and which can act as biologically adequate stimuli.

First, let us consider surface waves. Several surface-feeding fish species such as *Aplocheilus lineatus,* studied recently by Schwartz (1965), respond vividly to the concentric ripples caused by a struggling insect. The center of disturbance is localized with the lateral line organs. *Xenopus* is able to localize a struggling prey (Fig. 6) even when it is totally submerged. The amplitude of the vertical water displacements in surface waves diminishes rather quickly with increasing depth; the displacement amplitude near the submerged *Xenopus* was of the order of a fraction of a micron.

The second natural stimulus to the lateral line can occur in streams. When there are pronounced local velocity differences between adjacent bodies of water, and the fish gets into the boundary region of the flow, this can be sensed by the lateral line. A blinded minnow shows a rheotactic response to the water flow from an underwater outlet, and this reaction no longer occurs after sectioning of all lateral line nerves (Fig. 7).

The lateral line organs apparently are not involved in the rheotactic orientation toward large water currents that carry the whole fish away. Rheotaxis of this kind is based on visual or tactile contact of the fish with the solid underground. For substantial water currents, it makes no difference whether the lateral line organs are intact or are eliminated, even in blinded fish.

The lateral line organs are not involved in the coordination of swimming movements, on the basis of stimulation by water displacements along the fish's body such as are of necessity caused by the animal's locomotion. Blinded minnows lose their ability to swim freely in a

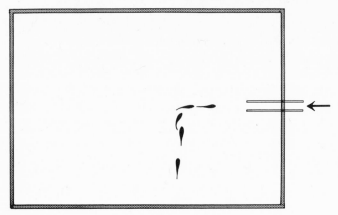

Fig. 7. Rheotactic response of a blinded minnow to a local water flow. (Successive positions are shown.)

normal coordinated manner after bilateral removal of their equilibrium organ (pars superior of the labyrinth). If the same operation is performed in minnows with the eyesight, however, they usually regain their normal swimming behavior within a few days, relying on visual stimuli. In neither case does it make any difference whether the lateral lines are left intact or put completely out of function.

Finally, perception of propagated sound waves has, until the present, never been shown to occur through the use of lateral line organs.

SPECIALIZED LATERAL LINE ORGANS

Apart from the ordinary lateral line organs, there is a specialized group of so-called "ampullary" lateral sense organs. Typical representatives of this group are the ampullae of Lorenzini in elasmobranchs (Fig. 8). What is the biological significance of these peculiar receptors?

My first experience with these sense organs dates back to 1935, when I was working at the Zoological Station of Naples and for the first time tried to stimulate the lateral lines of a blinded dogfish by moving a thin rod toward it. Time and again, the animal turned sharply away from the approaching rod at a distance of 5 to 8 cm, and I was enthusiastic about this apparently remarkable degree of mechanical sensitivity—until I replaced the iron rod that I had happened to use with a glass rod of the same diameter. Thereupon all such reactions failed to appear. At that time, this occurrence was rather disappointing to me, and just as Parker (1904) had done in his earlier experiments with catfish, I concluded that electric fields at the surface of the iron rod evidently acted as releasing stimuli and that mechanical forces were not involved.

I noticed, furthermore, that the iron rod released avoidance and flight only when it was brought toward the head of the fish, not if it approached the trunk. So I wrote in my notebook of those days: "Should perhaps the ampullae of Lorenzini be sensitive to electric stimuli?" But then I forgot about the whole thing until encountering Lissmann's (1958) highly interesting discoveries of the electrolocating freshwater fish.

Together with my co-worker Kalmijn (1963) and others, we took the case up where I had left it some 27 years earlier. Kalmijn first stated, in behavioral experiments, that dogfish and also rays are indeed most sensitive to minute local potential differences in the surrounding sea-water. Artificial electric stimuli induced characteristic reflexes.

In preliminary experiments, a threshold gradient of 0.1 $\mu$V per cm of seawater was determined. Recently, the heartbeat rhythm was used as an indicator, and it was found that the threshold lies even ten times lower—at 0.01 $\mu$V per cm. When the stimulus is applied (e.g., a square-wave pulse at a frequency of 5 cps), the heartbeat rhythm is immediately, but temporarily, slowed down.

Second, we wished to know whether the ampullae of Lorenzini— and *only* these—were indeed involved in the causation of the be-havioral reactions to these weak electrical stimuli. This was investi-

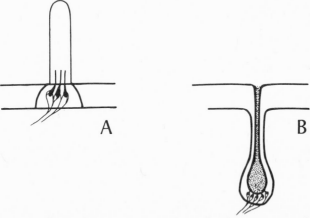

Fɪɢ. 8. (A) Ordinary lateral line organ (superficial neuromast with cupula). (B) Ampullary lateral line organ: the sensory cells are below the surface; there is no cupula, but rather a duct leading to an external opening and filled with gelatinous substance.

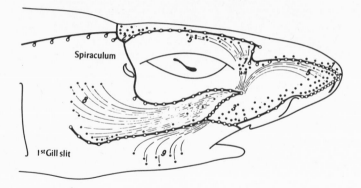

Spiraculum

1st Gill slit

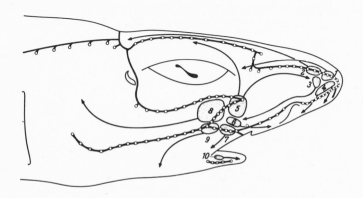

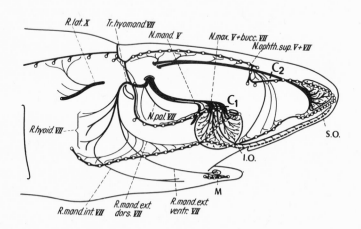

*R.lat.* X    *Tr.hyomand.* VII    *N.mand.* V    *N.max.* V+*bucc.* VII    *N.ophth.sup.* V+VII

C₂

C₁

*N.pal.* VII

*R.hyoid.* VII

S.O.

I.O.

M

*R.mand.int.* VII    *R.mand.ext. dors.* VII    *R.mand.ext. ventr.* VII

gated by means of a pair of special electrodes, with which a local alternating electric field could be produced and applied to a small area of a dogfish's head. The stimulus consisted of square-wave pulses at a frequency of 5 cps. The potential changes at both electrodes were opposite and symmetrical. When the electrodes were placed near the area between the spiracle and the first gill slit (Fig. 9), a threshold of about 3 $\mu$V per cm was determined.

Now, the N. maxillaris V and buccalis VII was cut at the right side just below the orbit. This caused the elimination of all ampullae of Lorenzini belonging to the infraorbital group, among them those of the group which have their openings in the stimulated area. As a consequence of this operation, the threshold was raised about ten times on stimulation of this area, although the ordinary lateral line organs and all other cutaneous receptors within this area were completely intact because they are innervated along different pathways. Furthermore, on stimulation of the corresponding area at the contralateral side, or on stimulation of the rostrum at either side, the threshold was unchanged.

Finally, after additional cutting of the same nerve at the opposite side and of both ophthalmic nerves to the rostrum, all ampullae of Lorenzini (except a few in the lower jaw) were put out of function. This caused complete insensitivity of the animal to weak electric fields up to 2000 $\mu$V per cm, if applied to any area on either side of the head. This was the highest stimulus value obtainable with our stimulating device.

These experiments thus prove, first, that the ampullae of Lorenzini can be used by the animal as electroreceptors; second, that the ampullae are only stimulated by potential changes occurring at their external opening; and finally, that neither the ordinary lateral line organs nor other skin receptors are involved.

So we come to the last and most difficult question: namely, what

---

FIG. 9. (Top) Head of a dogfish (*Scyliorhinus canicula*), with openings of the ampullae of Lorenzini (black spots) and lateral line canals with their openings (heavy black lines with open circles). Figures indicate openings of groups of ampullae having their blind ends with the sense cells united within a common capsule of connective tissue. (Center) Arrangement of all (10) ampullary capsules: numbers 1-4 and 5-9, respectively, are jointly surrounded by connective tissue so as to form the supraorbital group (within the rostrum) and the infraorbital group. Arrows indicate main direction of respective ampullar ducts. (Bottom) Innervation of Lorenzini ampullae and lateral line canals. C$_1$ and C$_2$, sites of nerve cuts; S.O., supraorbital; I.O., infraorbital; M, mandibular group of ampullae. (Note consequence of nerve cut at C$_1$: elimination of ampullar groups 8 and 9, whereas the canal organs in the area of their openings are spared.)

use do elasmobranchs make of these receptors, and what are the biologically adequate stimuli?

In electrophysiological experiments, the ampullae have been shown to respond not only to electrical but also to thermal and mechanical stimuli. Thermal stimuli, however, for various reasons can be safely ruled out as biologically adequate stimuli to the ampullae. And the behavior of blinded dogfishes definitely does not point to a special pressure sensitivity, but rather to the opposite. Electrical stimuli, on the other hand, are also effective in behavioral experiments. I may recall the oriented flight reaction of a blind *Scyliorhinus* at the approach of an iron rod.

Recently, a recording electrode was fixed to a strand of ampullar nerve fibers from the N. ophthalmicus superficialis V and VII and then fixed to the head of the animal. In this way it was possible to listen to and to look at what happened in the nerve at the approach of iron and plastic rods while the fish swam quietly around. It turned out that the ampullae involved, which had their openings at the ventral side of the rostrum, responded clearly to the muscle action potentials of the animal's own respiratory movements. A drastic and lasting burst of impulses occurred when an iron bar was brought to a distance of 15 cm from the fish. If, instead of the iron bar, a plastic bar of equal diameter was used, or even a coarser mechanical stimulus, no reaction at all occurred in these ampullary nerve fibers.

Besides artificial stimuli, potential changes of biological origin, such as the spread muscle potentials of a breathing flatfish, were successfully used. When these electrical stimuli were picked up from the flatfish in one tank and transmitted to another tank with a ray or a dogfish, at exactly the same amplitude, even at a distance of 10 cm, clear heartbeat responses were observed.

Finally, a dogfish could be conditioned, with the use of food, to respond to weak electric stimuli. The electrodes were buried under the sand at a distance of 5 or 10 cm from each other. Between both electrodes the strength of the 5-cps square-wave pulse stimulus was 0.4 $\mu$V per cm. In the experiments, the animal stopped when it passed over the hidden electrodes, next turning down and burrowing with its snout in the sand until it found first one electrode and then the other. A ray and another shark species were also successfully conditioned in the same way. Toward the end of the training period, the animals sometimes bit at the electrodes instead of at the food.

At one time Dr. Lissmann was somewhat reluctant to consider the ampullae of Lorenzini as electroreceptors, because elasmobranchs are not thought to possess an electrical locating system such as is found in gymnotids or mormyrids. But these weakly electric fish with location systems might represent specialized cases, like bats and porpoises do acoustically with their echolocation mechanism.

Although we do not yet know what kinds of electrical stimuli play a role in the normal life of elasmobranchs, we are now certain at least that most animals produce sufficient muscle potentials to make them detectable to sharks and rays at short range, and we also know that stimulus sources of this kind can be localized. Thus, the biological task of the ampullae of Lorenzini might closely resemble the task of the ordinary lateral line organs, except that mechanical forces are replaced by electrical stimuli.

## REFERENCES

Bergeijk, W. A. van (1963). Directional and nondirectional hearing in -fish, in *Marine Bio-Acoustics*. Pergamon Press, Oxford, pp. 281-299.

Dijkgraaf, S. (1963). The functioning and significance of the lateral-line organs. *Biol. Rev.* 38, 51-105.

———— and A. J. Kalmijn (1963). Untersuchungen über die Funktion der Lorenzinischen Ampullen. *Z. Vergleich. Physiol.* 47, 438-456.

Frisch, K. von, and H. Stetter (1932). Untersuchungen über den Sitz des Gehörsinnes bei der Elritze. *Z. Vergleich. Physiol.* 17, 686-801.

Lissmann, H. W. (1958). On the function and evolution of electric organs in fish. *J. Exptl. Biol.* 35, 156-191.

Moulton, J. M. (1960). Swimming sounds and the schooling of fishes. *Biol. Bull.* 119, 210-223.

Parker, G. H., and A. P. van Heusen (1917). The responses of the catfish, *Ameiurus nebulosus* to metallic and non-metallic rods. *Am. J. Physiol.* 44, 405-420.

Regnart, H. C. (1928). Investigations on the lateral sense organs of *Gadus merlangus*. *Proc. Univ. Durham Phil. Soc.* 8, 55-60.

Schwartz, E. (1965). Bau und Funktion der Seitenlinie des Streifenhechtlings (*Aplocheilus lineatus* Cuv. u. Val.). *Z.Vergleich. Physiol.* 50, 55-87.

Tinbergen, N. (1951). *The Study of Instinct*. Clarendon Press, Oxford.

LATERAL LINE DETECTORS (P. Cahn, ed.), 97–103, © 1967 Indiana University Press

# 8 ELECTROPHYSIOLOGICAL STUDIES ON THE TRUNK LATERAL LINE SYSTEM OF VARIOUS MARINE AND FRESHWATER TELEOSTS

E. E. SUCKLING

Department of Physiology
State University of New York
Downstate Medical Center
Brooklyn, New York

The present author is content to accept the concept that the lateral line system in the head region of most fish is related to the detection of water movement. The concept of "damming" of Dijkgraaf (1962) and the idea that the system is used to detect this or other disturbances of the usual stream line water flow as the fish moves appear to be well founded. There are indications, however, that the trunk lateral line system may be involved in more than this. Some of the indicators may be considered specious by some people in that they are of a teleological nature. For instance, if an engineer were designing a sensory system for a large fish, he would be bound to make use of the length of the fish as a base for triangulation or of a direction sensing system for arriving sonic or mechanical disturbances. We look for such an arrangement in the trunk lateral line system. Again, an engineer would like to utilize as much as possible of the energy of an arriving wave that is intercepted by a fish's body. Is the lateral line system, therefore, organized in some way so that an improved signal is obtained through energy collection by the whole fish's body?

If we inspect the lateral line scales of many common teleosts (many families of the order Perciformes, for instance), we find that the trunk lateral line sense organs are enclosed in a small tube in each scale. The conventional idea that these individual small tubes form a single continuous tube or enclosed canal does not seem to be borne out in the species we have examined (see Chap. 4). Each scale has a tiny opening to the water and some communication with the next tube, but appears to be more an independent unit than part of an elongated system. It is difficult to associate the structure seen with a function of water flow detection. It is also difficult to see how the structure can be an efficient collector of vibrational energy either as a pressure or as a movement detector.

For the above reasons and others, the present investigator has set himself the task of identifying more definitely an "adequate stimulus" for the trunk lateral line in teleosts and in investigating its function. He will be content when he is able to set up a reliable preparation in which some modality of stimulus at a very low energy level will consistently cause firing in fibers of the lateral line nerve. He will leave to other authorities the question of whether the fish really uses the system to modify its behavior. The present paper is intended to be in the nature of a review of efforts that have already been made, and thus various published material is quoted.

METHOD OF INVESTIGATION

**Techniques.** Conventional methods of electrophysiology were used. Fibers of the lateral line nerves were teased out and lifted onto electrodes. Impulses, when present after amplification, were observed on an oscilloscope and were photographed. A loudspeaker was often used in addition to visual monitoring, in order to identify nerve-fiber firing. Stimulation was done by stroking end-organ scales with a fine hairbrush, by directing streams of water onto scales, or by setting up vibrations in the water. The first series of experiments demonstrated that it was impossible to identify any response to a tone switched on manually because of the random or spontaneous activity of many nerve fibers. In later work, short bursts of tone synchronized with the oscilloscope sweep were used. If a tone burst occupied only part of the sweep duration, it was much easier to decide whether nerve impulses were related to the tone or not.

**Preparation.** All fish were spinalized and placed on their sides in various tanks containing circulating, aerated salt or fresh water. Water levels permitted the head, gills, and trunk of the fish to be immersed while an area behind the pectoral fin remained out of water and could be dissected.

In the case of tuna, an oxygenated water infusion into the mouth was necessary; in other fish, normal gill movements were sustained and passed enough water over the gills. Most recording was done on fibers of the ventral trunk of the lateral line nerve, located along the midline of the fish—sometimes fairly close to the surface, between myotomes and easily accessible, and in other cases (e.g., in tuna) lying fairly deep in the muscle. Nerve fibers were teased out under microscopic examination so that a few fibers at a time were laid across the fine silver-wire electrodes (Suckling and Suckling, 1964).

**Specimens Used.** Work was carried out at four locations, and local species from each area were used. These locations were: (1) Bimini in the Bahamas (reef fish caught by trap or line); (2) Mediterranean area at Banyuls-sur-Mer (rock or coastal fish, mainly from a trawl); (3) Brooklyn, New York (fish obtained from various local sources, including a trout hatchery, and some marine forms from nearby waters); (4) Honolulu (skipjack tuna). Table 1 in Chapter 4 lists actual species and numbers of specimens used.

RESULTS

**Efferent Activity.** In view of the possibility that efferent nerve-fiber control of lateral line organ sensitivity may exist, frequent searches were made for this activity. In fish possessing both dorsal and ventral lateral line nerves, activity apparently originating in the brain can usually be demonstrated in the dorsal branch. The activity is frequently in the form of short volleys of firing, such as two volleys per second with ten impulses in each volley. In four specimens of *Tilapia*, a careful search in both branches showed efferent activity in the dorsal branch and no efferent activity in the ventral branch. A comparative test of this kind was not made on earlier preparations showing dorsal branch activity, but it is quite possible that this is a usual situation.

Attempts were made to demonstrate that the efferent nerve impulses control the commonly occurring spontaneous activity that seems to originate at the end organs. On several occasions it was possible to record spontaneous activity from an uncut complete nerve trunk carefully freed (for a few millimeters) and lifted onto a recording electrode. When the nerve was then cut at another dissection site, a centimeter or so nearer the head, the spontaneous activity increased considerably. In other experiments a few seconds of electrical stimulation of the distal end of a cut nerve trunk was followed by an almost total cessation of spontaneous firing, which then recovered in 30 to 60 sec. This experiment could be repeated with consistency.

**Afferent Activity.** Many fibers of the lateral line system show spontaneous activity, and many do not. It has been observed in a number of preparations (Suckling and Suckling, 1964) that bursts of impulses in synchrony with the respiratory movements are obtained, presumably because of body movements that cause lateral line organs to fire. It is usually not difficult, in a preparation in good condition, to find fibers which are quiescent but in which activity can be set up if an appropriate lateral line organ scale is stroked with a fine hairbrush. When sensitive organs are located in this way, they can usually be stimulated by a jet of water directed at the scale. The turbulent edge of the jet is a more effective stimulator than the main center of the jet. Sensitivity to weak jets or slow flows of water has not been observed.

**Sensitivity to Vibratory Energy.** Vibratory stimuli were applied by the generation of vibrations in the water tank, or by the use of a loudspeaker in air near the soft tank walls (Suckling and Suckling, 1964). In Fig. 1 some of the results of this earlier work are represented. In this case, a water movement of less than 0.5 $\mu$ was shown to set up nerve impulses. In the case of trout and tuna (Suckling, 1965), no definite response to low-frequency vibration (50 to 200 cps) in the water was ever obtained, even with levels of vibration seen to be causing water surface movement or movement of electrode structures. In contrast, vibrations of normal speech in the room would sometimes set up nerve impulses (Suckling and Suckling, 1964).

**Sensitivity to Pressure Changes.** When a rigid test tank with a sealed lid was used, it was possible to look for a response to a pressure change caused by compressed air in the enclosed space over the fish. By this means it was possible to simulate a rapid change in the apparent depth of about 4 ft, for the fish. When six specimens of tautog (both species as listed earlier in Chap. 4), in which recording appeared to be normal and the organs to be sensitive, were treated in this way, no response in the lateral line nerve fibers could be detected. If in place of a static change in air pressure a vibratory effect was caused by a loudspeaker connected to the chamber by a rubber tube, a response could often be obtained. The burst of tone (at 60 to 150 cps) was monitored by a calibrated hydrophone. A level of about 20 dB above 1 dyne per sq cm rms was usually needed to obtain nerve impulses. This stimulus was considered to be substantially pure "pressure," with almost no water movement.

**Sensitivity to Electric Current.** Frequent checks have been made for the possible sensitivity of the trunk lateral line system to d-c electric fields in the water near the organs. No change in nerve firing has ever been found during such experiments.

**Sensitivity to Vibrations within the Body of the Fish.** In a number

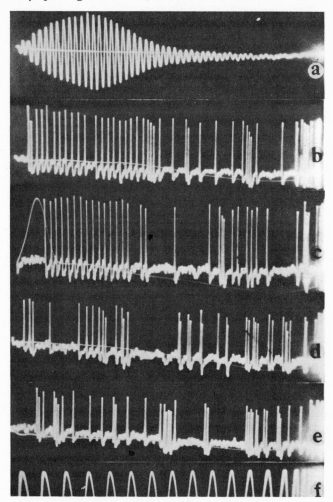

Fig. 1. Experiment showing impulses in the lateral line nerve during stimulation of various fishes, as described in Suckling and Suckling (1964). (a) Hydrophone output; (b), (c), (d), stronger to very weak tone levels; (e) no stimulation; (f) 50-cps timing signal. Water movement amplitude at (d) is less than 0.5 $\mu$.

of experiments, an unexpected sensitivity of the lateral line system was found to a stimulus that consisted of scratching across a scale of the fish with a fine needle. The scale could be detached and even placed onto any bare muscle surface from which the fish's skin had been removed for the effect to be demonstrable. Scratching with a needle across the rough-cut end of a plastic rod when the other end was touching the fish also produced bursts in the lateral line nerve fibers. The sensitivity to the effect was increased when the fish was out of the water (Suckling, 1962).

## DISCUSSION

The data presented in Suckling and Suckling's paper of 1964 is quite clear in its conclusion. In the species tested, a vibratory water movement of less than 0.5 $\mu$ at a frequency just below 200 cps caused firing in nerve fibers. The value of 0.5 $\mu$ was arrived at by measuring the motion of the walls of the soft plastic test tank. It was considered that no water movement of greater amplitude than the wall movement was likely. It is possible that the actual water movement at the site of stimulation was much less. It is also possible that the very small pressure component associated with the water movement caused stimulation. Further possibilities are that the water movement caused some motion of the whole fish, of part of it relative to the rest, or even pressure differentials within the fish. It is necessary to discuss why such results have not been achieved in other experimental series in which they might have been expected. These other series concern skipjack tuna and trout. At least ten apparently satisfactory experiments were run on each of these species, and in no case was any sensitivity to burst of vibratory stimuli found. The possible explanations include:

1. These fish may not be sensitive to vibratory stimuli. It is tempting to state that both tend to live in fast-moving or noisy waters, in which sensing by means of low-frequency vibrations would be far less practical than it would be in the quieter environments of the less-active rock and reef fish, in which sensitivity to vibrations has been demonstrated.

2. The experimental fish may not have been in normal physical condition. It is possible that fish confined to holding tanks for any length of time undergo changes in mucous secretion, or in other ways, that render the lateral line organs insensitive. The fish shown to be sensitive (Suckling and Suckling, 1964) had in nearly all cases been netted in the sea the previous day.

3. Experimental conditions were of necessity different in all cases, so that a difference in the actual vibration that reached or affected the fish may have existed. The only parameter of the stimulus that was monitored in all cases, the output of a hydrophone, does not reflect water movement.

4. Some requirement of efferent conditioning on the end organs may have been absent.

The experiments in which a scratching stimulus caused response gave an unexpected and rather vague result. These experiments suggested the possibility that energy may be able to be transferred efficiently to the hair cells from vibration within the body of the fish.

The experiments on efferent activity and its possible control over the end organs are interesting but not yet very meaningful. If, as seems possible, efferent activity in fibers in the dorsal branch of the nerve controls end organs that have their afferent fibers in the ventral branch, it should be possible to carry out experiments that may place the lateral line system with other sensory systems in which feedback from higher centers has been found to be of importance.

## REFERENCES

Dijkgraaf, S. ( 1962). The functioning and significance of the lateral line organs. *Biol. Rev.* 38, 51-105.

Suckling, E. E. ( 1962). Lateral line in fish; possible mode of action. *J. Acoust. Soc. Am.* 34, No. 1.

————— ( 1965). Mode of action of the lateral line organ receptors in fish. *Physiologist* 8, No. 3.

————— and J. A. Suckling ( 1964). Lateral line as a vibration receptor. *J. Acoust. Soc. Am.* 36, No. 11.

Suckling, J. A. ( 1967). Chapter 4, this volume.

LATERAL LINE DETECTORS (P. Cahn, ed.), 105–121, © 1967 Indiana University Press

# 9 FREQUENCY CHARACTERISTICS AND FUNCTIONAL SIGNIFICANCE OF THE LATERAL LINE ORGAN

JAN W. KUIPER

Department of Biophysics
University of Groningen
Groningen, The Netherlands

On the strength of considerable experimental evidence (see in particular Dijkgraaf, 1934, 1963, and his paper in this symposium), it is well established that fishes are able to localize moving objects in their vicinity by means of their lateral line organs. Some species with particularly well-developed lateral line receptors can do even more: they can locate stationary objects. The organ seems to respond to changes of the flow pattern in the water surrounding the fish. The cupula, resting on the macula, may be regarded as the functional unit of the lateral line organ, with which small water displacements are detected. Some light may be shed on the question of how this is done by studying the frequency characteristic of the organ. I have done this in the past by the application of elementary sinusoidal movements on the cupula. This particular form of stimulation was chosen because, according to Fourier's theorem, any signal can be represented by the sum of a number of sine and cosine functions.

This choice of stimulus does not imply that sinusoidal signals or, as an even more extreme view, sound was ever considered by me as the natural stimulus for the lateral line organ. Because of some recent publications, this statement is not superfluous (see Dijkgraaf, 1963, p. 59; and Kuiper, 1956, p. 146).

In the first part of this paper, I will briefly recapitulate some of my former work on this subject. In the second part, I will discuss the forces acting on the surface of the fish when the animal moves through nonrunning water and when a current from a certain direction strikes the body. The question will be raised as to which of these forces are likely to affect the cupula.

105

## THE LATERAL LINE ORGAN

In the bony skull of *Acerina cernua* there is found a system of furrows of about 2 mm width, which are locally covered by bony bridges. In the skin of the head, one can observe small pores between these bony bridges, which open into the furrows. After removal of the skin, a large cupula can be seen under each bridge. There are 25 such cupulae on each side of the head (see Fig. 1). When a small electrode is inserted through a pore and brought in the vicinity of a cupula, a potential change, called the microphonic effect, can be measured in response to movements in the water over the head (de Vries, 1948). When an oscillating water current is applied, the most striking property of the response is that its frequency is twice that of the stimulus (Jielof, Spoor, and de Vries, 1952; Kuiper, 1956).

In the years 1948-1956 both de Vries and I tried a number of stimuli on the lateral line organ, such as several kinds of water currents and vibrating needles and hairs. All stimuli that produced a movement of the cupula with respect to the macula proved effective in producing a microphonic potential. Eventually, I selected as the most useful stimulus a method in which the skin over the furrow, or even the cupula itself, was driven electromagnetically. This was accomplished by mounting a small magnet on the skin or on the cupula and causing vibration by means of an electromagnetic coil.

Direct observations on the amplitude and phase relations of the cu-

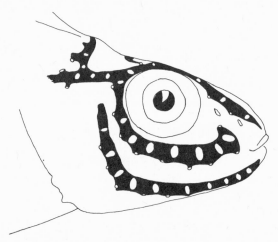

Fig. 1. Diagram of canals in the head of *Acerina cernua* and lateral line organs situated in them.

pula in response to sinusoidal stimuli were made with the aid of a water-immersion objective and a stroboscope directly coupled to the circuit driving the electromagnetic coil. From these observations, taken together with the electrical responses to a step-function displacement of the cupula, it was concluded that the cupula is very nearly critically damped and that its resonance frequency is about 100 cps. Similar conclusions were reached by Harris and van Bergeijk in the case of *Fundulus heteroclitus* (1962, and personal communication) and by Flock for *Lota vulgaris* (1965). The similarity in resonance frequency for different species is interesting in itself, but its possible significance remains as yet obscure.

Though there is until now no direct evidence for a causal relationship between the microphonic effect and the nerve responses in any one of the acousticolateral organs (for a recent discussion, see Davis, 1965), I will, for want of a better criterion, continue to use the amplitude of the microphonic effect as the measure of sensitivity of the lateral line organ.

That the microphonic effect is not a purely physical effect is sufficiently proved by its disappearance when the blood supply is stopped or when metabolic inhibitors are used. For instance, when Flaxedil, a substance with curare-like pharmacological effects, is brought into the lateral line canal in a concentration as small as $3 \cdot 10^{-4}M$, it causes a 50% reduction of the microphonic effect (Kuiper, 1955, 1956). This suggests that a chemical mediator is active in producing the microphonic effect, which is quite compatible with the delay time of about 1 msec (long enough for a chemical mediator) that can be derived from the phase relationship between the microphonic effect and the displacement of the cupula. Further evidence for the physiological origin of the microphonic potential can be found in the fact that potassium ions influence its amplitude, whereas sodium ions do not (Kuiper, 1956; Wersäll and Flock, 1964).

The frequency characteristics of the microphonic effect, though not always exactly similar for different specimens of the same species, always have a peak of maximum sensitivity between 50 and 150 cps. Within one animal, however, there is very little disparity between individual cupulae of the head (Fig. 2). Though we are not in possession of frequency characteristics for both the movement of the cupula *and* the microphonic potential in relation to stimuli to the cupula of the same magnitude (visual observation of the cupula responses requires rather unbiologically strong stimuli), we are nevertheless in a position to conclude, from the near-critically damped situation of the cupula alone, that there is no linear relationship between the ampli-

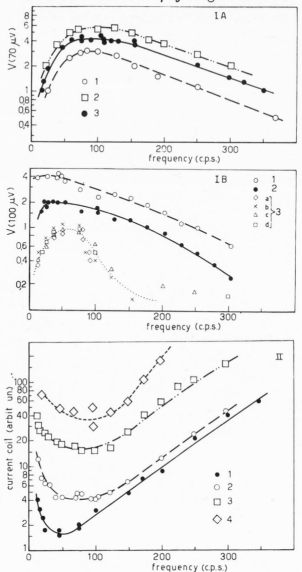

Fig. 2. I: Relation between applied frequency and microphonic potential for a constant amplitude of current through the driving coil (equal-force frequency characteristic). (A) Curves 1 and 2 represent the normal frequency characteristics of a cupula above which the skin and the bone bridge were removed. In this case the magnet was mounted directly on the cupula. Curve 3 was obtained from a cupula in the natural situation with the magnet mounted on the skin. (B) Curves 1 and 2 represent deviating frequency characteristics obtained from 2 cupulae situated in the supraorbital canal of one fish. Curve 3 represents a frequency characteristic

tude of the cupula displacement and that of the microphonic effect. The data fit better with the assumption that it is not the amplitude but the velocity of the cupula which is essential for the microphonic effect. (For more details, see Flock, 1965, 1966; Kuiper, 1956.)

*What stimuli does the fish perceive with its lateral line organ?* This question has for many years been a controversial one. It is self-evident that the instrumental properties of the cupula are not proof that these properties are made use of by the fish, and are actually perceived in its natural surroundings. Such proof can only be provided by behavior experiments, and it has, I think, been provided amply. I was able to condition blinded specimens of *Acerina cernua* to receive food after no more than 5 to 10 feedings by use of electromagnetic stimuli. The stimuli were delivered by means of a small magnet mounted on the skin over a lateral line furrow, as described above. The large electromagnetic coil ($\phi$ ca. 5 m, 400 windings, 1-ohm resistance), on which the fishes' aquarium was placed, was switched on and off with an electronic shutter in order to avoid transients in the current (rise time, 1 sec). The value of the current giving 50% positive reactions (snapping for food as soon as the current was switched on) was determined (see Fig. 3). From these data it was possible to calculate the order of magnitude of the displacement of the skin under natural conditions by measuring the gradient of the field of the electromagnet. The amplitude of the magnet on the skin of the fish was determined optically when the fish was tied to a holder over the coil. Because of the approximations involved, I cannot give an exact figure, but at the frequency of maximum sensitivity (75 cps) the threshold value lies at about 25 Å (extreme values, 5 and 50 Å). To exclude the possibility of stimulating other tactile organs in the skin or even the labyrinth with these stimuli, I cut the nerve leading to the four cupulae that were likely to be stimulated by the magnet on the skin. No reactions were observed even with the strongest currents used in these experiments, but when the magnet was subsequently mounted on the other

---

from another fish that is abnormal in a different way. Curves 3a and 3b were obtained from 2 cupulae in the supraorbital canal, and 3c and 3d from 2 cupulae in the infraorbital canal. Note that even in these cases there is great similarity between the responses of different cupulae in the same fish.

II: Relation between applied frequency and current through the driving coil necessary to obtain a constant response of microphonic potential (equal-response frequency characteristics). In curve 1 the response amplitude chosen was 75 $\mu V$; in curves 2, 3, and 4, all three of which were obtained in another fish, the response amplitudes chosen were 25, 75, and 100 $\mu V$, respectively. In all these cases the cupulae were driven by means of a magnet mounted on the skin (Kuiper, 1956).

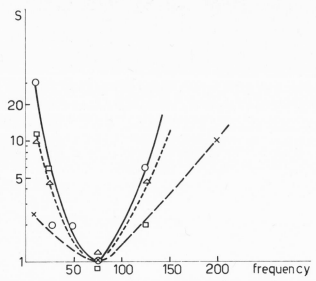

Fɪɢ. 3. Frequency characteristic of the conditioned behavioral response (search for food) on stimulation of the lateral line organ. S represents current through the driving coil, normalized in such a way that 1 is the current needed to obtain 50% positive reactions at 75 cps (Kuiper, 1956).

side of the head, where the nerves were left intact, the reactions were positive again without any new training. The frequency characteristic of the behavioral response is not unlike that of the microphonic potential; the maximum sensitivity is found in the same range. I therefore conclude that *Acerina cernua* is able to perceive low-frequency vibrations of the cupula and that the lateral line organ is most sensitive in the frequency range of 50 to 150 cps (Kuiper, 1956). With regard to the frequency discrimination abilities of *Acerina*, I have recently done a few preliminary experiments, which indicate that the animal can discriminate 50 cps from 150 cps.

Using less artificial stimuli, I confirmed Dijkgraaf's (1934, 1967) description of the fishes' ability to localize an object held in the experimenter's hand and their failure to do so when the same object is mechanically fixed. In addition, in the animals in which the nerves of four cupulae on one side of the head were cut through, I observed that, though the fish did notice the presence of the feeding bar held in the hand, it was not able at first to localize it correctly and that it regained this ability only after about ten feedings. This indicates that the lateral line organ is involved in the localization of moving objects (i.e., the involuntarily trembling hand) and that the elimination of less than 10% of the cupulae on the head has a significant effect.

EVALUATION OF FORCES ACTING ON THE CUPULA

The hydrodynamic forces that may act separately or in conjunction on the cupula are the following: pressure forces, viscous forces, elastic forces, and surface-tension forces. The latter can be neglected, however, since in this paper I will not consider amphibians, for which surface-tension forces are important, but only totally submerged fishes (see also Schwartz, 1967).

Viscous forces are responsible for the resistance experienced by a body moving in a fluid. Absolute viscosity is almost pressure-independent but varies with the temperature and is also influenced by impurities in the water, especially by the presence of hydrophilic colloids; salts, on the contrary, have only a minor effect. The kinematic coefficient $v$, defined as the absolute viscosity divided by the mass density, is often used in hydrodynamics. Elasticity is defined as the ratio between an increment of stress per unit area (or pressure intensity) and the resulting strain, which is the relative change in volume under the influence of stress.

In the following pages I will discuss some models in which, as is essentially the case in all models, the number of variables is reduced in order to gain some insight concerning the effectiveness of the above-mentioned forces on the lateral line organ.

1. A two-dimensional model: When a fish swims through the water, it thereby originates a continuous current along its body surface. Is such a current sufficient to provide a stimulus for a freestanding cupula of, for instance, a 10-cm specimen of *Phoxinus laevis*, the animal that has been extensively studied by Dijkgraaf (1934, 1967)? There are no significant data indicating that the organ is involved in normal locomotion (Dijkgraaf, 1963), or that cupulae become deformed by self-generated currents during normal swimming (Dijkgraaf, personal communication, 1966). Indeed, this was hardly to be expected, because the viscosity of the water gives rise to a loss of velocity of the water near the body surface. In this so-called "boundary layer," the friction losses occur. (In this particular case, we are dealing with a laminar flow; the larger fishes attain velocities in which turbulent flow becomes more likely.)

In Fig. 4 a dimensionless plot is given of the velocity distribution in this laminar boundary layer, as calculated by Blasius for a two-

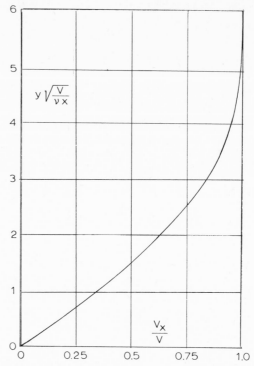

Fɪɢ. 4. Dimensionless plot of velocity distribution in laminar boundary layer (as calculated by Blasius) for a plane submerged in a streaming fluid. $V_x$ = velocity of fluid in the position defined as $(X,Y)$, where $X$ represents the distance from the leading edge of the plane in the direction of flow and $Y$ the distance from the plane; $\nu$ = kinematic viscosity.

dimensional model. For the moment, the fish is reduced to a plane, with a body length $L = 10^{-1}$ m and a velocity $V = 10L = 1$ m/sec; we find that the velocity of the fluid $V_x$ at the tip of a cupula of 100 $\mu$ in length $(Y = 10^{-4}$ m) situated mid-length on the body $(X = 5 \cdot 10^{-2})$ is no more than 5% of the velocity $V$ of the fish and that, in the case of a fish which moves ten times as slowly, $V_x$ becomes as small as 0.002$V$. The error that is made in using a two-dimensional instead of a three-dimensional model of the fish is small; even for $X = 10^{-2}$, Hansen's experimental data obtained with a plane fit the Blasius (1908) curve (Hansen, 1928).

The conclusion may be that only for very fast-swimming fish are the forces on such a freestanding cupula at all considerable. Fast-swimming fish do not have freestanding cupulae but only cupulae in canals. Also, the surface of the fish is covered with a mucous layer in which the whole freestanding cupula may be submerged. Since this mucus represents a nonnewtonian fluid, in which there is no fixed value of the viscosity constant, this layer will probably protect the cupula from shearing forces exerted by the fish's own movement.

2. A three-dimensional model: Most cupulae are not freestanding but are enclosed in canals that communicate with the outside world through small openings. This construction is rather similar to a differential Pitot system, that is, a system for measuring pressure differences along a surface. For the study of the pressure distribution at the surface of fishes, I will make use of a simple streamlined model like the one made of glass that is shown in Fig. 5. I feel justified in this, since already in 1888 Parson, a naval engineer who studied the forms of a

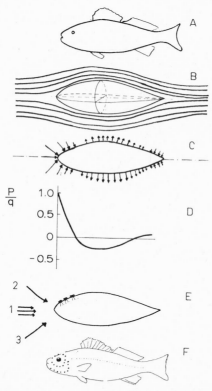

Fig. 5. (A) Silhouette of *A. cernua*. (B) Model of *A. cernua* in a current. (C) Direction of pressure exercised by current on the surface of the model. (D) Pressure distribution function for a current in the direction of the longitudinal axis of the model. (E) For a current from direction 2, the dorsal cupulae are on the pressure side; for a current from direction 3, they are on the suction side. (F) Distribution of the cupulae on the fish.

number of teleosts, remarked that the relation between the area of the cross section and the length of the body was essentially similar for different species of fish and that, in particular, the position of the greatest area of cross section was invariably found at 36% of the length of the fish's body, as measured from the front. Also, one must realize that the general shape of many fishes is remarkably constant during growth (Hecht, 1916).

As a suitable average model, I have therefore taken a body that is symmetrical along its longitudinal axis, and whose maximum diameter equals 1/5 of the total length; this maximum diameter is situated at 40% of the total length. The value of this maximum diameter is not so very important for the calculations that follow: bulkier or more slender models give qualitatively the same results.

In hydrodynamics, the pressure distribution function is expressed in a $p/q$ diagram. In such a diagram, $p$ is the pressure measured at a position indicated on the $x$ coordinate, and $q$ is the pressure in the surroundings, equaling $\frac{1}{2}\rho V^2$, in which $\rho$ is the specific density of the fluid and $V$ is its velocity. In Fig. 5 such a diagram is presented for our model as it is hit by a water current from the front. It is noticed that especially in the frontal region the pressure gradient is large. The direction of the current has a considerable effect on the pressure distribution function, as is indicated in Fig. 6. Different curves are obtained for the pressure and for the suction side of the body; for the dorsal and ventral pressure distribution functions it makes no difference whether the current strikes the body from the right or the left side, provided the same angle is involved.

On the basis of these data, I conclude that the pressure gradient in the fish is greatest on the head and that it is largely dependent on the direction of the current. Moreover, when these currents are local ones, the pressure on the head varies with time. It is not surprising, therefore, that it is on the head that the lateral line organ reaches its greatest development, when it is pressure that forms the stimulus. In the cupulae enclosed in canals, the pressure fluctuations are mediated through the elastic skin extending between the bone bridges or, as in herrings (Wohlfahrt, 1937), through small ramifying tubes that form the communication between the lateral line canal and the outside. Pressure differences between such openings located on either side of a cupula will produce a fluid displacement in the canal, and hence affect the cupula.

In freestanding cupulae also, it is likely that small pressure variations form the stimulus. If we assume that the mucus embedding the cupulae has elastic properties, then the pressure differences on either

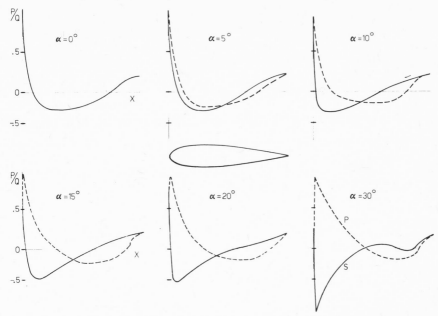

FIG. 6. Pressure distribution on a model for currents from different directions
($\alpha$). For the solid curve, the measured points are situated on the pressure side;
for the dashed curve, on the suction side of the model.

side of the cupula may be transmitted by the elastic deformation of
the mucous layer. It is understandable, in this way, that rapid pressure
fluctuations will produce corresponding oscillations or vibrations of
the cupula, which are quite well evaluated by the fishes, as has been
extensively shown by Dijkgraaf, even if these oscillations of the cupula
are not likely to be so perfectly sinusoidal in the natural surroundings
as in my experimental setup.

The localization of nonmoving objects that is performed by some
species of fish with exceptionally well-developed lateral line organs
fits in the picture. When a fish approaches a stationary object, the current pattern around the fish undergoes a change that is reflected by a
change in the pressure distribution on the fish's body. When, for instance, the model of a fish with a diameter $d$ is moved along the wall
of a tank at a distance $m$ from the wall, then the drag is significantly
larger at $m = 2d$ than at $m \geqslant 3d$ (see also Hertel, 1963), so that indeed
a fish with a sensitive lateral line organ must be able to notice it.

*What signals are detected by the lateral line organ?* The more com-
plexly organized sense organs, like the eyes and ears of higher animals,
are used as instruments to detect spatial and temporal energy distribu-

tions of light and sound, and not simply for registering the presence of light and sound. Must we classify the lateral line organ as a primitive receptor, noticing only the presence of currents, or may we consider the spatial localization of a moving prey by means of the currents it produces as a rather complex procedure requiring a more sophisticated organ? I am inclined to think the latter is the case (see also Tavolga, 1967), and that the organ is probably able to discern different configurations or patterns of currents, such as the patterns generated by members of the same species during courtship and other activities or by different species of prey.

There is little data available on the currents generated by swimming fish. Experiments in which a fish swam over a thin layer of milk placed at the bottom of a black dish were filmed by Rosen (1959, 1961), showing that vortices with a vertical axis were generated in a special spatial arrangement. In this particular case, however, we should realize that the vortices are standing on a solid surface; when a fish swims at a substantial distance from the bottom, the vortex filaments will have to be closed and different current patterns must be expected.

Another technique was used by Walters (1967); in his experiments the fish swam in a suspension of the birefringent clay mineral Bentonite, which also produced a stationary current pattern behind the fish. Though no clear three-dimensional picture is available at the moment, it seems likely that the shape and size of the fins and the manner of moving them affects the current pattern, so that the possibility of species-specific patterns would not seem too remote. This would mean that a fish, following in the wake of another, can detect its current patterns, giving him some clue of what moves ahead. Breder (1965), following a similar line of thought, suggested that these currents are involved in the schooling behavior of fishes. However, further experimental evidence will be needed in order to decide about the value of this concept.

REFERENCES

Blasius, H. (1908). Grenzschichten in Flüssigkeiten mit kleiner Reibung. Z. *Math. Physik* 56, 1; cited by Schlichting, 1960.
Breder, C. M. (1965). Vortices and fish schools. *Zoologica* 50, 97-114.
Davis, H. (1965). A model for transducer action in the cochlea. *Cold Spring Harbor Symp. Quant. Biol.* 30, 181-190.
Dijkgraaf, S. (1934). Untersuchungen über die Funktion der Seitenorgane an Fischen. Z. *Vergleich. Physiol.* 20, 162-214.
——— (1963). The functioning and significance of the lateral-line organs. *Biol. Rev.* 38, 51-105.

—— (1967). Chapter 7, this volume.

Flock, A. (1965). Electron microscopic and electrophysiological studies on the lateral line canal organ. Thesis, Stockholm.

—— (1966). Transducing mechanisms in the lateral-line canal organ receptors. *Cold Spring Harbor Symp. Quant. Biol.* 30, 133-146.

Hansen, N. (1928). Die Geschwindigkeitsverteilung in der Grenzschicht an einer eingetauchten Platte. *Z. Angew. Math. Mech.* 8, 3; also NACA.TM 585 (1930).

Harris, G., and W. A. van Bergeijk (1962). Evidence that the lateral-line organ responds to near-field displacements of sound sources in water. *J. Acoust. Soc. Am.* 34, 1831.

Hecht, S. (1916). Form and growth in fishes. *J. Morph.* 27, 379-400.

Hertel, H. (1963). *Struktur-Form-Bewegung.* Krausskopf-Verlag, Mainz.

Jielof, R., A. Spoor, and Hl. de Vries. (1952). The microphonic activity of the lateral line. *J. Physiol. (London)* 116, 137.

Kuiper, J. W. (1955). The effect of curare on the microphonic effect. *Proc. Intern. Physiol. Congr., Brussels.*

—— (1956). The microphonic effect of the lateral line organ. Publication Biophysical Group, Natuurkundig Laboratorium, Groningen.

Parson, H de B. (1888). The displacements and the area curves of fish. *Trans. Am. Soc. Mech. Eng.* 9, 679-695.

Rosen, M. W. (1959). Waterflow about a swimming fish. *Tech. Publ. U.S. Naval Test Station, China Lake, Calif.;* NOTS TP 2298, 1-94.

—— (1961). Experiments with swimming fish and dolphins. American Society of Mechanical Engineers, New York, Rept. 61-WA-203.

Schwartz, E. (1967). Chapter 10, this volume.

Schlichting, H. (1960). *Boundary Layer Theory,* 4th ed. McGraw-Hill, New York.

Tavolga, W. (1967). Chapter 32, this volume.

de Vries, Hl. (1948). Die Reizschwelle der Sinnesorgane als physiologisches Problem. *Experentia* 4, 205.

Walters, V. (1967). Chapter 24, this volume.

Wersäll, J., and A. Flock. (1964). Suppression and restoration of the microphonic output from the lateral line organ after local application of streptomycin. *Life Sci.* 3, 1151.

Wohlfahrt, T. A. (1937). Anatomische Untersuchungen über die Seitenkanale der Sardine (Clupea pilchardus Walb). *Z. Morph. Oekol. Tiere* 33, 381-412.

## COMMENTS

ROSEN: In 1958, in the work referred to by Dr. Kuiper, I performed a series of hydrodynamic experiments with live fish. In these investigations I discovered the existence of a strange system of vortices in the flow about the body of actively swimming fish (see Figs. 1 and 2). The existence of such a system, generated by fish, had not previously been known. Prior to that time, it was a generally accepted theory that the water flow around fish was smooth, streamlined, laminar flow, free of vortices or turbulence.

This experimental work was done on the fresh-water schooling fish *Brachydanio albolineatus* (Rosen, 1959). It was discovered that each concave undulating curve of the fish's body contained one (and only one) large discrete unit vortex, spinning about a vertical axis. The vortices were generated just

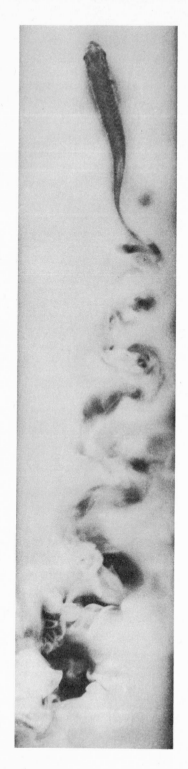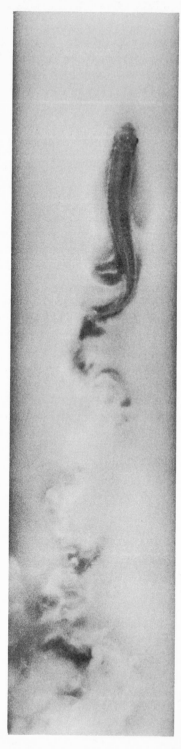

FIG. 1. Discovery of fish vortex system by Rosen in 1958. The flow about the body of a swimming fish, never before seen, was discovered to be a strange system of vortices. Each curve of the body contains one large vortex. As the animal swims, its undulating form weaves itself in and out between these spinning fluid units. Fish and water operate together in a precisely synchronized machinery-like motion. Vortex cores visible as dark centers, later developing spiral arms (upper). Lower: fish's body is engaged with three vortices; the elliptical vortex on right side has just been generated near fish's head.

FIG. 2. Rosen's experimental discovery (1958) of large elliptical vortex in spray about the body of a leaping Pacific white sided dolphin (*Lagenorhynchus obliquidens*). Axis of vortex, centered near dorsal fin, is transverse to the dolphin's body.

behind the gills, one with each stroke of the body, first on one side of the fish's form and then on the other, growing in size as the fish moved forward. Each vortex rotated in a direction opposite to its predecessor, and as the fish swam, it weaved its undulating body smoothly in and out between these cyclonic units as they developed. The fish's undulatory wave motion and the rotating vortices operated together, as if they were one precisely synchronized piece of machinery.

After leaving the tail, the vortex centers were aligned in a single line coinciding with the path of the fish's head. Twin spiral arms unwound from each vortex and linked themselves with the arms of the preceding and folowing vortices, forming a trail resembling a sinusoidal wave. There was neither a forward nor a backward movement of the vortex centers, and no net rearward flow of water could be detected when the fish's velocity was reasonably steady. When the fish started out from a dead stop, or accelerated, then a rearward movement of water was seen, and this consisted of the rapid unwinding of a vortex arm.

The properties and motions of this vortex system are unlike those of Karman vortex streets, which are produced by flow about spheres or blunt inanimate objects and which have two rows of moving vortices and a well-defined central current.

In further experiments, I used a dye rather than a milky layer below the fish. In the dye experiments, only the water coming directly off the fish's body was made visible. The same vortex system was found as was discovered by the milk-layer experiments, verifying that these vortices actually exist at the sides of the fish, not merely below it.

In addition, the existence of cross-recross water filaments was detected in the dye investigations. These filaments were found flowing obliquely underneath the lower edge of the fish and were seen feeding directly into the center of a vortex. Such cross-recross flow filaments, also previously unknown, seem to close the vortices in a chain about the fish in the third dimension of depth.

Following the fish investigations, I performed a number of hydrodynamic experiments with full-grown live porpoises, *Lagenorhynchus obliquidens* (Pacific white-sided dolphin). These mammals swim by undulating up and down, and their caudal fin lies in a horizontal plane—at 90° to that of fish. It was reasoned that, if these animals generated vortices, they should revolve about horizontal axes. Three types of experiments were performed: boundary spray visualization, dye directly on the skin of the porpoise, and an underwater "particle curtain" through which the animal was trained to swim. All three types of experiments revealed that the porpoise generated a very large elliptical vortex system above its body and in its trail. Each vortex did indeed revolve about a horizontal axis, and the system seemed almost identical in its properties and behavior to that of the fish. The flow of water about live, naturally swimming porpoises had never before been seen. The work with the porpoises is described in two of my published reports (Rosen, 1959, 1961).

It is probable that this vortex system is a basic phenomenon present for all aquatic animals that obtain propulsion by means of undulation, including the largest of whales. The strength may vary from one species to another. From the observed behavior of the vortex system, I have proposed the vortex peg undulatory theory of propulsion, as explained in the above-noted references. This theory states that the undulating body and fins of the fish react with each vortex, pushing against it as if it were a fixed roller peg. By means of the pressure field within each vortex, the animal obtains the thrust required for propulsion. The theory postulates that the fish recovers a portion of the energy originally absorbed by the vortex itself, making the system a regenerative energy process of considerable efficiency.

Although I am not a biologist (my fields being hydrodynamic propulsion, fluid dynamics, and propulsion power plants), it is my belief the lateral line of fishes senses each vortex and enables the fish to adjust its undulations in swimming to conform and synchronize with the position and motion of the water in each vortex, enabling it to propel itself with efficiency.

WALTERS: In my studies on fish swimming in Bentonite I have seen this vortex production, and I can substantiate your claim that the vortex trail does not move but is stationary. I have never seen, however, a systematic production of vortices along the sides of the body. Occasionally, a fish in acceleration will send out a little jet that will create turbulence and will cause separation of the boundary layer. But I have found that in a fish such as the eel, which is perfectly streamlined all the way back, there is no vortex production.

TAVOLGA: Dr. Breder recently made use of your vortex-trail analyses in a theoretical study of the role of the vortices in the schooling of fishes. He proposed that the stream of vortices helps keep the fish at specific distances from one another.

LINDGREN: If the fish is moving forward, it is necessary for the wave flow to move backward in relation to a fixed frame of reference. It may be that Dr. Walters did not see any backward flow because his fish were in a Bentonite gel. The vortex trail described by Mr. Rosen cannot be considered a true three-dimensional pattern, and since the fish is a three-dimensional body, the true vortex range is not shown by this technique.

# 10 ANALYSIS OF SURFACE-WAVE PERCEPTION IN SOME TELEOSTS

ERICH SCHWARTZ

Zoophysiologisches Institut
University of Tübingen
Tübingen, Germany

Because of its interesting morphology and physiology, a large number of studies have been made on the lateral line system in fishes and aquatic amphibians. Leydig (1850) discovered its sensory nature, and Hofer (1908) presented evidence that these organs are sensitive to weak water currents. Dijkgraaf (1934, 1947, 1956) improved upon Hofer's results. He demonstrated that the lateral line organs are sensitive to displacements of water particles produced by what he called a "damming phenomena," which occurs in front of moving objects. More recently, Görner (1961, 1963) described individual lateral line sense organs of the clawed frog *Xenopus laevis,* and how these responded differently to water displacements of various directions. The functioning of an end organ as a receptor with directional sensitivity appears closely related to the ultrastructure of the neuromast cells, that is, to the arrangement of the stereocilia and the kinocilium of the sensory cells.

The participation of lateral line sense organs in low-frequency sound perception has often been questioned since Parker's experiments in 1904. Only a few studies with classical conditioning have shown positive results. However, Harris and van Bergeijk (1962) demonstrated that the acting stimulus is not the propagated pressure wave but the water displacement produced by the vibrating stimulator. This limits the perceptible range to the near field of the sound source.

Both aspects, the directional sensitivity to water displacement and the sensitivity to vibrations of lateral line sense organs, are relevant to this paper. Observations that certain fish take food from the water surface in darkness as quickly as in daylight suggested the present study. The experimental animals selected are classified as surface-feeding fish, varieties that prefer the quiet shallow waters of streams and lakes. At night they remain at the water surface, and enucleated animals were found, most of the time, in contact with the surface film.

Dropping food into the water causes ripples at the water surface that are in turn propagated. These waves, however, are different from sound waves: normally they are low-frequency transverse waves. The propagation velocity of the waves depends on the frequency. In most experiments it was approximately 95 cm per sec. Surface fish obviously perceive these waves. The aim of this paper is to demonstrate by behavioral experiments the directional sensitivity of lateral line end organs in fishes, and also that these organs can behave as vibratory sensors.

RESPONSES TO SURFACE WAVES

Blinded *Aplocheilus lineatus* Cuv. and Val. and *Fundulus notatus* Raf. often respond spontaneously to disturbances of the water surface produced by dipping a small glass rod into the water. Their responses are oriented toward the center of the disturbance. A floundering fly anywhere on the water surface, for instance, will quickly be captured by the fish. Repeated trials at distances of up to 90 cm revealed that the fish respond immediately after the propagated surface waves have passed them. The average time between stimulus and response of *F. notatus*, determined with movie frames (64 fr per sec), was 0.05 sec; the shortest time measured was 0.038 sec. Since the investigated species never responded prior to the arrival of the slowly propagated surface waves, one can rule out the possibility that the fish responded to pressure waves, which are propagated more than a thousand times faster than surface waves.

The above-mentioned species do not respond when they lose contact with the surface film. Other fish such as the mudminnow *Umbra limi* Kirtland, however, which often frequent surface waters, respond to surface waves even if they stay several centimeters below the surface; but the response is delayed according to the depth of the fish. Such a response is also reported for *X. laevis* (Dijkgraaf, 1947).

*F. notatus* perceive waves up to a distance of 80 to 90 cm, whereas *A. lineatus* respond to waves generated up to 105 cm away. (Fig. 1, here the relative range of distance perception, is for *Fundulus* only.) The responses of the fish were always directional toward the wave source, but they varied considerably in duration and strength, depending on the distance of the fish from the source. Response to waves that originated from a distant source (60 cm) was performed slowly and ceased after a distance of 20 to 25 cm. Waves produced close to the fish

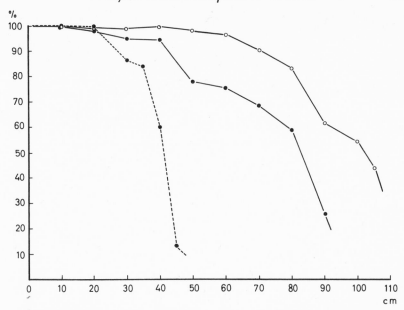

FIG. 1. Absolute (————) and relative (– – – –) range of distance perception of surface waves. Each circle represents 384 trials with 7 animals. ●: *Fundulus natatus;* ○: *Aplocheilus lineatus.*

(within 20 cm) evoke a quick and vigorous reaction, with a rate of movement that corresponds to the distance of the wave source. The ability of *F. notatus* to localize the wave source is illustrated in Fig. 2. The fish attained the highest score (86.5%, 384 trials) when the wave source was 4 cm away. The precision of the reactions decreases with increasing distance, and correspondingly the variation of the responses increases from 2.5 to 7 cm. Also the number of reactions short of the target become larger. The undershooting may be caused by the way the stimulus was presented. This was done by dipping glass rods, one at a time, into the water. Floundering prey produce continuous waves at the water surface; therefore, the fish localize such prey much better.

The fish orient well to surface waves originating from a single point source. When confronted by two waves produced simultaneously by a bipronged fork, the fish always swim to the nearest wave source; that is, the wave front that strikes the fish first determines the response. However, if the second wave is stronger than the first, the fish may switch to the second wave source. When the fish is confronted by a wave source on both sides, at exactly the same distance away from him, he does not respond to either one. The fish could not distinguish between two identical waves presented simultaneously. If the wave

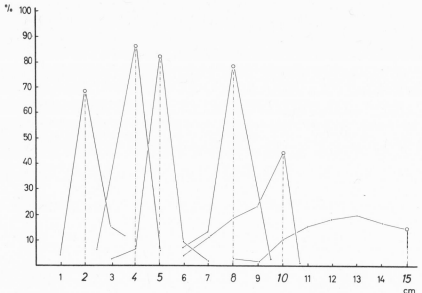

Fɪɢ. 2. Localization of wave source at 2, 4, 5, 8, 10, and 15 cm distance by *F. notatus.*

sources are located anterior to the fish, maintaining exactly the same distance from him, the fish swims along the same course, along the midline of the two sources. The movements are differentiated as follows: close to the wave source they react weakly and briefly, but farther away a stronger and longer-lasting response is elicited. In other words, the smaller the angle between the fish's mouth and the two wave sources, the more vigorous the response.

The question to be asked now is: what are the sensory structures that enable fish to perform these reactions?

MORPHOLOGY

The sensory organs engaged in surface-wave perception are located on top of the strongly flattened head (Fig. 3). Both the canal organs in *F. notatus* and the superficial organs in *A. lineatus* are arranged in three groups, composed of organs located symmetrically on both sides of the head. The freestanding organs of *A. lineatus* bear a flaglike cupula. The end organs point in different directions and therefore form different angles with the midline of the fish. Without going into detail, we recognize that the organs of the nasal group form acute angles, and the organs of the supraorbital mostly obtuse and right

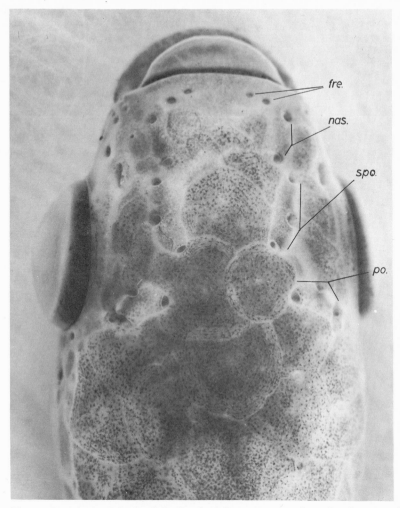

Fig. 3. Dorsal view of top of the head of *F. notatus* revealing distribution and arrangement of lateral line canals. nas, nasal canal; spo, supraorbital canal; po, postorbital canal; fre, freestanding organ.

angles. The arrangement of the organs is quite similar in both species and leads to the assumption that it is a functional one.

## PERCEPTUAL FIELD OF SEPARATE AND GROUPED SENSE ORGANS

Intact fishes are able to locate a wave source. If parts of the lateral line system are eliminated, however, both perception and response are affected. The best method of doing this is by cauterization of specific organs with a hot wire. This operation does not produce any adverse changes in the fish's behavior. To study the function of an individual organ, several free standing organs of *A. lineatus* and canal organs of *F. notatus* were tested. *A. lineatus* with only one intact end organ, located at an angle of 5 to 10°, responded only to waves approaching the fish anteriorly. Other organs are sensitive only to waves that originate laterally. Only those waves which act approximately parallel to the longitudinal axis of the organ—and hence the cupula—evoke a response, but not those perpendicular to it. Thus the perception of a stimulus depends on the directional sensitivity of the individual end organ. The response of such a fish with a single functioning end organ, however, is poorly oriented.

The directional sensitivity also limits the perceptual field of the groups of organs (Fig. 4). Each of these three groups in *A. lineatus* is especially sensitive to waves approaching the fish from a specific direction: that is, the nasal group of neuromasts are most sensitive to anterior waves, the supraorbital to lateral and slightly anterior waves, and the postorbital to posterior-directed waves. These groups also represent, according to the arrangement of the individual organs, different sections of the original perceptual field. For instance, the nasal one represents a section of 55°; the supraorbital, 160°; and the postorbital, 130°. The perceptual fields of these groups overlap one another, and the degree of overlapping seems to be important for the ability to respond precisely.

Generally, waves produced within the perceptual field of an individual organ or of a group evoke fairly well-defined directional responses, whereas near the margins the accuracy of the responses diminishes considerably. Striking differences were observed in the duration of responses. For instance, after removal of nasal or supraorbital organs on both sides of the head, the responses fell short of the wave source. Responses due to only intact postorbital organs ceased after a very short time. The responses appeared to be highly stereotyped. Removal of postorbital organs did not impair the accuracy of localization in the anterior and lateral perceptual field. Although the nasal and supraorbital organs are separated morphologically, they function as a unit and appear responsible for the estimation of distance.

Removal of sensory organs on one side of the head causes the fish to be disoriented. Elimination of the sensory organs on one side of the body forces the fish to move to the other side if the waves are presented anteriorly. Consequently, indication of direction of the wave source results from the collaboration of symmetrically located organs. The

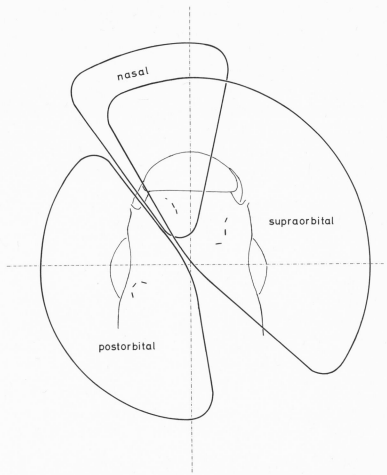

Fɪɢ. 4. Perceptual field of the nasal, supraorbital, and postorbital group of sense organs of *A. lineatus*. The symmetrically located fields and organs are not illustrated.

most frequent overlapping of the perceptual fields of individual organs occurs in front of the fish. A wave from this area stimulates at least 6 to 8 individual organs and, therefore, allows an accurate localization.

THE STIMULUS PARAMETER

It has been shown that surface feeders orient to surface waves and, under certain conditions, even localize their origin. This ability is possible only through close interaction of individual end organs. Consequently, we must ask: what indicates the distance of a wave source? During the following test the fishes were exposed to waves of a constant frequency. The intensity of the waves was adjusted in such a way that the fish detected the wave source at less than 10 cm distance. During the second test, the intense waves provided a response at about 60 cm distance. In both cases, the waves were of the same frequency (wavelength) and intensity when the fishes responded. Despite these facts, the fish performed correctly according to the distance of the wave source. In the first test they localized the source with a quick and vigorous reaction, whereas in the second they showed a weak, but long-lasting, directional response. This result suggests that the curvature of the waves, the only remaining variable, may be the decisive factor.

The radiating waves generated at a point became more and more expanded with increasing distance. The front of these waves was strongly curved near their source but became less curved as they progressed. The rate of change of the wave arc therefore is strongest within the first centimeters of the wave propagation. As demonstrated, localization is limited to a relatively short range. Trials with differently shaped wave sources simulating different distances (Schwartz, 1965) confused the fishes. They reacted to the simulated distance, and not to the actual distance. Therefore, we conclude that the curvature of the wave arc is the relevant factor responsible for the differentiated reactions.

We do not know enough about the mechanical properties and the transducing mechanism of these sensory organs. They can, however, be considered as analyzing receptors. The specific information delivered to the brain is due to the receptor's location on the head. Because of the directional sensitivity of these organs, this first information is modified according to the direction of the stimulus. Water particles that compose surface waves carry out orbital motions and produce a displacement perpendicular to the direction of the radiating waves. Since fishes perceive only a small section of the whole wave, a wave that is not propagated as much can involve a greater variety in the direction of displacement than a wave that travels far. A wave front that is not curved very much will act upon the sense organs by way of slightly different angles than a strongly curved one, although both waves originated from the same direction. Only through interaction of many individual organs will the fish receive enough information to perform a localization.

Two surface waves that strike the fish simultaneously will stimulate, independently, the individual sense organs on both sides of the head through the same angle. Those vectors of the stimuli which are opposed in their effect can be neglected, and only those which have the same effect will evoke a response. Therefore, the closer the fish is to the wave source—that is, the more lateral the wave sources are—the slower is the response.

## SENSITIVITY TO VIBRATIONS

A local deformation of the water surface forms oscillations. Floundering insects on the water surface also produce continuous oscillations, perceived by surface feeders. Surface waves, however, do not have a constant propagation speed in a specific medium, as do pressure waves (sound). The propagation speed of surface waves depends on the wavelength (Fig. 5). At $\lambda = 1.7$ cm (equal to a frequency of 13.4 cps), the propagation speed is at its minimum, at 23 cm/sec. In the lower-frequency range it increases rapidly, while in the higher-frequency range it increases slowly. The differences between surface waves and sound waves are relevant. Now, it is of interest to test these fish for their responses to surface waves of different frequency. The method has been described previously (Schwartz, 1965). However, it

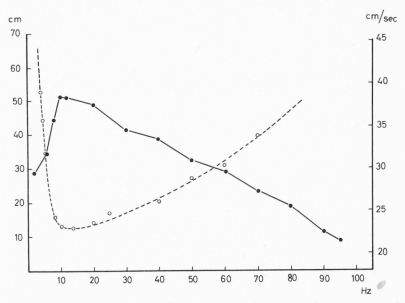

FIG. 5. Propagation speed of surface waves (– – – –), in centimeters per second, and sensitivity of lateral line organs of *A. lineatus* (———) in centimeters of distance from wave source, depending on frequency (cps).

should be added here that the intensity of the waves remained the same throughout the test. The unbroken curve in Fig. 5 represents the responses of *A. lineatus*. The sensitivity of the fish, expressed as the distance in centimeters from the wave source at which they responded, is plotted against the frequency of the waves. *A. lineatus* responded best to waves of 10 to 12 cps. The threshold seemed to be raised with increasing frequency; the animals must then be closer to the wave source to detect waves. Only a few responses could be obtained above 95 cps. The sensitivity decreased very rapidly in the frequency range below 10 cps, whereas it decreased slowly in the higher range.

The curve representing the propagation velocity is just the opposite of that mentioned above. Since the propagation velocity is a characteristic feature of surface waves, it can be concluded that the sensitivity of the lateral line sense organs of *A. lineatus* is inversely proportional to the propagation velocity.

SIGNIFICANCE

Lateral line sense organs of a great number of fishes, especially of the Cyprinodontes I have studied (Schwartz, 1966), seem to function also as vibratory receptors. The perceptible vibrations, the surface waves, are of a different physical nature than sound waves. Therefore the present paper does not support the notion of a participation of the lateral line system in sound perception; instead, it emphasizes the displacement-sensitive character of these sense organs.

Certain fishes classified as surface feeders are able to sense surface waves. Pelagic fish, such as *Umbra limi* and *Fundulus diaphanous,* can also sense surface waves, but they respond poorly compared with surface fishes.

Since surface fishes live very close to the water surface, their upward visual field (and hence the aerial window) is smaller than that in fish frequenting deeper water. Vision at the water surface (water-air interface) is practically impossible because of reflections and refractions of light. Yet surface feeders take food (prey) predominantly from the surface. These fishes seem to compensate the dead band between the upward and downward visual field by means of their lateral line, which appears to be highly specialized. In the present case, the lateral line supplements the vision of the fishes quite strongly.

REFERENCES

Dijkgraaf, S. (1934). Untersuchungen über die Funktion der Seitenorgane an Fischen. *Z. Vergleich. Physiol.* 20, 162-214.

———— (1947). Über die Reizung des Ferntastsinns bei Fischen und Amphibien. *Experientia* 3, 206-208.

———— (1956). Elektrophysiologische Untersuchungen an der Seitenlinie von *Xenopus laevis*. *Experientia* 12, 276-278.

Görner, P. (1961). Beitrag zum Bau und zur Arbeitsweise des Seitenorgans von *Xenopus laevis*. *Verhandl. Deut. Ges. Zool.* 193-198.

———— (1963). Untersuchungen zur Morphologie und Elektrophysiologie des Seitenorgans vom Krallenfrosch (*Xenopus laevis*). *Z. Vergleich. Physiol.* 47, 316-338.

Harris, G. G., and W. A. van Bergeijk (1962). Evidence that the lateral line organ responds to water displacements. *J. Acoust. Soc. Am.* 34 (12), 1831-1841.

Hofer, B. (1908). Studien über die Hautsinnesorgane der Fische I. Die Funktion der Seitenorgane bei den Fischen. *Ber Kgl. Bayer. Biol. Versuchssta. München* 1, 115-164.

Leydig, F. (1850). Über die Schleimkanäle der Knochenfische. *Müller's Arch. Anat. Physiol. wiss. Med.* 1850.

Parker, G. H. (1904). The function of the lateral line organs in fishes. *Bull. Bur. Com. Fisheries* 24.

Schwartz, E. (1965). Bau und Funktion der Seitenlinie des Streifenhechtlings *Aplocheilus lineatus*. *Z. Vergleich. Physiol.* 50, 55-87.

———— and A. D. Hasler (1966). Perception of surface waves by the blackstripe topminnow *Fundulus notatus* (Cyprinodontidae). *J. Fisheries Res. Board Can.* 23, 1331-1352.

## COMMENTS

LOWENSTEIN: I think it's very interesting that the fish can detect at all when one side is not functioning. I think it's possible that the swimming movement is controlled also by the lateral line organs.

SCHWARTZ: Actually I don't say that the swimming movement as such is controlled by the lateral line organ. The movements of the fish toward the wave source are certainly influenced by the waves. The fish will obtain information on the waves by means of the lateral line organs, during the swimming phase. The sensitivity of the fish is remarkably lower during movement; therefore the results reported were obtained only with fish hovering at the surface.

WILLIAMS: Were you ever able to get these fish to respond far enough from the source so that you might rule out the possibility that they are responding before the wave arrives?

SCHWARTZ: The analysis of movies of some experiments reveals most impressively that the fishes respond immediately after the first surface wave has passed them, and never before. This has been examined at distances of up to 100 cm. The shortest reaction time measured was 0.038 sec. Therefore we really can rule out sound perception.

VAN BERGEIJK: I want to take issue with you on the way you plot the propagation processes (Fig. 5). It comes out very nicely, that is, as the same curve—except, of course, that it is negative. I don't see what this would have to do with a relevant stimulus parameter. I would suppose that amplitude would be important, but the wavelengths are going to change in the same way.

One thing that will happen, too, is that at the lowest velocity the output will be larger for a given input; and what I want to raise mostly is the question of which is the relevant parameter to measure here. Is it the total energy you put into the water that determines what he gets? Obviously not, because you'd get a flat curve if you were doing this. Is it the amplitude at the point where the fish's organ is? I should think that this is the first thing to look for which seems to fit with other things we know, but I think the propagation velocity here is hiding the real parameter.

SCHWARTZ: Since the frequency test has been performed with waves of constant amplitude, I believe the propagation speed is an important factor. However, further experiments must be made to clarify these questions.

RASMUSSEN: Did you say at the surface you were able to detect the wave? Because we all know that in any surface there's an orbital motion underneath it and that the lower you get in the water the less the linear dimension of this orbital movement, so that there is a maximum right at the surface. It doesn't seem there's much reason to explain why the fish respond right at the surface but would not respond a little bit below. As it got deeper, the direction of the displacement would still be the same as it would be on the surface.

SCHWARTZ: The investigated surface fishes do not respond to surface waves if they lose contact with the water surface. I am aware of the physical facts, but I still can't explain why the fish don't respond. It is even possible that they perceive the stimulus in such a case. I am going to look into this with a different method than was used here. Other fishes show a positive response, but with a time delay.

LATERAL LINE DETECTORS (P. Cahn, ed.), 135–161, © 1967 Indiana University Press

# 11 SPONTANEOUS AND EVOKED ACTIVITY FROM THE *XENOPUS LAEVIS* LATERAL LINE

GERARD G. HARRIS AND ÅKE FLOCK †

Sensory and Perceptual Processes Department
Bell Telephone Laboratories, Inc.
Murray Hill, New Jersey

Neural responses from the lateral line organ of *Xenopus laevis* have been studied by Dijkgraaf (1956), Murray (1956), Görner (1963), and by Harris and Milne (1966). Previous experiments (Görner, 1963; Harris and Milne, 1966) have studied the spontaneous and evoked activity from a single stitch in vitro and have emphasized the information which this organ is sensitive to and the manner in which it is encoded. We wish to describe some in vitro experiments on the effect of antidromic firing of the whole nerve trunk on the spontaneous and evoked activity from a single stitch. The purpose of these experiments is to gain some insight into the process of impulse generation by hair cells. Since some of the conclusions depend upon the specific anatomy of the innervation in *Xenopus,* we shall first deal briefly with a few of the salient features.

## ANATOMICAL INTRODUCTION

Figure 1 shows the arrangement of the lateral line organs on *Xenopus.* The organ consists of rows of stitches. The upper and middle lateral rows, following the nomenclature of Murray (1955), are easily accessible and have been studied most. For each row of stitches, a nerve trunk leaves the thorax behind the shoulder and courses down the skin alongside its row. Each stitch consists of a number of neuromasts placed in an almost linear array. Branches leave the nerve trunk to innervate each stitch. Murray (1955) describes two large myelinated fibers that branch to innervate each neuromast in the stitch. Görner

† On leave from Gustaf V Research Institute and from the Department of Otolaryngology, Karolinska Sjukhuset, Stockholm, Sweden.

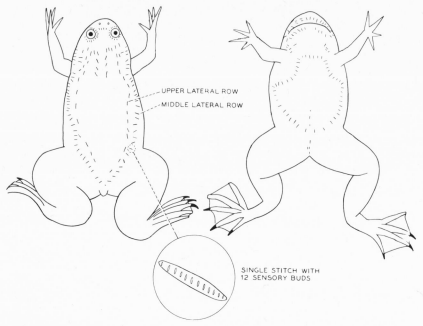

UPPER LATERAL ROW
MIDDLE LATERAL ROW

SINGLE STITCH WITH
12 SENSORY BUDS

Fig. 1. Diagram of the lateral line organ of *Xenopus laevis*. (After Harris and Milne, 1966.)

(1963) found small myelinated fibers in the branches as well. These features can be seen if we section the nerve trunk leading to the middle lateral row.

Figure 2 shows a phase contrast photomicrograph of the nerve trunk to the middle lateral row. Three branches can be seen, each with two large myelinated fibers (about 8 $\mu$) and one or more small myelinated fibers. The number of large fibers is conserved in the trunk; that is, the two large fibers from each branch do not combine with other fibers and so retain the specificity of their original stitch, at least to the ganglion (Murray, 1955). In physiological experiments both Görner (1963) and Harris and Milne (1966) found only two types of nerve pulses from a single stitch. These pulses show sensitivity in antiparallel directions. In the case of the middle lateral row, one is sensitive to velocities toward the tail, the other toward the head. One of the delights of this particular preparation is that by isolating a single stitch one may record from two fibers by using only a macroelectrode on the main nerve trunk.

The arrow in Fig. 2 points to a very small myelinated fiber. An electromicrograph (Petraitis, 1964) of this region is shown in Fig. 3.

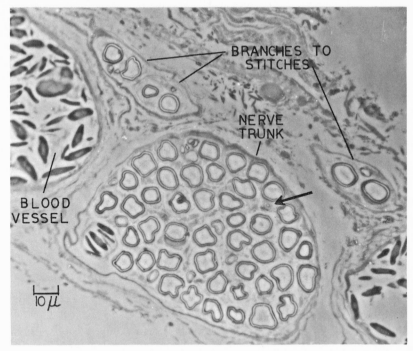

BRANCHES TO STITCHES

NERVE TRUNK

BLOOD VESSEL

10 μ

FIG. 2. Phase photomicrograph of the nerve trunk to the middle lateral row, showing three branch nerves. The region near the arrow is enlarged in Fig. 3. (Harris and Milne, 1966.)

Alongside the small myelinated fiber is a group of six unmyelinated fibers in a single Schwann cell. Exhaustive determinations have not been made, but it appears that the unmyelinated fibers can branch to many stitches. Flock (1967) has found both afferent and efferent types of synaptic endings on the hair cells. Since in vitro preparations of a single stitch give only two types of pulses, which can be attributed to the two large fibers, it is tempting to suggest that the unmyelinated fibers and small myelinated fibers are efferent. Görner (1967), indeed, has evidence that the small myelinated fibers are efferent, but with as yet unknown effect.

The two large fibers to a stitch branch to each neuromast in what Murray (1955) has described as a tram-line fashion. A schematic of this branching to two neuromasts is shown in Fig. 4. Flock (1967) finds that the nerves lose their myelination before penetrating the basement membrane. The point to be emphasized here is that the neuromasts are quite separate and are connected only by the nerve fibers.

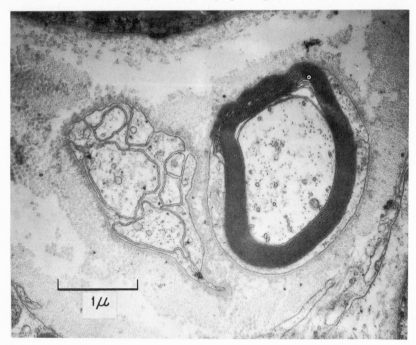

FIG. 3. Electromicrograph of a portion of the nerve trunk in Fig. 2, showing a small myelinated fiber and six unmyelinated fibers surrounded by a Schwann cell. (Courtesy of R. Petraitis.)

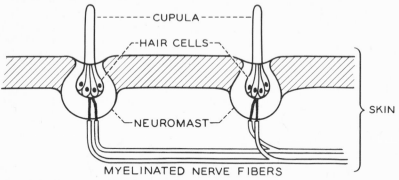

FIG. 4. Schematic drawing of the large myelinated fibers branching to two neuromasts. (After Harris and Milne, 1966.)

EXPERIMENTAL PREPARATION

The method of preparation is similar to that described by Harris and Milne (1966) and by Görner (1963). The animal is cooled to near 0°C

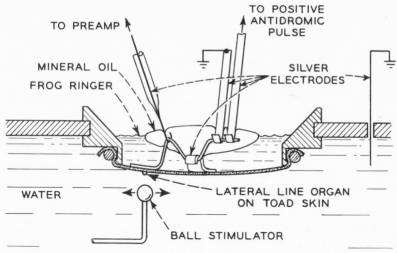

TO POSITIVE
ANTIDROMIC
PULSE

TO PREAMP

MINERAL OIL
FROG RINGER

SILVER
ELECTRODES

WATER

LATERAL LINE ORGAN
ON TOAD SKIN

BALL STIMULATOR

FIG. 5. Schematic of experimental arrangement.

in water from its own tank and then pithed. A piece of skin from the
back is cut off the animal while in the cold water and placed over the
bottom of a nylon cylinder to form a pan. The pan is then placed in a
tank as shown in Fig. 5. The water on the outside of the skin is the
tank water in which the toad was living. Frog Ringer is placed inside
the pan. A stitch is selected, and the nerve trunk is carefully dissected
loose from the skin so as to leave only the selected stitch joined to the
nerve trunk. A pool of mineral oil is placed on the Ringers, and the
nerve trunk is threaded through the electrodes, i.e., around a recording electrode in the oil, down to a grounding electrode in the Ringers,
back up again to a grounding electrode in the oil, and then to an
electrode for antidromic stimulation. Mechanical stimulation was supplied by moving a 3-mm-diameter ball in the direction of maximum
sensitivity. During an experiment the ball displacement was kept constant, and the stimulus magnitude was varied by changing the distance
between ball and skin.

Careful design of the grounding and stimulating electrode enabled
artifacts at the recording electrode to be reduced considerably. The
antidromic artifact plus the antidromic volley did not saturate the preamplifier. The antidromic firing of the nerve had a clear threshold
effect, as seen in Fig. 6. It was found convenient to hold the voltage
of a rectangular pulse constant and to vary its duration. In this particular preparation, the threshold occurred between 0.020 and 0.021
msec for a pulse amplitude of 0.5 volt. The threshold was sharp although the duration required for threshold could vary during an ex-

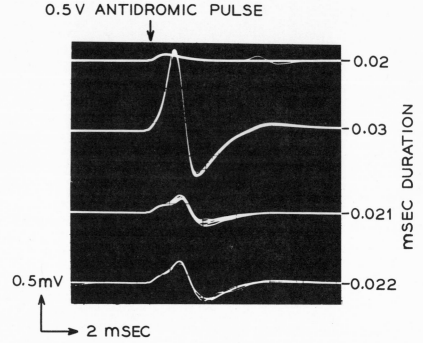

Fɪɢ. 6. Oscilloscope trace of the artifact and antidromic volley produced by an antidromic stimulus and picked up by the recording electrode. The antidromic stimulus was a rectangular voltage pulse of constant amplitude and variable duration. The threshold is between 0.020 and 0.021 msec in duration.

periment, possibly owing to fatigue or to adaptation. The delay between the artifact and the nerve volley is about 1 msec, which means a velocity of about 10 m per sec. This velocity is presumably for the large myelinated fibers. Volleys from the small myelinated fibers or the unmyelinated fibers were not seen. They either could not be separated from the main volley because of the small length of nerve or were so small that they could not be detected in the noise.

Both the mechanical stimulus and the antidromic pulse were triggered at a separately variable time after a master trigger. The master trigger was repeated at a rate of from 1 to 5 times per sec.

The recording electrode picked up spontaneous and evoked activity from both large fibers connected to the selected stitch, as well as the antidromic volley. After amplification the signal was processed by an electronic circuit that could be adjusted to discriminate between the two types of pulses from both fibers. A scope intensifier could then be used to intensify the trace at the time of selection of a particular type

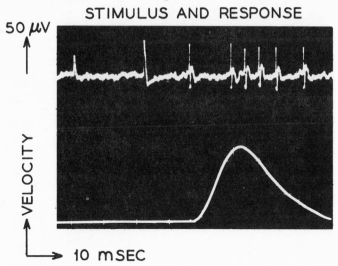

## STIMULUS AND RESPONSE

50 μV

VELOCITY

10 mSEC

FIG. 7. Oscilloscope trace of the velocity of the mechanical stimulus (lower), together with a trace showing a repetitive, evoked response (upper). Note the point of intensification at the bottom of the overshoot of the evoked pulses.

of pulse. Figure 7 shows, on the lower trace, the velocity of the mechanical stimulus. The upper trace shows a typical repetitive response. The overshoot of the pulse has an intensified spot. At times no vertical input is put on the trace, and the selected nerve pulse shows as a bright spot at the time of its occurrence (see Fig. 16). Many successive stimuli can be shown in the same picture by displacing the trace vertically between each stimulus presentation. The data from an experiment is recorded on FM tape and subsequently digitalized to be processed on a computer.

RESULTS

It is well known that the lateral line nerves of *Xenopus* are spontaneously active. Figure 8 shows some properties of this spontaneous activity from a single fiber. An interval histogram of the spontaneous activity is plotted in Fig. 8A. The abscissa is the time between successive nerve pulses (in msec), and the ordinate is the number of such intervals per msec of increment. The height of this interval distribution at a given interval is representative of the probability of occurrence of that interval. There is a characteristic absence of intervals less than about 10 msec duration. The probability rises to a maximum and then declines for long intervals in what we shall see is a more or

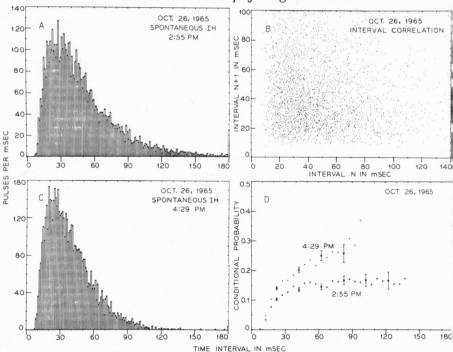

FIG. 8. Spontaneous activity from toad, October 26, 1965. (A) Internal histogram of spontaneous activity taken at 2:55 P.M. (B) Scatter plot to test correlation of successive intervals; no correlation is observed. (C) Spontaneous interval histogram taken at 4:29 P.M. (D) Conditional probability of firing: defined as the probability of firing in the time interval $t$ to $(t + 1)$, conditional on the nonfiring during the previous $t$ msec. A higher plateau corresponds to a higher spontaneous rate.

less exponential tail. The histogram in Fig. 8C is taken from the same preparation at a later time. The rate of spontaneous activity has gone up, and the shape of the interval histogram is different. The difference in shape cannot be explained by a simple scale contraction along the time axis. This fact can easily be seen in these figures by noting that the time interval for no response is the same for both rates of spontaneous activity. The rate of spontaneous activity depends, among other things, on the local oxygen supply. In this particular experiment a bubble of oxygen was placed in the frog Ringer over the stitch, with the result that the oxygen content was not constant.

A convenient way of replotting these data is to plot the probability $p_k$ of firing in the next msec, conditional on the fact that the nerve has not fired during the specified interval. The value of $p_k$ for an interval of $k$ msec can easily be found by dividing the number of intervals that occur in the next msec box by the total number of intervals larger than the given interval. For a Poisson distribution of intervals, which would give an exponential tail in an interval histogram, $p_k$ is a constant. This type of conditional probability is plotted in Fig. 8D for both interval histograms shown on the left of the figure. The conditional probability is zero for about 10 msec and rises to a more or less constant value in about 60 msec. The errors shown at representative points are the standard deviations. As the interval increases, the error increases since the number of samples decreases. We see from this plot that after a nerve fires it slowly recovers to a statistical process independent of previous history (constant $p_k$).

We can next ask the question: does the firing of a nerve erase the memory of previous firings? Or to put it in another way: are successive intervals correlated? For instance, do short intervals follow long intervals? Any correlation can be seen by plotting the $N$th interval vs. the ($N$th + 1) interval. A correlation would be seen as a local grouping; such a scatter plot is seen in Fig. 8B. No evidence of correlation can be found, which means that the process giving rise to spontaneous activity is at least in the first order statistically independent and is probably independent to higher orders.

Two more examples of spontaneous interval histograms and associated plots of conditional probability are seen in Fig. 9. The shapes of the interval histograms can be quite different, but the conditional probabilities have the property of recovery to a constant value.

These facts about the spontaneous activity demonstrated by Harris and Milne (1966) are also supported by the present experiment. They reported another property of the spontaneous activity of both fibers from a single stitch, that is, that the spontaneous activity from one fiber is independent of the spontaneous activity in the other fiber except perhaps for a slight ($\sim$5%) positive correlation during the first 40 msec. Remember that these two fibers are probably connected to neighboring hair cells. The fact of independence was used to argue against Brownian motion of the cupula as the origin of the spontaneous activity.

A characteristic dead time of about 10 msec is highly unusual when one considers the innervation of the neuromasts from a single stitch. Consider the following argument. If the origin of the spontaneous activity is in the individual neuromasts, then the activity of one neuromast should be independent of the activity in another neuromast. If this is so, the minimum dead interval is determined by the recovery time of the nerve and should be less than 4 msec (this value is ob-

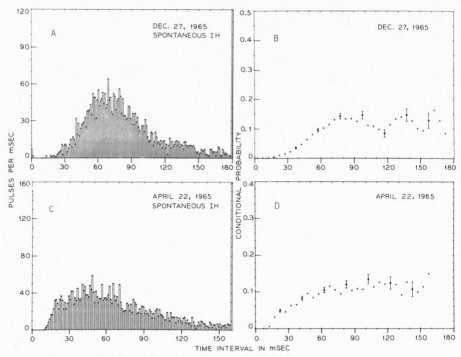

Fig. 9. Spontaneous interval histograms and conditional probability plots from two different animals. (A) and (B) December 27, 1965; (C) and (D) April 22, 1965.

tained from evoked activity). To get around this difficulty, Harris and Milne (1966) hypothesized that, when one neuromast fires the nerve, the nerve spike antidromically invades all the other neuromasts from the same stitch and, so to say, resets a process that contributes to the rate of spontaneous activity.

We can test this hypothesis by antidromically firing the nerve artificially and seeing what happens to the spontaneous activity. We thus want to look at the interval histogram—however, not the interval histogram from the previous spontaneous spike but from the time of the antidromic volley. Figure 10 shows the superposition of a number (~60) of traces with antidromic firing. Before the antidromic volley occurs, there are spots indicating spontaneous activity. After the antidromic volley there is a time of inhibition followed by a slow recovery. The region of inhibition is much longer than either the recovery time of the nerve or the recovery time of the amplifier. The inhibition could be due to the hypothesized resetting process, but it could also be due to the firing of efferent inhibitory nerves. In order to distinguish between

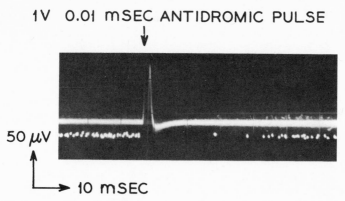

**1V  0.01 mSEC ANTIDROMIC PULSE**

50 μV

10 mSEC

Fig. 10. Superposition of oscilloscope traces showing the effect of an antidromic volley on spontaneous activity. The region of inhibition after the antidromic volley is similar to the inhibition after a spontaneous nerve pulse.

these two possibilities, we can compare the plots of the conditional probability after an antidromic volley with the conditional probability after spontaneous activity. This is done for two different preparations in Fig. 11.

In Fig. 11A the conditional probabilities from the preparation shown in Fig. 8 are repeated, together with a plot of the conditional probability after an antidromic volley. We would expect this plot to be shifted to a greater time by about 4 msec, thus allowing for double the travel time from the recording electrode to the stitch. When this shift is accounted for, one sees that the recovery after an antidromic volley closely follows the recovery after a spontaneous pulse. The data for the antidromic case were taken at a time between the two spontaneous runs, and it is not clear whether the differences shown are real differences or are merely due to variations in rate of spontaneous activity. The plots in Fig. 11B and D show cases where the data for the antidromic volley were taken immediately after the data for the spontaneous activity. The data for Fig. 11D were taken about 40 min after the data for Fig. 11B. In both of these plots the recovery after an antidromic firing is close to but slightly slower than that after spontaneous firing.

The plot in Fig. 11C is for the same preparation as those on the right, but the data were taken later in the experiment and after the cupulae were scraped off. Before the cupulae were scraped off, the preparation was sensitive to a mechanical stimulus and produced evoked activity; afterward there was no evoked activity. That there is any spontaneous activity at all is strong proof that the spontaneous

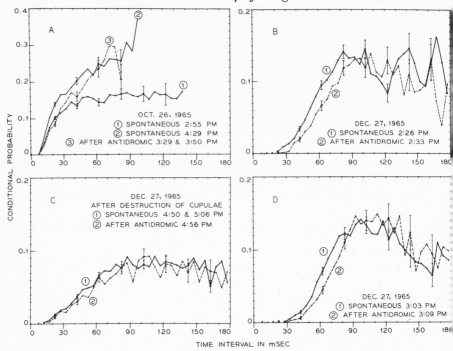

Fig. 11. Conditional probability of spontaneous activity after spontaneous activity and after an antidromic volley. (A) October 26, 1965. (B) December 27, 1965, at 2:26 P.M. (C) December 27, 1965, after destruction of the cupulae. (D) December 27, 1965, at 3:30 P.M. (before destruction of cupula). The recovery after antidromic volley is slightly slower than after a spontaneous firing.

activity is inherent in the process through which the hair cell fires the nerve and is not caused by Brownian motion of the cupula. We also see from this plot that the spontaneous activity recovers from an antidromic volley in a manner quite similar to its recovery after spontaneous firing.

We take the whole of this data to indicate that the recovery of a stitch from an antidromic volley is similar to the recovery of a stitch after spontaneous firing, and that this strongly suggests that the hypothesis of an antidromic invasion of the neighboring neuromasts is correct.

What could be the source of the slightly slower recovery after an antidromic volley? The artificial antidromic firing of a nerve volley is different from the antidromic invasion due to spontaneous activity in two ways. First, an artificial volley invades all the neuromasts in a standard sequence. A natural antidromic invasion would not invade the originating neuromasts and would not have a unique invasion pattern. Second, an artificial volley can produce excitation of efferent nerves, whereas the spontaneous activity cannot.

Figure 12 shows another preparation that also has this difference in recovery. Figure 12A shows the interval histogram for spontaneous activity similar to the ones we have seen before. Figure 12C is the histogram for intervals between the *first* and *second* pulse after an antidromic volley. You will be reminded by the scatter plot in Fig. 12D that a spontaneous pulse washes out all memory of previous activity. Thus the histogram for intervals between the first and second pulse after an antidromic volley should be the same as the spontaneous interval histogram. This appears to be the case. The calculated mean and standard deviations for these distributions also bear this out. The histogram for intervals between the antidromic volley and the first pulse is shown in Fig. 12B. The slower recovery can be seen and is

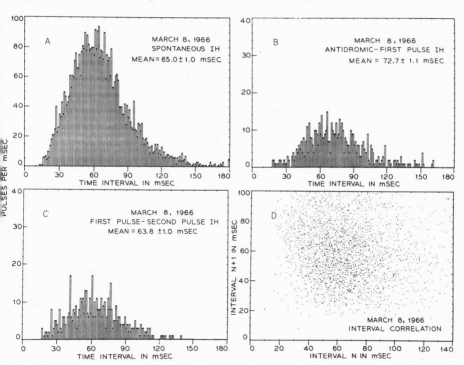

Fig. 12. Spontaneous activity for toad, March 8, 1966. (A) Spontaneous interval histogram. (B) Antidromic volley–first pulse interval histogram. (C) First pulse–second pulse after antidromic-volley interval histogram. (D) Correlation plot for spontaneous activity. Because there is no correlation, the first pulse–second pulse interval histogram should be similar to the spontaneous interval histogram.

borne out by the fact that the mean and standard deviations are larger than those for spontaneous activity.

In some preparations this discrepancy is more pronounced. Figure 13 shows a case where the spontaneous interval histogram and the antidromic first-pulse histogram are significantly different. The spontaneous interval histogram in Fig. 13A shows a high peak for small intervals and a tail. In Fig. 13C the histogram of intervals between the first and second pulses after an antidromic volley has this same appearance. On the right side are the antidromic volley first-pulse interval histograms for two durations of antidromic pulse. Each distribution lacks the peak at small intervals. The values of means of the intervals after an antidromic volley are larger than the mean of the intervals after a spontaneous firing. Differences this large suggest that at times there are additional processes going on. One such possible process is hinted at in Fig. 14. The upper picture shows a superposi-

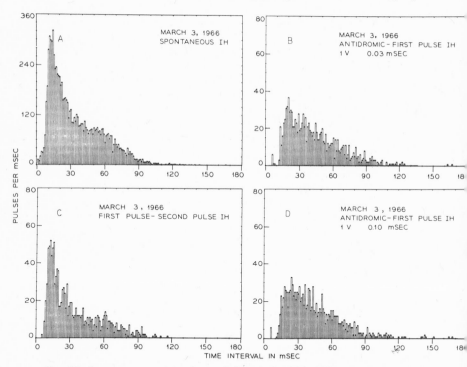

Fɪɢ. 13. Spontaneous activity for toad, March 3, 1966. (A) Spontaneous interval histogram exhibiting a double hump. (B) Antidromic–first pulse interval histogram with absence of first hump. (C) First pulse–second pulse interval histogram similar to that in (A). (D) Antidromic–first pulse interval histogram after a more intense antidromic stimulus. No significant difference is seen from the plot in (B).

0.5 V ANTIDROMIC PULSE

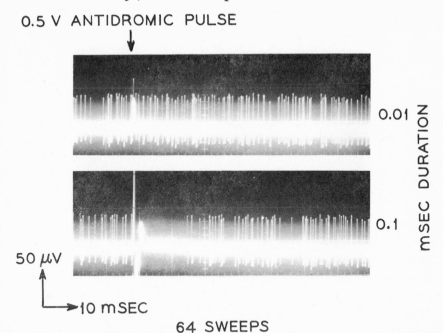

50 μV

10 mSEC

64 SWEEPS

FIG. 14. Superimposed oscilloscope traces of spontaneous activity (above), and spontaneous activity with an antidromic volley (below). Besides a region of inhibition immediately after the volley, there is a suggestion of an inhibitory region about 40 msec after the volley.

tion of a number of traces of spontaneous activity. The lower picture shows a superposition of traces with an antidromic volley. There is an inhibition of pulses immediately after the volley and a possible inhibition occurring about 40 msec after the volley. Statistical fluctuations cannot be ruled out in such a picture, but there were other cases where there appeared a second time of inhibition about 30 to 40 msec after the volley. It is tempting to calculate a velocity of nerve propagation, assuming that this later inhibition is due to efferent activity in the small unmyelinated fibers. The velocity comes out to be between 0.5 and 1 m per sec—a not unreasonable velocity for unmyelinated fibers about 0.5 μ in diameter.

Much stronger evidence for a secondary delayed inhibition was obtained from the preparation of March 10, 1966. Data from this preparation are shown in Fig. 15. Figure 15A shows the interval histogram for spontaneous activity. Figure 15C shows the antidromic first-pulse interval histogram with a significantly slower recovery: Figure 15B shows a PST histogram for the same antidromic run. (A PST histo-

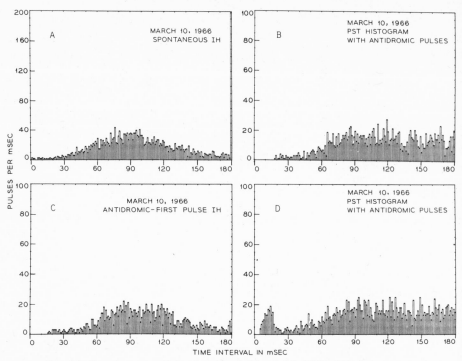

FIG. 15. Spontaneous activity from toad, March 10, 1966. (A) Spontaneous interval histogram. (B) Post-stimulus-time (PST) histogram after an antidromic volley. (C) Antidromic–first pulse histogram of the same date as in (B). (D) Post-stimulus-time histogram after an antidromic volley; the nerve was moved between the data shown in (C). In (D) there is no immediate inhibition, but an inhibited region 30 msec after the antidromic volley.

gram is different from an interval histogram in that all pulses occurring after the antidromic volley are plotted, not only the first pulse. An inhibitory interval shows up better in this type of plot.) In this preparation we moved the position of the antidromic electrodes along the nerve in an attempt to see whether we could obtain different types of inhibition. At one point we obtained the situation shown in Fig. 15D. There is no inhibition close to the antidromic volley, but there is a region of inhibition about 30 msec after the volley. By again moving the nerve, the situation resembling that shown in Fig. 15B was obtained, but only for a short while. Even though the obtaining of such a preparation has a substantial element of chance, this one result is strongly suggestive of a secondary inhibition, probably due to the small unmyelinated fibers.

EVOKED ACTIVITY

A mechanical stimulus produces repetitive evoked activity, with the rate of repetition dependent on the stimulus strength. Both Görner (1963) and Harris and Milne (1966) found the repetition rate to be an increasing function of the velocity. Harris and Milne (1966) found that variability of the epoch of the first pulse was often larger than the variability of the first pulse–second pulse interval. This effect can be illustrated in Fig. 16, which shows both an antidromic volley and the response to a mechanical stimulus. Superimposed on a representative trace is a display. In this type of display each horizontal row of dots represents one stimulus presentation. The dots occur at the time of a nerve spike. For the moment, neglect the region of time just after the antidromic volley and concentrate on the evoked response. This response is represented by vertical rows of dots, with each row representing one nerve pulse of the repetitive response. The scatter in the row illustrates the variability of the response. Note that the time of occurrence of the second row is often closely correlated with the time

## ANTIDROMIC AND STIMULUS

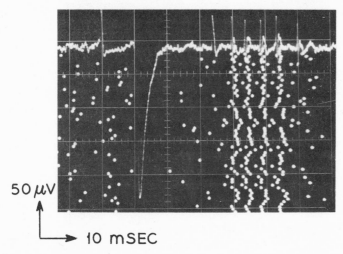

50 μV

10 mSEC

FIG. 16. Oscilloscope dot display of a response to a mechanical stimulus that is preceded by an antidromic volley. Each horizontal line of dots represents the response to one stimulus presentation. A representative trace is also given. The variability of the repetitive evoked response can be seen as a vertical scatter. The scatter of the second pulse is correlated with the first scatter. (March 3, 1966; see Fig. 18.)

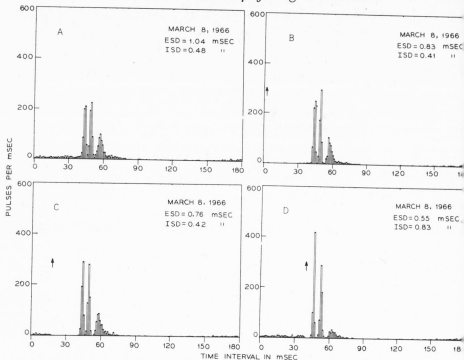

FIG. 17. Response to antidromic volley and mechanical stimulus, March 8, 1966. (A) Mechanical stimulus alone. (B) Mechanical stimulus plus antidromic volley occurring 40 msec before. (C) Antidromic volley occurring 25 msec before. (D) Antidromic volley occurring 10 msec before. The variability decreases as the time of the antidromic volley becomes closer to the evoked time of the response. (ESD = standard deviation of the epoch of the first evoked pulse. ISD = standard deviation of the interval between the first and second evoked pulses.)

of occurrence of the first row. Harris and Milne (1966) found that as long as the first interval was less than about 15 msec the interval variability was less than the variability of the epoch of the first pulse. This result suggested a process which resulted in random spontaneous activity. The mechanical stimulus would increase the rate of this process, but the rate increase would start at some unknown point in a process already going on, which would consequently produce a variability of nerve-spike latency. A sustained stimulus would result in another pulse, but the threshold would be higher, so that the variability in the interpulse interval should be smaller.

One method of testing this suggestion was to obtain a preparation that exhibited both evoked activity and antidromic inhibition, and then to study the effect of the relative time between the antidromic volley and the mechanical stimulus on the variability of the evoked response. Four such preparations were obtained, one of which is illustrated in Fig. 17. We are interested in changing the relative time between the mechanical stimulus and the antidromic volley and studying the variability of the evoked response. A series of four data runs from one preparation is shown. Figure 17A shows a PST histogram when there is the mechanical stimulus and no antidromic volley. There is a level of spontaneous activity before the evoked response, and then after the evoked response there is a period of inhibition, followed by a gradual recovery. When the antidromic volley is applied, the spontaneous activity is inhibited. As the time of the antidromic volley, represented by the arrow in Fig. 17B, C, and D, is moved closer to the time of the evoked response, the variability of the evoked response significantly diminishes, as can be seen in Fig. 17C and D. This series

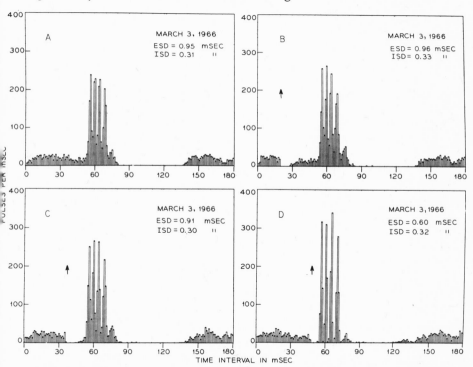

Fig. 18. Response to antidromic volley and mechanical stimulus, March 3, 1966. (A) Mechanical stimulus only. (B) Antidromic volley occurring 35 msec before. (C) Antidromic volley occurring 20 msec before. (D) Antidromic volley occurring 8 msec before. The region of inhibition for this toad is much shorter than for the toad of March 8; thus the antidromic volley must be closer before a reduction of variability takes place. (See Fig. 17 caption for explanation of ESD and ISD.)

is taken from a preparation in which the recovery from the antidromic volley is relatively slow. Figure 18A-D shows a comparable series of four plots from a preparation that displays a shorter recovery period. In this case, the decrease in variability does not occur until the antidromic volley is correspondingly closer to the evoked response. If one moves the antidromic volley very close, the evoked response is pushed back by the recovery time of the nerve. If one moves closer still, some of the evoked activity occurs before the antidromic volley reaches the stitch. The variability then takes a sudden jump.

## DISCUSSION

In this paper we are interested in the knowledge of the operation of the lateral line organ of *Xenopus* that can be obtained from antidromic firing of the nerve. The type of information which this organ processes and the way that it integrates into the behavior of the animal have been discussed in published works (Görner, 1963; Harris and Milne, 1966) and elsewhere in this volume (Görner, 1967). For the purposes of the present discussion, we shall assume that the hair cell is a specialized sense cell which transduces a displacement into a release of quantal amounts of as yet unknown chemical transmitter to a synapse with an afferent nerve. This transmitter substance then evokes a response in the nerve that may end in an all-or-none regenerative response. To be more specific, Fig. 19 gives a schematic representation of the hair cell–nerve connection that can provide a heuristic framework for discussion.

The stimulus to the hair cell appears to be the shear displacement of the cupula relative to the top of the hair cell (Flock, 1965). Arguments can be advanced that the stereocilia are firmly embedded in the cupula and so move with it (Harris, 1966). In line with these arguments, we shall assume that it is the motion of the sensing hairs relative to the top of the hair cell which is the proper stimulus. It is well known that there is a microphonic potential associated with vibratory displacement of the cupula. For the present discussion it is not necessary to assume that the microphonic potential as such is a causal link in the sensory process or that it correlates with a causal process at the hair-bearing end of the sensory cell which governs the release of a quantal amount of chemical transmitter at the synapse with the afferent nerve ending. The afferent synapses (Flock, 1967) appear to be similar in structure to axodendritic synapses and, more particularly, to other types of sensory cell–dendritic synapses, showing the typical features of a chemical synapse. Presynaptic vesicles inside

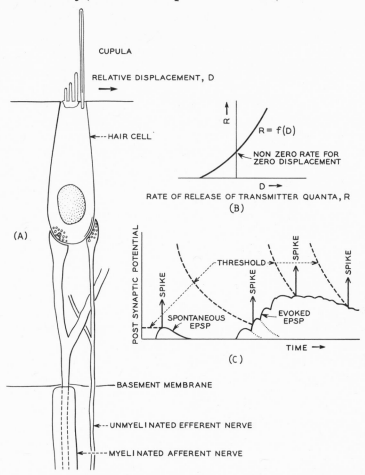

FIG. 19. (A) Schematic diagram of a cupula–hair cell–nerve connection used as a heuristic aid in the discussion. (B) Input-output function between the input, which is the relative displacement of cupula and hair cell, and the output, which is the rate of release of quantal units of chemical transmitter. The essential feature is a positive slope and a nonzero rate for zero displacement. (C) Qualitative relationship between excitatory postsynaptic potential, threshold, and nerve firing. In this illustration, one quantal unit is sufficient to fire the nerve.

the hair cell tentatively represent quantal packages of transmitter substance that are ultimately released into the synaptic space.

Even though it is not necessary to make assumptions about the role of the microphonic potential, it is tempting and convenient to do so. Katz and Miledi (1965) have shown that packets of chemical transmitter (acetylcholine) are released from a nerve terminal by negative electric pulses applied to its surface. There was a delay between the application of a pulse and the secretion of acetylcholine. This suggests that the secretion of acetylcholine is the end product of a sequence of reaction steps set off by the displacement of the membrane potential. There may be a similar chain of events in the hair cell. In the cochlea a nerve impulse is initiated when the microphonic potential outside the top of the hair cell is in the negative phase. Because of the presence of two types of hair cells, it is not possible to be as definite about the hair cells in the lateral line organ of *Xenopus*. It is reasonable, however, that this is also the case. If this is so, the operation of the hair cell can be separated into two parts. The first step involves a displacement at the sensory hairs that causes a depolarization of the membrane potential, and then the depolarization initiates the release of chemical transmitter. The first process would be peculiar to mechanical receptors, while the second process could be quite general and be similar in most receptor cells and also in axonal terminations where a conductive-regenerative membrane depolarization results in a release of chemical transmitter.

Once the transmitter is released, an excitatory postsynaptic potential (EPSP) is produced across the postsynaptic membrane. The EPSP spreads to a region of the nerve membrane that is regenerative. There the EPSPs from the hair cells innervated by that fiber summate. When a threshold (Th) is reached, the regenerative part of the nerve fires. The threshold momentarily goes way up, then recovers to an equilibrium level (Th'). Initially after a firing $Th \gg Th'$, and subsequently Th decays to the value Th'. It could also happen that for a while Th is less than Th'.

This organ is spontaneously active. Antidromic firing of the whole nerve can reset the conditional probability of a spontaneous firing in a manner that is similar to the resetting after a spontaneous firing of the nerve. The differences, which may be evidence for efferent activity, will be discussed later. The similarity supports the hypothesis that when the nerve branch innervating one neuromast fires, the pulse antidromically invades the branches leading to the other neuromasts in the same stitch. Thus the conditional probability is reset for all the neuromasts when one fires. This hypothesis implies that the resetting process is in or near the regenerative portion of the nerve, and not in the hair cells. The recovery of the conditional probability may be due to the recovery of the threshold for firing the nerve. The long time constant of recovery ($\sim$50 msec) also argues for location in the nerve, rather than a location in the hair cell, for the recovery process.

The spontaneous activity can be inhibited by movement of the cupula. Typically, when one nerve is excited, the other is inhibited. This can be explained by having a finite rate of release of chemical transmitter when the cupula is in the undisplaced position. When the cupula is displaced in the direction from the stereocilia toward the kinocilium, the cell is depolarized and the rate of release of chemical transmitter increases. When the cupula is displaced in the opposite direction, the rate of release of transmitter decreases. This would mean that the spontaneous activity is caused by release of chemical transmitter, which occurs even with no mechanical stimulus.

This model of the origin of spontaneous activity utilizes a threshold Th which varies but which has no high-frequency fluctuations. The postsynaptic membrane potential fluctuates because of a statistical release of quantal units of transmitter. An alternative model accounting for spontaneous activity is one with a fluctuating threshold. There will always be a certain fluctuation of potential across any membrane. Derksen and Verveen (1966) have measured the membrane potential noise at a single node of Ranvier of frog sciatic nerve. From their data, one can calculate a root-mean-square noise of 0.5 mV between frequency limits of 10 to 10,000 rad per sec. It is unlikely that this is large enough to set off the nerve spontaneously. Moreover, if this were the source of spontaneous activity, then one would have to explain the inhibition during a mechanical stimulus by another different and parallel process such as release of a chemical inhibitor, which would increase the threshold or reduce the threshold noise levels. It is more convenient to envision a single process of transmitter release. The rate of release is positive for zero displacement and has a positive slope for displacements in the direction of the kinocilium. The sum of resulting EPSPs is sometimes large enough to produce a firing of the nerve. Of course, the threshold does fluctuate and will contribute somewhat to the variability of firing, but we are suggesting that the source of the spontaneous activity is the quantal release of chemical transmitter.

If we follow this hypothesis that the spontaneous activity is caused by the quantal release of transmitter, then it becomes crucial to ask how many quantal units are needed for the EPSP to reach threshold. The interpretation of our results for evoked activity will depend upon whether one or more than one quantal unit is necessary to reach the equilibrium threshold Th'. Specifically, we can consider the origin of the variance in the time of the first evoked pulse. If only one quantal unit is needed, then the origin of the variance must be in the process in the hair cell resulting in the release of a quantal unit. With zero displacement, transmitter is released at a certain rate with a certain statistical distribution. When a displacement suddenly occurs, the rate goes up; but the hair cells are already in various stages of the release process, which consequently varies the time of first release. For the second pulse the threshold is higher but is decreasing rapidly, resulting in a smaller time variance.

If more than one quantal unit is needed to reach threshold, then there will be another source of variance of the time of occurrence of the first pulse besides that just described. A unit EPSP will have a time course probably of a few milliseconds. When increase in the rate of release occurs, the postsynaptic membrane would not be at its resting potential but would have some distribution of values between resting potential and threshold. The time it takes to reach threshold would depend on the postsynaptic membrane potential at the time of stimulation, and thus a varying membrane potential would be a source of time variance.

The decrease in variance of the first evoked pulse after an antidromic stimulus would, in the model we are considering, depend on the increased threshold. A second and possibly longer-acting effect could come from efferent activity, which might also be present in antidromic stimulation.

Flock (1967) has found both afferent and efferent types of synaptic endings on the hair-cell bodies. It is not known whether there are any efferent endings on the afferent nerves themselves. Our data (especially that of March 10, 1966) indicate the possibility of a delayed inhibitory effect about 30 msec after the antidromic volley. Because of this long delay, we assume that this particular inhibition is associated with the small unmyelinated fibers rather than with the small myelinated fibers. The efferent endings on the hair cells could act to reduce the rate of transmitter release. Nothing is known about how this is achieved—whether the inhibition affects the membrane potential or acts by direct interference with the transmitter release mechanism. The function of the small myelinated fibers is still unknown (Görner, 1967). Further work must be done with anatomical and physiological studies on the role of these efferent nerve fibers.

There have been a number of recent studies on the statistical distribution of nerve firings (Gerstein and Mandelbrot, 1964; Hagiwara, 1954; Viernstein and Grossman, 1961; Goldberg, Adrian, and Smith, 1964; Stein, 1965). The model discussed here is similar to the shot noise model discussed by Stein (1965), with the addition of a variable threshold. In the present model the source of noise is in the quantal nature of the transmitter release and its nonzero rate of release with zero displacement. It is necessary to obtain further data on the hair-cell operation before the model can be tested quantitatively. Especially interesting would be the determination of the number of quantal units necessary for a nerve firing.

## REFERENCES

Derksen, H. E., and A. A. Verveen (1966). Fluctuations of resting neural membrane potential. *Science* 151, 1388-1389.

Dijkgraaf, S. (1956). Elektrophysiologische Untersuchungen an der seitenlinie vom *Xenopus laevis. Experientia (Basel)* 12, 276-278.

Flock, Å. (1965). Electron microscopic and electrophysiological studies on the lateral line canal organ. *Acta Oto-Laryngol. Suppl.* 199, 1-90.

———— (1967). Chapter 12, this volume.

Gerstein, G. L., and B. Mandelbrot (1964). Random walk models for the spike activity of a single neuron. *Biophys. J.* 4, 41-68.

Goldberg, J. M., H. O. Adrian, and F. D. Smith (1964). Response of neurons of the superior olivary complex of the cat to acoustic stimuli of long duration. *J. Neurophysiol.* 27, 706, 749.

Görner, P. (1963). Untersuchungen zur Morphologie und Electrophysiologie der Seitenlinienorgans vom Krallenfrosch (*Xenopus laevis,* Daudin). *Z. Vergleich. Physiol.* 47, 316-388.

———— (1967). Chapter 13, this volume.

Hagiwara, S. (1954). Analysis of interval fluctuations of the sensory nerve impulse. *Japan. J. Physiol.* 4, 234-240.

Harris, G. G. (1966). Brownian motion and the threshold of hearing. VIII International Congress of Audiology, Mexico.

———— and D. C. Milne (1966). Input-output characteristics of the lateral-line sense-organs of *Xenopus laevis. J. Acoust. Soc. Am.* 40, 32-42.

Katz, B. and R. Miledi (1965). Release of acetylcholine from a nerve terminal by electric pulses of variable strength and duration. *Nature (London)* 207, 1097-1098.

Murray, R. W. (1955). The lateralis organs and their innervation in *Xenopus laevis. Quart. J. Microscop. Sci.* 96, 351-361.

———— (1956). The response of the lateralis organs of *Xenopus laevis* to electrical stimulation by direct current. *J. Physiol. (London)* 134, 408-420.

Petraitis, R. (1964). Private communication.

Stein, R. B. (1965). A theoretical analysis of neuronal variability. *Biophys. J.* 5, 173-194.

Viernstein, L. S., and R. G. Grossman (1961). Neural discharge patterns, in C. Cherry (ed.). *Fourth London Symposium on Information Theory.* Academic Press, New York, pp. 252-269.

## COMMENTS

BENNETT: Do you feel that the unresponsiveness following antidromic stimulation is slightly longer than that following autodromic, or than that following a spontaneous event? Could one component of this delay be the conduction time from one neuromast to the adjacent one? Then one would have a longer time to recover following an antidromic stimulus than with an autodromic.

HARRIS: The nerves don't get that small until they are inside the neuro-masts. We've estimated that there's about a 4-msec delay due to travel time in the nerve. The pulse must get down to the recording electrode, that is, down to the neuromast and back again, so that this might explain part of the difference. But the difference is about 10 to 15 msec. Can you explain 15 msec? That is the problem.

TEAS: In your scatter diagram, you've called it random in relation to the probability curves on the shorter interval. If you had done your scatter plot on only shorter intervals, then you would have correlation. Your scatter plot runs the whole duration of your histogram.

HARRIS: The scatter plot only shows first-order independence. In this type of process, it's hard to see how you'd have any higher orders of correlation if you didn't have a first-order one.

GÖRNER: Did you record spikes from the thin fibers?

HARRIS: What you saw in the figure was an antidromic volley, a whole nerve volley. We didn't pick up a branch as you did. We would like to be able to look at this volley 20 msec later. Right now, you couldn't see anything; it's in the noise, but with an averaging technique you could really see whether there was a small persistent peak.

GÖRNER: What was the distance between stimulating and recording? It's sometimes dangerous to record, but it cannot be avoided when you don't know whether the unmyelinated fibers are stimulated or not. You only suggest that they are stimulated.

HARRIS: We don't know for sure.

GÖRNER: If you lowered your stimulating amplitude so that only the thick afferent fibers were stimulated and looked at the effect, it might be that this effect would be the same.

HARRIS: We have varied the amplitude of the antidromic duration and have looked at the shape of the recovery. It doesn't change very much. I think it would be very nice to do this very carefully.

KUIPER: Have you some data on the effects of temperature on this particular result?

HARRIS: No, the preparation was always maintained near room temperature. Why do you ask?

KUIPER: You can also think of Brownian motion effects and of thermal noise on the membrane level.

HARRIS: What I said was that I guessed that the spontaneous firing was because of the statistical way that the hair cell was operating all the time. Of course, there'd be noise in the membrane potentials, but it's small compared with the first. I don't think it's Brownian motion of the cupula, and I've done some calculations on the ear, and there are some interesting arguments we could go into.

GÖRNER: Getting down to the last point: you said you stimulated with longer duration and got a longer delay in recovery. How long was that delay?

HARRIS: I should expect that you would need 5 to 10 msec. We rarely went up that high, mostly only a millisecond. But we did get a delayed inhibition sometimes.

LATERAL LINE DETECTORS (P. Cahn, ed.), 163–197, © 1967 Indiana University Press

# 12 ULTRASTRUCTURE AND FUNCTION IN THE LATERAL LINE ORGANS

ÅKE FLOCK †

Visual and Acoustic Research Division
Bell Telephone Laboratories, Inc.
Murray Hill, New Jersey

The lateral line organs are developed from the same embryological anlage as the organs of equilibrium and hearing in the inner ear (van Bergeijk, 1967). In all these organs having different uses the sensory unit, the hair cell and its innervating nerve fibers, has a common basic structure, and its functional principles are believed to be the same. The hair cell is basically a directionally sensitive displacement detector, sensitive to motions in the order of Ångstrom units. Working on this basic mechanism, the hair cell is used to subserve a multitude of functions. For instance, it serves the sense organs of the inner ear as a detector of angular accelerations in the three planes of space (semicircular canals), and of linear accelerations and changes of position in the field of gravity (utricle, saccule); it also serves as a frequency analyzer (cochlea, amphibian and basilar papilla). Thus the biological significance of the various organs may differ considerably, while the adequate stimulus for the sensory cell is still the same, namely, displacement of the sensory hairs. It is by mechanical coupling to auxiliary structures of different types that specific response to particular types of stimuli is achieved (Pumphrey, 1950). The range of performance of the lateral line organs is therefore restricted mainly by the capacity of the hair cells, and the stimulus parameter to which the organ is sensitive depends on how the organ is mechanically exposed to the environment.

By virtue of their relatively simple structure and their accessibility for controlled physiological experimentation, the lateral line organs may serve as basic models of the acousticolateral system from which insight can be gained into the peripheral mechanisms of sensory perception. Understanding of the physiology of the organ as a whole

† On leave from Gustaf V Research Institute and from the Department of Otolaryngology, Karolinska Sjukhuset, Stockholm, Sweden.

depends, logically, on knowledge of the function of its components. It will be attempted here to describe the fine structure of the sensory cells, their innervation, the supporting cells, and the cupula, all in relation to their function. After a general description of the organization of the lateral line sensory organs, the different elements of the organ will be considered, as far as possible, in the order in which they are successively engaged in the process of sensory perception. The ultrastructure will constitute, therefore, a matrix upon which we may discuss the functioning of the lateral line organ.

## MATERIAL AND METHODS

The freestanding organ was studied in the South African clawed toad, *Xenopus laevis*. The organs were fixed in vivo in the anesthetized and pithed toad by bathing a selected group of organs in a local pool of 1% osmium tetroxide buffered with veronal acetate (Rhodin, 1954). After having been rinsed in Ringer solution, each stitch was carefully dissected out and processed for embedding in Epon (Luft, 1961). For phase-contrast microscopy, 1-$\mu$-thick sections were cut on an LKB Ultrotome III, collected from distilled water, and mounted with Epon on slides. If such sections were to be used with light microscopy, they were stained with toluidine blue (Richardson et al., 1960). For electron microscopy, ultrathin sections were collected on copper grids and stained with uranyl acetate and lead citrate. Electron microscopy on the freestanding organs of the toad was performed with a Hitachi HS7-S.

The canal organ was studied in the burbot *Lota vulgaris*, which is a freshwater codfish. The organs were fixed with the same fixative by perfusion of the lateral line canal and were processed for light and electron microscopy in the same way as for the toad. The ultrastructure, which was investigated with a Siemens Elmiscop I, has been extensively described elsewhere (Flock, 1965a).

## GENERAL STRUCTURE

There are two types of lateral line mechanoreceptor organs: freestanding, or epidermal, organs and canal organs. The organs are distributed in rows on the head and along the body in fishes and water-living amphibia. The more primitive freestanding organs are situated in the epidermis, with a gelatinous cupula projecting into the surrounding water. In cyclostomes, in aquatic amphibia, and in some fishes this is the only type of organ present, but in most fishes a number of sensory areas are sunk in furrows in the skin that ultimately close into canals. The canal system is especially elaborate on the head (Dijkgraaf, 1963). However, where canal organs occur, freestanding organs are generally still present along the canals (Fig. 1).

The sensory epithelium (neuromast) is composed of mechanoreceptor cells partially surrounded by supporting cells. From the top of each receptor cell protrudes a bundle of sensory hairs, to which a gelatinous cupula is attached. At their basal ends, the hair cells are contacted by the terminal branches of innervating nerve fibers (Fig. 3). Water motion causes a displacement of the cupula, which through the sensory hairs activates the receptor mechanism whereby the flow of impulses in the innervating nerve fibers is regulated. This process will

FISH (*GADUS LOTA*)

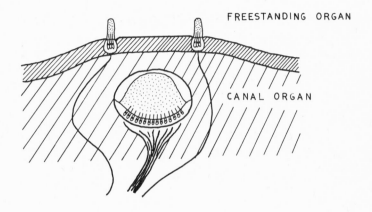

TOAD (*XENOPUS*)

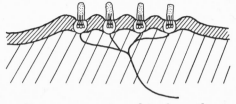

Fig. 1. Freestanding organs are situated in the epidermis, with the gelatinous cupula projecting into the surrounding water; whereas canal organs, which are present in most fishes, are enclosed in canals beneath the skin.

be discussed in detail below, after a brief description of the morphology characteristic of each type of organ.

### THE FREESTANDING ORGAN

The freestanding organs of *Xenopus* were first described by Maurer
(1895), who recognized their sensory function. The histology of these
organs has been investigated by Murray (1955) and Görner (1963).

The organs occur in groups of 3 to 12 neuromasts, alternating with
tactile bodies, and are lined up in a row on a slightly elevated ridge
that (because of its appearance) is sometimes referred to as a "stitch"
(Fig. 2). In fish, freestanding organs commonly appear singly. The
hair cells are arranged in an oblong band in a shallow groove in the
center of the onion-shaped organ and are distributed in two similar
groups confined to the two ends of the sensory area. The number of
cells in each neuromast may vary from 20 to 60. These are slender
cells about 30 to 40 μ long, with basal nuclei, and are surrounded by
supporting cells that extend about 80 μ from the surface down to the
basal membrane (Fig. 3). Thus the hair cells end halfway down the

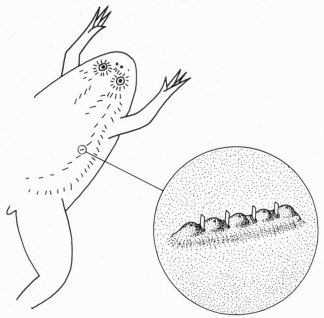

Fig. 2. In the *Xenopus* toad, groups of freestanding organs are lined up in rows
on the body of the animal. The insert is an enlargement of one stitch containing
four neuromasts.

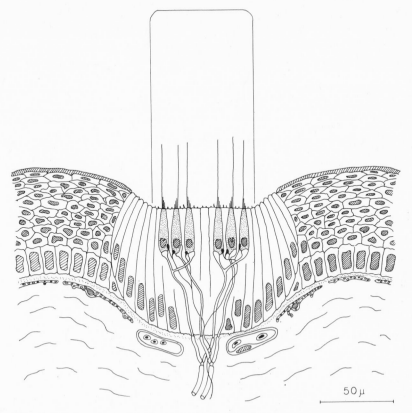

Fig. 3. The sensory epithelium of the freestanding neuromast in X. *laevis* is composed of hair cells embraced by supporting cells. From the top of each receptor cell protrudes a bundle of sensory hairs to which the cupula is attached. Water motion causes a displacement of the cupula, which through the sensory hairs activates the receptor mechanism and controls the frequency of nerve impulses in the innervating nerve fibers. The exact course of the afferent (white endings) and postulated efferent (black endings) terminal nerve branches is not known.

sensory epithelium and are surrounded by supporting cells on all but the apical surface.

The sensory region is surrounded by concentric layers of supporting cells, called the mantle cells, which also extend through the depth of the organ but which become progressively shorter toward the periphery. The innervation of the organ will be described later.

THE CANAL ORGAN

At the time of its discovery in L. *vulgaris* by Steno (1664) and thereafter, the lateral line system was generally considered mucus-secret-

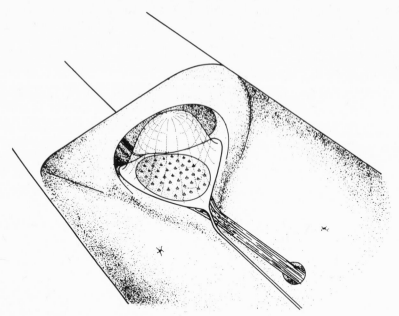

FIG. 4. In the canal organ the sensory area forms an oval disc upon which the dome-shaped cupula rests.

ing, until Leydig presented histological evidence of its sensory nature in 1850.

The canal organs are situated at the bottom of the lateral line canal, where each sensory area forms an oval disc upon which the dome-shaped cupula rests. A peripheral zone of mantle cells surrounds the sensory area (Fig. 4). In *L. vulgaris* the system of canals communicates with the exterior only through one rostral and one caudal pore on each side of the body (Hyrtl, 1866), whereas in other fishes there is usually one pore near each organ.

### THE CUPULA

The adequate stimulus for the sensory cells is the shear displacement of the base of the cupula, where the sensory hairs are attached, relative to the surface at the sensory epithelium. In a number of species the cupula has been shown to be sensitive to some function of water motion, such as displacement, velocity, or acceleration. Harris and van Bergeijk (1962) have shown that the organ responds to the near-field displacement of vibrating sources in water rather than to the pressure component.

The cupula has often escaped the attention it merits as the source of stimulus input to the sensory cells. Since it plays an important role in the sensory process, its structure and function will be described here in some detail, especially with reference to the connection between the cupula and the hair cells.

**In Vivo Examination.** The cupula is highly fragile and is also subject to considerable shrinkage when treated by routine histological methods. The shrinkage caused by fixation, in many cases, detaches the cupula from the sensory hairs; moreover, after fixation, the cupula becomes stiffer and more brittle. It may even break loose entirely and be washed away during dehydration. Because of these difficulties, histological examination has in many cases failed to reveal its existence.

A more appropriate, and also easier, procedure is in vivo examination of the exposed cupula, which also permits observation of its mechanical behavior. The cupula of *L. vulgaris* is birefringent and can often be seen directly in a dissecting microscope when the light source is properly aimed. This is true also in *Acerina cernua* (Jielof et al., 1952), but apparently not in *Fundulus heteroclitus* (van Bergeijk and Alexander, 1962). To observe its outlines and its movement, it is usually necessary to stain or otherwise define its outlines. Different vital stains, such as methylene blue, have been used, either dissolved in the aquarium water (Denny, 1937; Sato, 1962) or applied directly to the organ. With India ink, which does not dissolve but remains a suspension of particles in water, the cupula can be seen in negative contrast in a pool of "stain" solution (Steinhausen, 1933) or when a jet of ink is directed at the organ from a pipette. The contours of the cupula can be outlined most distinctly, however, by having small visible particles adhere to its surface. For this purpose, ZnO (Jielof et al., 1952), aluminum powder (Kuiper, 1956), or silicate crystals (Flock, 1965a) have been used. Such contour outlining is easily achieved by directing against the organ a fine jet of silicate crystals (grinding powder for microtome knives) suspended in water by shaking or ultrasonic agitation. After sedimentation of the large-sized particles, a supernatant containing particles of appropriate size can be sucked into a micropipette and applied to the surface of the cupula, where the particles get caught in the fine meshwork of fibrils constituting the cupular matrix.

**Mechanical Properties of the Cupula.** The physical properties of the cupula in the canal organ of *A. cernua* have been extensively studied by Jielof et al. (1952), de Vries (1956), and Kuiper (1956). Their studies yielded important information on the behavior of the cupula

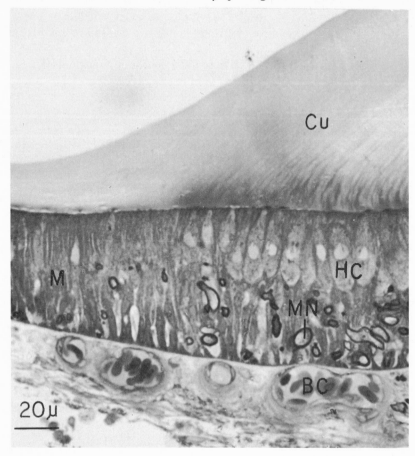

FIG. 5. The cupula (Cu) in the canal organ covers not only the region of hair cells (HC) but also the zone of mantle cells (M). Inside the epithelium, myelinated nerve fibers (MN) are seen, and below the epithelium blood capillaries (BC) form an extensive network. *L. vulgaris,* Toluidine-blue-stained Epon section (×640).

under dynamic and static stimulation, as observed under high magnification and in stroboscopic illumination.

The cupula in *Lota* is dome-shaped and covers the sensory area as well as the mantle cells (Figs. 4 and 5). It almost fills the canal, with the top reaching the roof of the canal, which is constricted in this region by a ridge of connective tissue (Fig. 4). When the cupula is probed at its base with a micromanipulator, it is seen to slide as a whole over the sensory epithelium in the direction of the applied pressure, either along or across the canal with equal ease. When pressure is applied higher up, the wall of the cupula is plastic and yields; thus a larger displacement is needed to cause the same shearing displacement of the base relative to the epithelium. Closer to the top the cupula is even more plastic and also bends somewhat. These observations are in agreement with those of Jielof et al. (1952) in *A. cernua*. When the displacement of the base of the cupula approaches 10 $\mu$, the force needed to produce further displacement increases rapidly, and a displacement limit is reached. This limit is apparently achieved either because the sensory epithelium is now displaced with the cupula when the pressure is applied close to the base or because the cupula bends when pressure is applied close to the top. Displacements of this magnitude are probably close to the maximum also for the vibrating cupula in the exposed organ, since this is about the amplitude at which the microphonic potential saturates (Jielof et al., 1952; Kuiper, 1956; Flock, 1965a). In the natural situation, with the cupula still in a closed canal, the maximal vibration amplitudes reached are certainly much smaller, and have been reported to be less than 1 $\mu$ by Kuiper (1956). This does not exclude the possibility that in the natural situation the fluid in the canal may transiently be displaced 10 $\mu$, or even more, by accident or by normal body motion. In such cases, it would be of physiological importance to have the stiffness of the cupula matched in such a way that part of it would yield and bend at supramaximal stimulation, and so avoid damage to the sensory cells. On electron-microscopic examination, there is no detectable mechanical injury to the hair cells even when the upper part of the cupula is blown out by perfusion of the canal.

The cupular substance can be partially removed by water jets of traumatic velocity or by mechanical manipulation. It is consistently found that the basal circumference corresponding to the mantle cell zone and the basal part over the sensory area has the highest stiffness and is most resistant to mechanical strain. A similar "wall" has been described in the canal organ of *A. cernua* by Jielof et al. (1952) and by Kuiper (1956), although it is regarded by these authors as being a structure distinct from the cupula, and it was believed by Jielof et al. to be "only a supporting tissue." That this is not the case in *L. vulgaris* can be demonstrated electron-microscopically: the stiffer peripheral wall is composed of the same fibrillar material as is the rest of the cupula, only the material is more densely packed. This peripheral wall may well be the "hyaline tube" observed by Schulze a century ago (1861).

The examination of the freestanding cupulae is much more difficult because of their small size and fragility. The histology of the cupula

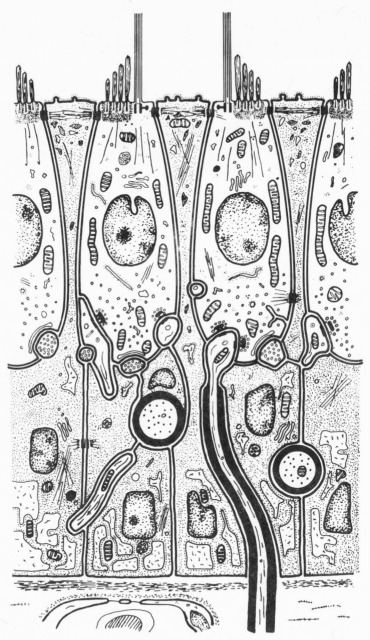

FIG. 6. Schematic drawing of the ultrastructure of the sensory epithelium of the lateral line canal organ in *L. vulgaris.*

has been described by Denny (1937), Sato (1962), and Iwai (1967). Thosmopolous (1957) and Sato (1962) have investigated its polysaccharide histochemistry. The freestanding cupula is displaced by minute water motions (Schulze, 1861; Dijkgraaf, 1934). Longer cupulae also bend, as observed by Cahn and Shaw (1962) in swimming larvae. At rest, however, the cupula returns to a perpendicular position because of its elastic properties. In their work Cahn and Shaw include a useful list of the literature in which cupulae have been described.

Görner (1963) has described the cupulae of the *Xenopus* toad as an extremely flat, flaglike structure, rising about 100 $\mu$ above the neuromast surface. The distal end is quite flaccid and bends in currents directed at its broad side, whereas it is stiff to currents hitting the narrow side. Shear forces are transmitted best along the longitudinal axis. The displacement of the cupula, and thus the response of the organ, is proportional to relative water velocity, since in this direction the main force on the cupula is due to viscous drag. A more complete discussion of the mechanics of this organ is given by Görner (1963) and by Harris and Milne (1966).

## THE SENSORY HAIR BUNDLE AND ITS ATTACHMENT TO THE CUPULA

From the apical end of each receptor cell a bundle of sensory hairs protrude into the overlying cupula (Figs. 3 and 6). Each bundle is composed of 40 to 50 stereocilia arranged in a hexagonal pattern behind an asymmetrically located kinocilium (Figs. 7 and 8). Each stereocilium is anchored in a granular, cuticular plate in the top to the hair cell by a fibrillar rootlet that is an intracellular extension of fibrils which make up the bulk of the stereocilium (Fig. 9). The stereocilium is surrounded by a plasma membrane, which forms a tube with a diameter of 0.15 to 0.2 $\mu$. This tube tapers down to a minimum of 0.1 $\mu$ above the cell surface, where it becomes continuous with the apical cell membrane. The length of the stereocilia increases stepwise toward the kinocilium and ranges from 0.5 to 5 $\mu$. The kinocilium shows the typical arrangement of 9 peripheral double-barreled tubules surrounding a central pair of simple tubules (Fig. 10). It is about 40 $\mu$ long and has a diameter of 0.25 to 0.3 $\mu$. The two central tubules do not penetrate the cell proper but end about 0.3 $\mu$ above the cell surface. However, the peripheral tubules are continuous with 9 triplicate tubules that form the wall of a basal body located in the periphery of the cell, in an area devoid of cuticular substance (Figs. 9 and 10).

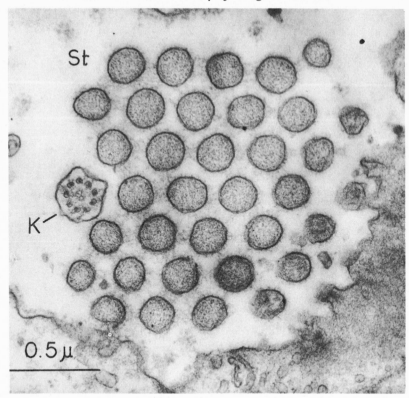

Fig. 7. A cross section through the sensory hair bundle in a canal organ hair cell shows the regular arrangement of the stereocilia (St) lined up behind the peripherally located kinocilium (K). A meshwork of fibrils is interwoven among the stereocilia. *L. vulgaris* (×53,000).

The cupular substance consists of a network of microfibrils about 100 Å long, which are conspicuously concentrated above the hair cells (Fig. 11). The fibrils can be seen to intertwine with the hair bundle where they attach to the surface of the stereocilia and the kinocilium (Figs. 7 and 8). This connection is believed to serve the mechanical transmission of cupular displacement to the sensory cells (Flock, 1965a). Kimura (1966) has recently demonstrated a similar situation in the organ of Corti where the sensory hairs are attached to the tectorial membrane.

In the fresh cupula of *A. cernua,* Jielof et al. (1952) observed vertical striations that seemed to extend from the sensory cells. Vertical striations have also been seen in the freshly dissected cupula of *Fundulus* by Denny (1937) and by van Bergeijk and Alexander (1962),

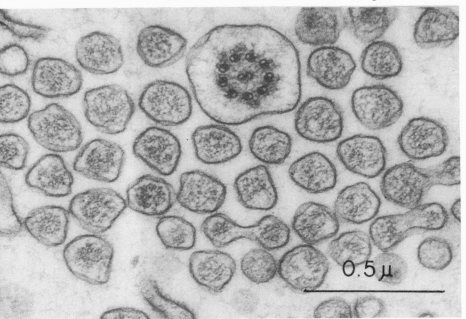

Fɪɢ. 8. The sensory hairs in the freestanding organ are not so regularly arranged as in the canal organ, and the stereocilia extend further toward the sides with respect to the kinocilium. *X. laevis* (×64,000).

and in histological preparations by other authors (Emery, 1880; Katsuki, Mizuhira, and Yoshino, 1951; Kuiper, 1956). These vertical striations or fibers, as well as those which originate above supporting cell interfaces (Denny, 1937), probably represent condensation of the finely fibrillar cupular matrix observed with the electron microscope.

A periodic horizontal striation parallel to the surface of the sensory epithelium has also been observed in stained sections (Emery, 1880; Denny, 1937; van Bergeijk and Alexander, 1962). Kuiper (1956) has observed that the cupula is capable of considerable growth, and it has been suggested that the horizontal striations represent periodic changes in the growth rate of the cupula (Denny, 1937; Petraitis, 1966). It is seen with the electron microscope that these horizontal striations are also analogous to an aggregation of cupular material.

TRANSFER OF CUPULAR MOTION TO THE HAIR CELL

As elaborated by Harris (1966), optimal transfer of cupular motion to the hair cells, and thereby a high sensitivity of the organ, would be

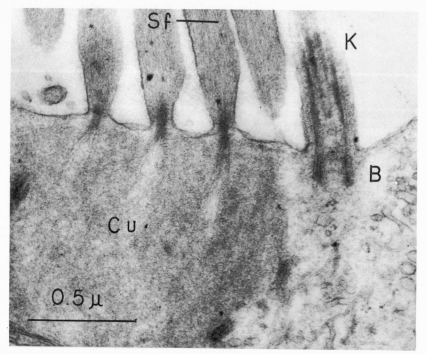

Fig. 9. The stereocilia contain fibrils (Sf) that penetrate into the cuticular plate (Cu). The peripheral filaments of the kinocilium (K) are continuous with the wall of the basal body (B), which is located in an area devoid of cuticular substance. *L. vulgaris* ($\times$58,000).

acquired if three prerequisite conditions were met: (1) The cupula should be comparatively rigidly coupled only to the sensory hairs and (2) slide on a low-friction interface over the surface of (3) a stiff disk of sensory epithelium. In the following paragraphs it will be examined to what extent these conditions are met in the canal organ.

In a single receptor cell, the surface of the stereocilia plus the kinocilium is about 150 $\mu$, or 30 times that of the cell surface without cilia, which is elliptic and has an area of about 5 $\mu$. The force transferred to the hair cell by shearing displacement of the cupula is therefore larger by a factor of at least 30 than that transferred to a flat-surfaced supporting cell of the same size, even if the cupular fibrils were attached also to the supporting-cell surface with an equal density of attachment points. However, the cupula probably is not attached to the supporting cells, because it slides over the sensory epithelium with apparently little friction, as described above. This implies the presence

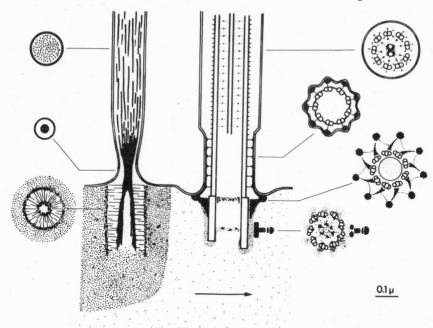

Fig. 10. Based on serial sections, a schematic reconstruction of the kinocilium with its basal body and a stereocilium. The arrow indicates the direction of excitatory displacement.

of a viscous subcupular layer separating the cupula from the surface of the sensory epithelium. In a recent article on the role of the supporting cells in the canal organ of *F. heteroclitus,* Petraitis (1966) proposed that the cupula is formed by coalescence of secretory products from the supporting cells occurring at the base of the cupula. A low-friction subcupular space would be maintained by the continuous secretion from the supporting cells. However, the sensory hairs probably are not coupled through viscous drag in the subcupular space, as proposed by Petraitis (1966), but they extend through the cupular space into the cupula—or rather, the cupula is polymerized between and around the sensory hairs, thus assuring a direct mechanical coupling to the cupular fibrils (Fig. 7). That this is probably so is seen also from the fact that the phase angle of the microphonic potential follows that of the displacement of the cupula with respect to the driving force and not the velocity (Kuiper, 1956; Harris and van Bergeijk, 1962; Flock, 1965a).

The apical ends of the sensory cells are interlocked in a rigid frame of supporting cells that are attached to one another and to the hair

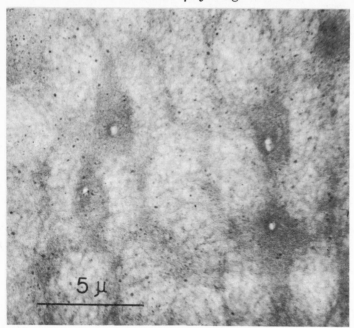

Fig. 11. This section through the cupula cut parallel to and above the sensory epithelium shows that the cupular material is conspicuously concentrated above each of four hair cells. During preparation the kinocilia have been pulled out, leaving clear canals. *L. vulgaris* (×5,800).

cells at specialized zones of cell junctions (Fig. 12). At the surface of the epithelium the cell membranes of adjoining cell surfaces fuse into a tight junction (zonula occludens of Farquhar and Palade, 1963). Below this level, the two cell membranes are again separate but become mechanically connected around the apical circumference by desmosomes, which are patches of sandwiched disclike thickenings of the opposing cell membranes (Fig. 13). Deeper down, further interlocking is ensured by interdigitating foldings of the cell membranes (Fig. 12). The hair cells are joined to the surrounding supporting cells by tight junctions and desmosomes, while interdigitations are usually seen only between supporting cells. Tight junctions and desmosomes are found also in the organ of Corti, and Beagley (1965) has shown that these junctions are particularly resistant to the mechanical stress of traumatic acoustic exposure severe enough to cause physical damage to other parts of the sense organ. Apart from its purely mechanical function, the tight junction probably has an important function as a high-resistance ionic barrier between fluid compartments of different ionic composition. This point will be further considered in a later section.

To summarize, it appears that the hair cells are firmly fixed in a rigid platform of supporting cells and that the sensory hairs are firmly attached to the cupula, which is free to move by shearing displacement

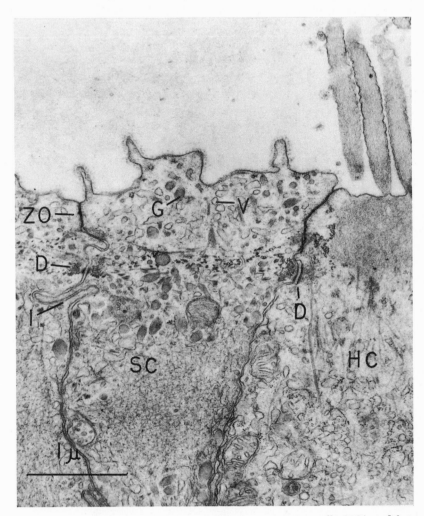

FIG. 12. Apical interfaces between neighboring supporting cells (SC) and hair cells (HC) are joined by tight junctions (ZO), desmosomes (D), and interdigitations (I). Apart from serving mechanical attachment, the tight junction also constitutes a high-resistance ionic barrier between fluid compartments of different ionic composition. In the supporting cell are seen dense secretory granules (G), vacuoles (V), and supporting fibrils. *L. vulgaris* (×27,000).

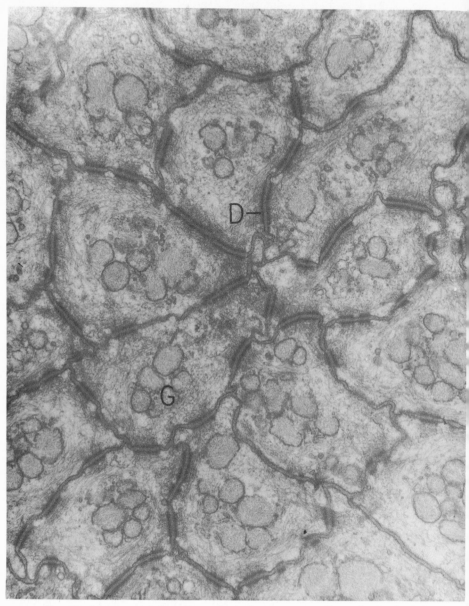

Fig. 13. Section cut below the surface of supporting cells at the level of the desmosomes (D) that mechanically join the cells. In the center of each cell are seen granules (G) that are believed to contribute their secretory material to form the cupular material. *X. laevis* (×25,000).

on a low-friction viscous subcupular interface. The design of this system meets the theoretical requirements for optimal sensitivity, since close to the sensory threshold the displacement of the cupula is distributed to the sensory elements with the addition of a minimum of thermal noise motion (see Harris, 1966).

## HAIR CELLS AND MICROPHONIC POTENTIAL; MORPHOLOGICAL BASIS OF DIRECTIONAL SENSITIVITY

The sensory hairs act to transmit the mechanical energy of cupular displacement to the mechano-sensitive site in the apical end of the hair cell where the receptor mechanism is activated. As a result of displacement of the sensory hairs a graded potential is generated, probably by the action of the hair cells. In vibration-sensitive organs, such as the lateral line organ, vibratory stimulation causes an alternating potential change, the microphonic potential discovered by de Vries (1948). In more slowly adapting organs, for instance, the crista ampullaris in the semicircular canals, steady potential shifts accompany sustained static displacement (Trincker, 1957). Conversely, with experimental stimulation a microphonic response can be evoked from the crista (de Vries and Bleeker, 1949) and steady potentials from the organ of Corti (Békésy, 1960). The sign and amplitude of the potential change is, however, in all cases correlated in a consistent and seemingly meaningful way to the directional sensitivity of the sensory unit; that is, the response is dependent on the direction in which the hair bundle is displaced. When the bundle is displaced in a direction from the stereocilia toward the kinocilium, a negative microphonic or a steady displacement potential is generated above the hair cell. This negative potential is accompanied in the nerve by the initiation of a nerve impulse or, in the case of maintained displacement, an increase of nerve impulse frequency. Displacement in this direction will be referred to as excitatory, while displacement in the opposite direction, from the kinocilium toward the stereocilia, is inhibitory and causes a positive potential and a decrease in nerve discharge rate. It is conspicuous that the directional sensitivity coincides with the asymmetric position of the kinocilium in the sensory hair bundle—a fact which implies that this morphological polarization reflects a functional polarization responsible for directional sensitivity. This hypothesis is illustrated in Fig. 14. It is possible to map the orientation of the hair cells with the electron microscope. The directional sensitivity of an entire organ and the response of the organ to stimuli of any chosen direction can be predicted on the basis of the above hypothesis. In the crista ampullaris (Lowen-

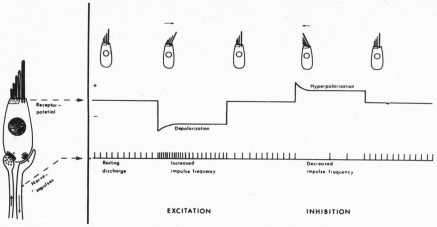

FIG. 14. Diagrammatic illustration of the proposed theory of hair-cell function, showing the relation between receptor potential and nerve impulse frequency when the sensory hairs are inclined toward or away from the kinocilium. (Modified from Flock, 1965a.)

stein and Wersäll, 1959) and in the organ of Corti (Flock et al., 1962), all hair cells face in the same direction, and the microphonic potential, which is the summed output of all hair cells, therefore follows the frequency of the stimulus. In the lateral line organ (Fig. 15), adjacent hair cells are oriented with their kinocilia facing in opposite directions. The hair cells are polarized along the canal in the canal organ (Flock and Wersäll, 1962) or along the long axis of the sensory area in the freestanding organ (Kalmijn, 1963). Figure 16 illustrates how this dual orientation explains the earlier puzzling double frequency of the microphonics in the canal organ, first observed by de Vries (1948). For a

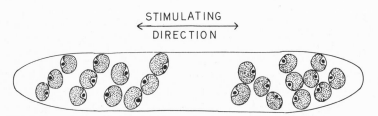

FIG. 15. Adjacent hair cells are oriented with their kinocilia pointing in opposite directions, along the long axis of the sensory area. Here, in the freestanding organ of X. *laevis*, the kinocilium is indicated as a black dot in the periphery of each cell.

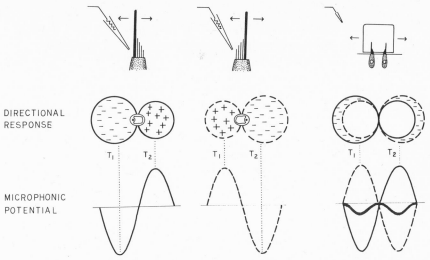

Fɪɢ. 16. Diagram to illustrate the generation of double microphonics in the lateral line organ. Hypothetically, displacement of the sensory hair bundle in a direction from the stereocilia toward the kinocilium depolarizes the cell, recorded as a negative potential above the hair cell. Antiparallel displacement causes hyperpolarization. In the first half-period ($T_1$) of one cycle of cupular displacement, hair cells A and B, which are oriented in opposite directions, are depolarized and hyperpolarized, respectively. During the second half period ($T_2$), the signs are reversed. When recording the summed output of several cells, the responses subtract and leave a distortion product twice the frequency of the stimulus to be recorded by the electrode.

more extensive discussion on this theme, one should refer to Flock (1965). In the saccule and the lagena (Lowenstein et al., 1964) and in the utricle and the amphibian papilla (Flock, 1964; Flock and Flock, 1966), the pattern is more complicated, yet consistent with electrophysiological findings.

When recording, as we do, with an external electrode, the simultaneously generated potentials from the two groups of hair cells will be subtracted. The microphonics recorded in this way therefore does not proportionately represent the hair-cell activity, as was earlier believed, but constitutes the distortion product between the opposed responses when the hair cells work outside their linear range. That the microphonics behaves as a distortion product has been concluded on other grounds by Harris and van Bergeijk (1962). Whether working outside the linear range also means working outside the physiological range is not clear, but it does not appear to be so, since the minimal calculated displacements at which second-order microphonics have been recorded are less than 0.08 $\mu$ in Harris and van Bergeijk's (1962) experiments, less than 1 $\mu$ in Kuiper's (1956), and less than 0.08 $\mu$ in Flock's (1965a). Displacements of this order should be well within the physiological operation of the hair cell. In the amphibian papilla of the bullfrog, double orientation of hair cells also occurs (Flock and Flock, 1966). Second-order microphonics can be recorded from this organ at sound pressure levels as low as 45 dB, which are certainly physiological (Capranica et al., 1966).

The presence of two functionally opposed groups of sensory units is reflected in the nerve trunk, where Sand (1937) demonstrated that there are two groups of nerve fibers which are excited and inhibited by antiparallel displacements. This dichotomy exists also in the free-standing organ of *Xenopus* (Görner, 1963; Harris and Milne, 1966), which is particularly well suited for studies on nerve activity, as will appear from later sections dealing with the anatomy of innervation and with processes of impulse initiation.

THE ROLE OF THE KINOCILIUM

The directional sensitivity of the hair cell is indicated not only by the position of the kinocilium in relation to the stereocilia but also, on an ultrastructural level, by the asymmetric arrangement of the component filaments of the kinocilium and by the presence of a basal foot. The basal foot protrudes from the basal body in a direction away from the stereocilia, that is, in the direction of excitatory stimulation (Fig. 10). The presence of a basal foot with a similar relation to the functional polarization of the cell has been observed in the ray labyrinth (Lowenstein et al., 1964) and in the macula utriculi of *L. vulgaris* (Flock, 1964).

It is interesting to observe in motile cilia the correlation of an analogous morphological polarization of the kinocilium and its basal body to the beating direction of the cilia (Gibbons, 1961; Afzelius, 1961), a fact that directs our attention to the presence of modified cilia also in other sense organs. It has been suggested by Lowenstein et al. (1964) that the kinocilium may act as a motile cilium in reverse by responding to passive deformation in a certain direction with the initiation of electric change, as proposed for the tympanic organ by Gray and Pumphrey (1958).

That the kinocilium plays an important role in the excitatory process indeed seems to be true in the freestanding lateral line organ of the salamander *Necturus maculosus*, in which the hair cells are equipped only with a kinocilium that projects into the cupula (Flock, 1967). Afferent nerve impulses have been recorded by Schmidt (1965), but it remains to be shown that this organ exhibits angular sensitivity. It is pertinent to recall, at this point, that the hair cells of the organ of Corti exhibit distinct directional sensitivity (Békésy, 1960), in spite of the fact that they lack the kinocilium (Engström and Wersäll, 1958). Yet the cochlear inner and outer hair cells invariably possess a centriole, which is the structural equivalent to the basal body of the kinocilium and which, in the outer hair cells, indicates by its position the directional sensitivity of the cell. The presence of such a centriole has recently been shown also in the human cochlea by Kimura et al. (1965). Kikuchi and Hilding (1965) and Kimura (1966) recently demonstrated that the hair cells in the developing organ of Corti of the mouse do possess a kinocilium that is shed shortly after partus, leaving behind its intracellular portion, which constitutes the centriole of the mature cell. Also, in sections from a 24-week human embryo, a cilium has been found to protrude from the centriole of the external hair cells (Wedenberg and Wersäll, 1965; Wersäll and Flock, 1966). It is not justified on this basis to interpret, as one might be tempted to do, the shedding of the extracellular portion of the kinocilium as a necessary differentiation prerequisite to high-frequency discrimination in hair cells, since a fully developed kinocilium is present in the bullfrog basilar papilla, which is a hearing organ in which the best frequency of primary auditory neurons is centered around 1400 Hz (Frishkopf and Goldstein, 1963). Also, the presence of a kinocilium in the cochlea of birds has been reported by Vinnikov et al. (1965). The functional significance of the kinocilium is therefore still obscure. The kinocilium or its basal body is possibly engaged in organizing during development, and maintaining throughout life, the polarization of the functional elements in the mechanosensitive membrane on which directional sensitivity depends. It cannot be excluded that the kinocilium or the basal body may also be actively engaged in the transducer process, for instance, by regulating the conductance of the sensitive membrane in response to mechanical deformation.

TRANSDUCTION IN HAIR CELLS

The question of whether the microphonic potential acts as a causal event in the sensory process in hair cells (Davis, 1965) or is an epiphenomenon (Grundfest, 1965) will remain unresolved until this process has been studied by intracellular recordings from hair cells. For a discussion on the significance of the microphonic potential, it is useful to consider briefly the basis for generation and transmission of electric potentials in excitable biological membranes.

Electrogenesis in neurons, and also in receptor cells, is based on the potential difference between the inside and the outside of the cell. This electrical polarization is established and maintained across the semipermeable cell membrane by the different distribution of ions with different equilibrium potentials on the two sides of the cell membrane. The main ions concerned are $Na^+$ and $K^+$. $K^+$ is found in high concentration intracellularly where the potential is negative, and $Na^+$ is high extracellularly. These ions are not distributed in electrochemical equilibrium: there is an inward electromotor force for $Na^+$ and an outward force for $K^+$. $Cl^-$ often seems to be distributed closer to equilibrium and is in higher concentration on the outside. This membrane polarization is maintained by an active transport of ions against their concentration gradients, a process that requires energy supplied by the metabolic processes of the cell. At electrogenesis the conductance of the excitable membrane is suddenly increased, thus allowing the ions to pass more freely across the membrane along their electrochemical potential gradients. The associated change in transmembrane potential can be recorded extra- or intracellularly with microelectrodes and is of opposite polarity on the two sides of the membrane. Excitable membranes belong to two classes, distinguished by two different modes of electrogenesis: the sensitive membrane can be chemically or electrically excitable. For a given unit of membrane, only one mode of activation is possible (Grundfest, 1965). At the input of neurons (dendritic or somatic postsynaptic membranes), the release of a chemical transmitter substance from the presynaptic ending causes a conductance change that gives rise to a graded generator potential in the postsynaptic area. This postsynaptic potential spreads electronically to the point on the axon where the electrically excitable membrane takes over. In this region the permeability is a function of membrane potential, and once a critical threshold is reached, a regenerative self-sustained all-or-nothing impulse develops and travels down the axon. When the impulse reaches the nerve ending, it causes the release of chemical transmitter. The secretion of transmitter substance is probably induced by the potential change inside the nerve terminal caused by the nerve impulse.

The functional analogy between neurons and sensory cells has often been pointed out (Davis, 1961), and in a number of cases of primary sensory cells the distinction is quite subtle, for example, in the crustacean stretch receptor (Alexandrowicz, 1951). Here the stimulus energy acts to change the conductance of the sensitive membrane, which is now specifically modified for mechanical excitability. As a result, a receptor potential is generated that is graded with respect to stimulus intensity and acts on the electrically excitable membrane to determine by its magnitude the rate of firing of the afferent nerve fiber (Eyzaguirre and Kuffler, 1955).

The lateral line organ hair cells differ from primary sensory neurons in that they are specialized sensory cells interposed between the stimulus and afferent bipolar ganglion cells, the nerve endings of which make synaptic contact with the bottom of the hair cell (Figs. 3 and 6). In the central nervous system and in the motor end plate, synaptic vesicles in the presynaptic ending represent one site of binding of transmitter substance, which is discharged in quantal units into the synaptic cleft during excitation. Inside the hair cell a cluster of vesicles surrounds a dense synaptic body at the area of synaptic contact between nerve ending and hair cell (Fig. 17). The hair cell is therefore presynaptic, relative to this type of nerve ending which is afferent in nature. There are also nerve endings of a second type, in which the vesicles are inside the nerve endings (Fig. 18). The latter type of endings is believed to represent terminals of efferent fibers, and their possible functional significance will be discussed later. Figure 19 illustrates the schematic structure and tentative function of these nerve endings. From morphological analogy it is inferred that in the lateral line organs impulse activity in the afferent nerve fiber is initiated and controlled by the hair cell through the release of a chemical transmitter contained in quantal amounts in the synaptic vesicles surrounding the synaptic body. This hypothesis is more extensively discussed elsewhere in this volume (Harris and Flock, 1967).

If we assume that, by secreting transmitter substance, the basal innervated end of the hair cell resembles in its action the presynaptic terminal of a neuron, how is this process controlled by the hair cell, and what is the significance of the microphonic potential?

Little is known about how the release of transmitter is triggered in presynaptic terminals. Bishop (1956) and Eccles (1959) infer that the terminals are subject to depolarization on the arrival of the nerve impulse. The most compelling evidence was furnished recently by Katz and Miledi (1965), who showed that in the muscle motor end plate, where electrical excitability was blocked by tetrodotoxin, negative electric pulses applied to the nerve ending initiated transmitter release evidenced by depolarizing postsynaptic potentials. On this basis, it may be suggested that in hair cells intracellular potential changes are instrumental in controlling the rate of release of transmitter at the afferent synapse. The potential could be controlled by the stimulus through a change in conductance of the apical membrane to one or more species of ions, in response to mechanical distortion caused by

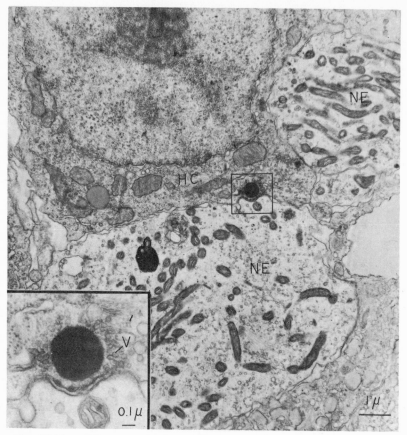

Fig. 17. Two afferent nerve endings (NE) contact the base of a hair cell (HC). Inserted is the magnified synaptic body surrounded by synaptic vesicles (V). These vesicles tentatively contain a transmitter substance (×9,000).

lateral displacement of the sensory hairs. If the conductance is increased to allow ion fluxes that depolarize the cell, the rate of transmitter release increases; when the cell is hyperpolarized, the discharge rate decreases. The microphonic potential may then be the extracellular sign of such potential changes and, in this interpretation, is causal in the sensory process. The sign of the measured potentials conform with this idea. Supporting such a hypothesis is the fact that the microphonic potential is sensitive to changes in ion concentration in the surrounding fluid, as well as to d-c polarizing potentials across the cochlear partition (Tasaki and Fernández, 1952). It is also influenced by pharmacological agents known to interfere with ion transport acorss excitable

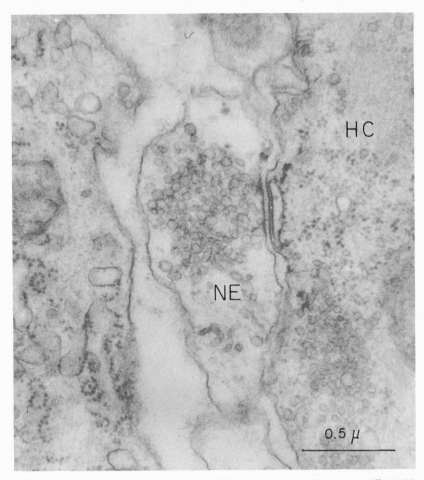

Fig. 18. A vesiculated nerve ending (NE) in contact with a hair cell (HC) contains numerous synaptic vesicles. Such endings probably represent terminals of efferent centrifugal fibers capable of controlling the activity of the hair cell (×52,000).

membranes. This has been demonstrated in the cochlea (Tanaka and Katsuki, 1966; Katsuki et al., 1966) and in the lateral line organ (Kuiper, 1956). In this respect, the microphonic potential is similar to receptor potentials in other mechanoreceptors such as the crustacean stretch receptor (Eyzaguirre and Kuffler, 1955), the muscle spindle (Ottoson, 1964), and the Pacinian corpuscle (Gray and Sato, 1953), where transduction involves ion fluxes controlled by stimulus-induced permeability changes.

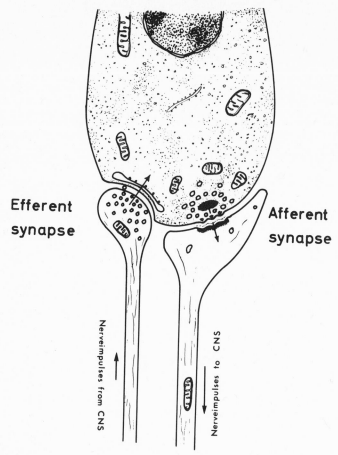

**Efferent synapse**

**Afferent synapse**

Nerveimpulses from CNS

Nerveimpulses to CNS

Fig. 19. The hair cells are innervated by two types of nerve endings distinguished by the location of synaptic vesicles inside the hair cell or inside the nerve ending. These are considered afferent and efferent synapses, respectively. (From Flock, 1965a.)

## IONIC ENVIRONMENT AND TIGHT JUNCTIONS

The function of the hair cell would depend on a stimulus-controlled flow of ions across the apical membrane. In the labyrinthine organs, the ionic environment at the surface of the sensory cells can be efficiently controlled by specific secretory structures, such as the stria vascularis. The endolymph has a high concentration of $K^+$ and $Na^+$. Also in the canal organ of *L. vulgaris*, high concentrations of $K^+$ and $Na^+$ have been measured (Wersäll and Flock, 1964). It is more difficult to see how hair cells in freestanding organs in freshwater fishes and amphibians can work on a similar principle, since these organs have their surface exposed to the outside water. It is possible to stain for $Na^+$ ions specifically with potassium antimonate, which forms an electron-dense deposit marking the presence of $Na^+$ ions for electron microscopic identification (Komnick and Komnick, 1963). Using this technique, a particularly high concentration of $Na^+$ ions has been demonstrated in the cupula in the freestanding organs of the *Xenopus* toad and the salamander *N. maculosus,* as well as in the canal organ of *Lota* (Flock, 1967). The extent of deposit appears to be proportional to the density of the cupular substance, and possibly $Na^+$ ions are loosely coupled to free negative radicals of mucopolysaccharides that constitute the cupular matrix. Sodium seems to be secreted by the supporting cells in the sensory area as well as in the mantle-cell zone. On this basis, it is conceivable that the hair cells in freestanding organs may also function in an ionic environment similar to that of enclosed labyrinthine or lateral line organs, since the sensory hairs and the apical membrane are in contact with the ionic composition of the cupula and the' subcupular space rather than with the surrounding seawater.

These studies also demonstrate that the tight junctions between the apical interfaces of supporting and sensory cells provide a barrier to $Na^+$ ions. Tight junctions are seen between epithelial cells separating media of different composition and have been suggested to prevent intercellular diffusion of ions and molecules (Muir and Peters, 1962) and probably also water (Farquhar and Palade, 1963). A high ohmic resistance (6.0 Mohm) of the canal walls of the ampulla of Lorenzini has been observed by Waltman (1966) and was attributed by him to the ionic impermeability of the tight junctions.

It is concluded that, besides providing mechanical stability for the sensory epithelia, the tight junctions may play an important role in the function of the acousticolateral organs in constituting a high-resistance barrier preventing ion flow between fluid compartments, across which the hair cells work on the basis of ionic electrochemical potential gradients.

The hair cell is interposed in parallel between two fluid compartments separated by a high resistance—on the one hand, the lateral canal fluid (or more correctly, the subcupular space) and, on the other, the intercellular fluid in the sensory epithelium. That the two must be separated is clear also because the nerve fibers innervating the hair cells could not function in the unusually high $K^+$ concentration to which the epithelium surface is exposed.

INNERVATION

The nerve trunk innervating each canal organ of *Lota* comprises both myelinated and unmyelinated fibers. The myelinated fibers range from 1 to 25 $\mu$ in diameter, and they are distributed in two distinct groups with mean diameters of 4 and 12 $\mu$, respectively. The innervation and the function of the nerve fibers can be most conveniently studied in the freestanding organs of the *Xenopus* toad. In this animal, all neuromasts within one stitch are innervated by two large myelinated fibers, 8 to 15 $\mu$ in diameter, each of which divides and supplies one branch to each neuromast within the stitch (Murray, 1955). The stitch may be innervated also by one or two thin myelinated fibers, 1 to 5 $\mu$ in diameter. The thin fibers are sometimes totally absent (Murray, 1955), or they do not always innervate all neuromasts within the stitch (Flock, 1967). Unmyelinated fibers are also present. The two large fibers are spontaneously active (Murray, 1956; Dijkgraaf, 1956). Harris and Milne (1966) have concluded that the origin of this activity is not Brownian motion of the cupula, and the fact that the spontaneous activity persists when the cupula is removed (Harris and Flock, 1967) supports the conclusion that its origin is more likely inherent in the process by which the hair cell fires the nerve. These fibers can be excited or inhibited by water displacements in opposite directions (Görner, 1963; Harris and Milne, 1966). They are excited in antiparallel directions: when one is excited, the other is inhibited, and vice versa—a fact which indicates that they are functionally coupled to the two groups of hair cells with opposite orientations. However, this remains to be morphologically verified. The structure of the afferent nerve endings has been described earlier in relation to how the hair cell may cause the firing of the nerve.

Görner (1967) has shown that the thin myelinated fibers carry efferent impulses, but he was unable to detect any influence of their activity on the firing of the thick afferent fibers. Their function is still unknown, as is the manner in which they terminate in the sensory epithelium. Vesiculated nerve endings which make contact with the hair cells and which are presumed to represent efferent terminals were first described by Hama (1962, 1965). Such endings are also present in other canal organs (Pomes-Delaveuve, 1964; Flock, 1965a), as well as in the freestanding organ (Figs. 18 and 19). Equivalent nerve endings in the organ of Corti degenerate after sectioning of the crossed olivocochlear tract, which is efferent in nature; and Fex (1962) has shown that electric stimulation of these fibers causes inhibition of the auditory nerve response. In experiments involving antidromic firing of the nerve to the *Xenopus* stitch, Harris and Flock (1967) observed inhibition of the spontaneous activity with a latency of 30 msec. Such a long latency could be attributed to nerve fibers with a slow conduction velocity of the order expected for nonmyelinated fibers. The nonmyelinated fibers in the lateral line nerve could therefore represent an inhibitory pathway that serves to decrease the sensory input through the action of the vesiculated nerve endings on the hair cell. How the inhibitory action is brought about can only be speculated. Inhibitory synapses on neurons and, in some known cases, in receptors act by secreting a transmitter substance that causes a short circuit by selectively increasing the membrane conductance to ions which tend to repolarize the cell (Kuffler, 1958). By acting in a similar manner to repolarize or hyperpolarize the cell, the action of efferent nerve endings on hair cells could lead to inhibition of the nerve discharge if the rate of excitatory transmitter release at the afferent synapse is a function of the intracellular hair-cell potential.

REFERENCES

Afzelius, B. (1961). The fine structure of the cilia from ctenophore swimming-plates. *J. Biophys. Biochim. Cytol.* 9, 383.

Alexandrowicz, J. S. (1951). Muscle receptor organs in the abdomen of *Homarus vulgaris* and *Palinurus vulgaris*. *Quart. J. Microscop. Sci.* 92, 163.

Beagley, H. A. (1965). Acoustic trauma in the guinea pig. Part II. Electron microscopy including the morphology of cell junctions in the organ of Corti. *Acta Oto-Laryngol.* 60, 479.

Békésy, G. (1960). *Experiments in Hearing.* McGraw-Hill, New York.

Bergeijk, W. A. van (1967). The evolution of vertebrate hearing, in W. Neff (ed.), *Contributions to Sensory Physiology*, Vol. 2. Academic Press, New York.

────── and S. Alexander (1962). Lateral line canal organs on the head of *Fundulus heteroclitus*. *J. Morphol.* 110, 333.

Bishop, G. H. (1956). Natural history of the nerve impulse. *Physiol. Rev.* 36, 376.

Cahn, P. H., and E. Shaw (1962). The first demonstration of lateral line cupulae of Mugiliformes, *Copeia* 1, 109.

Capranica, R. R., A. Flock, and L. S. Frishkopf (1966). The microphonic potential from the amphibian papilla in the bullfrog. *J. Acoust. Soc. Am.* 40, 1262.

Davis, H. (1961). Some principles of sensory receptor action. *Physiol. Rev.* 41, 391.

────── (1965). A model for transducer action in the cochlea. *Cold Spring Harbor Symp. Quant. Biol.* 30, 181.

Denny, M. (1937). The lateral line system of the teleost *Fundulus heteroclitus*. *J. Comp. Neurol.* 68, 49.

Dijkgraaf, S. (1934). Untersuchungen über die funktion der Seitenorgane an fischen. *Z. Vergleich. Physiol.* 20, 162.

―――― (1956). Elektrophysiologische Untersuchungen an der Seitenlinie von *Xenopus laevis. Experientia* 12, 276.

―――― (1963). The functioning and significance of the lateral-line organs. *Biol. Rev.* 38, 1.

Eccles, J. C. (1959). Neuron physiology—introduction, in J. Field (ed.), *Handbook of Physiology*, Vol. 1. American Physiological Society, Washington, D.C., p. 59.

Emery, C. (1880). Le Specie del Genere Fierasfer nel Golfo de Napoli e Regioni limitrofe. Fauna e Flora des Golfes von Neapel, II. Leipzig.

Engström, H., and J. Wersäll (1958). The ultrastructural organization of the organ of Corti and of the vestibular sensory epithelia. *Exptl. Cell Res.* 5, 460.

Eyzaguirre, C., and S. W. Kuffler (1955). Processes of excitation in the dendrites and in the soma of single isolated sensory nerve cells of the lobster and crayfish. *J. Gen. Physiol.* 39, 87.

Farquhar, M. G., and G. E. Palade (1963). Functional complexes in various epithelia. *J. Cell Biol.* 17, 375.

Fex, J. (1962). Auditory activity in centrifugal and centripetal cochlear fibers in cat, a study of a feedback system. *Acta Physiol. Scand.* 55, 189.

Flock, A. (1964). Structure of the macula utriculi with special reference to directional interplay of sensory responses as revealed by morphological polarization. *J. Cell Biol.* 22, 413.

―――― (1965a). Electron microscopic and electrophysiologic studies on the lateral line canal organ. *Acta Oto-Laryngol. Suppl.* 199, 1.

―――― (1965b). Transducing mechanisms in the lateral line canal organ receptors. *Cold Spring Harbor Symp. Quant. Biol.* 30, 133.

―――― (1967). Ultrastructure of the lateral line organ in the salamander. In preparation.

―――― and B. Flock (1966). Ultrastructure of the amphibian papilla in the bullfrog. *J. Acoust. Soc. Am.* 40, 1262.

―――― and J. Wersäll (1962). A study of the orientation of the sensory hairs of the receptor cells in the lateral line organ of fish, with special reference to the function of the receptors. *J. Cell Biol.* 15, 19.

――――, R. Kimura, P.-G. Lundquist, and J. Wersäll (1962). Morphological basis of directional sensitivity of the outer hair cells in the organ of Corti. *J. Acoust. Soc. Am.* 34, 1351.

Frishkopf, L. S., and M. H. Goldstein (1963). Response to acoustic stimuli from single units in the eighth nerve in the bullfrog. *J. Acoust. Soc. Am.* 35, 1219.

Gibbons, E. R. (1961). The relationship between the fine structure and direction of beat in gill cilia of a lamellibranch mollusc. *J. Biophys. Biochem. Cytol.* 11, 179.

Görner, P. (1963). Untersuchungen zur Morphologie und Electrophysiologie des Seitenlinieorgans vom Krallenfrosch (*Xenopus laevis* Daudin). *Z. Vergleich. Physiol.* 47, 316.

―――― (1967). Chapter 12, this volume.

Gray, E. G., and R. J. Pumphrey (1958). Ultra-structure of the insect ear. *Nature* (*London*) 181, 618.

Gray, J., and M. Sato (1953). Properties of the receptor potential in Pacinian corpuscles. *J. Physiol.* (*London*) 122, 610.

Grundfest, H. (1965). Electrophysiology and pharmacology of different components of bioelectric transducers, *Cold Spring Harbor Symp. Quant. Biol.* 30, 1.

Hama, K. (1962). Fine structure of the lateral line organ of the Japanese sea eel, in *Electron Microscopy*, Vol. 2. (S. Breese, ed.), Academic Press, New York, N4.

————— (1965). Some observations on the fine structure of the lateral line organ of the Japanese sea eel *Lyncozymba* Nystrom. *J. Cell Biol.* 24, 193.

Harris, G. G. (1966). Brownian motion in the cochlear partition. *J. Acoust. Soc. Am.* 40, 1264.

————— and W. A. van Bergeijk (1962). Evidence that the lateral-line organ responds to the near field displacements of sound sources in water. *J. Acoust. Soc. Am.* 34, 1831.

————— and A. Flock (1967). Chapter 11, this volume.

————— and D. C. Milne (1966). Input-output characteristics of the lateral-line sense-organs of *Xenopus laevis*. *J. Acoust. Soc. Am.* 39.

Hyrtl, J. (1866). Der Seitenkanal von *Lota*, *Sitzber. Kaiser Akad. Wiss. Wien* 1, 551.

Iwai, T. (1967). Chapter 3, this volume.

Jielof, R., A. Spoor, and H. de Vries (1952). The microphonic activity of the lateral line. *J. Physiol. (London)* 116, 137.

Kalmijn, A. J. (1963). As cited by Dijkgraaf, 1963, and Görner, 1963.

Katsuki, Y., V. Mizuhira, and S. Yoshino (1951). On the end organ of the acoustico-lateralis system of fish. *Japan. J. Physiol.* 2, 93.

—————, K. Yanagisawa, and J. Kanzaki (1966). Tetraethylammonium and tetrodotoxin: effects on cochlear potentials. *Science* 151, 1544.

Katz, B., and R. Miledi (1965). Release of acetylcholine from a nerve terminal by electric pulses of variable strength and duration. *Nature (London)* 207, 1097.

Kikuchi, K., and J. Hilding (1965). The defective organ of Corti in shaker-1 mice. *Acta Oto-Laryngol.* 60, 207.

Kimura, R. (1966). Hairs of the cochlear sensory cells and their attachment to the tectorial membrane. *Acta Oto-Laryngol.* 61, 55.

—————, H. Schuknecht, and T. Sando (1965). Fine morphology of the sensory cells in the organ of Corti of man. *Acta Oto-Laryngol.* 58, 390.

Komnick, H., and U. Komnick (1963). Elektronenmikroskopische Untersuchungen zur Funktionellen Morphologie des Ionentransportes in der Salzdrüse von *Larus argentatus*. *Z. Zellforsch.* 60, 163.

Kuffler, S. W. (1958). Synaptic inhibitory mechanisms, properties of dendrites and problems of excitation in isolated sensory nerve cells. *Exptl. Cell Res. Suppl.* 5, 493.

Kuiper, J. W. (1956). The Microphonic Effect of the Lateral Line Organ. Thesis. Groningen, Netherlands.

Leydig, F. (1850). Über die Schleimkanäle der Knochenfische. *Müller's Arch. Anat. Physiol.* 170.

Lowenstein, O. E., and J. Wersäll (1959). A functional interpretation of the electron microscopic structure of the sensory hairs in the cristae of the elasmobranch *Raja clavata* in terms of directional sensitivity. *Nature (London)* 184, 1807.

—————, M. Osborne, and J. Wersäll (1964). Structure and innervation of the sensory epithelia in the labyrinth of the thornback ray (*Raja clavata*). *Proc. Roy. Soc. (London)* B129, 256.

Luft, J. H. (1961). Improvements in epoxy resin embedding methods. *J. Biophys. Biochem. Cytol.* 9, 409.

Maurer, F. (1895). *Die Epidermis und ihre Abkömmlinge.* Engelmann, Leipzig.

Muir, A. R., and A. Peters (1962). Quintuple-layered membrane junctions at terminal bars between endothelial cells. *J. Cell Biol.* 12, 443.

Murray, R. W. (1955). The lateralis organs and their innervation in *Xenopus laevis. Quart. J. Microscop. Sci.* 96, 351.

—— (1956). The response of the lateralis organs of *Xenopus laevis* to electrical stimulation by direct current. *J. Physiol. (London)* 134, 408.

Ottoson, D. (1964). The effect of sodium deficiency on the response of the isolated muscle spindle. *J. Physiol. (London)* 171, 109.

Petraitis, R. (1966). Fine structure of supporting cells in the lateral-line canal-organ in *Fundulus. J. Morphol.* 118, 367.

Pomes-Delaveuve, B. (1964a). Quelques observations sur l'ultrastructure des cellules sensorielles des neuromastes du Goujon: *Gobio fluviatilis* (Cuv. Val.). *Compt. Rend.* 258, 4846.

—— (1964b). Particularités morphologiques de la région synaptique des cellules sensorielles des neuromastes du Goujon, *Gobio fluviatilis* (Cuv. Val.). *Compt. Rend.* 258, 6222.

Pumphrey, R. J. (1950). Hearing. *Symp. Soc. Exptl. Biol.* 4, 3.

Rhodin, J. (1954). *Correlation of Ultrastructural Organization and Function in Normal and Experimentally Changed Proximal Convoluted Tubuli Cells of the Mouse Kidney.* Aktiebolaget, Godvil, Stockholm.

Richardson, K. C., L. Jarett, and F. N. Finke (1960). Embedding in epoxy resins for ultra thin sectioning in electron microscopy. *Stain Technol.* 35, 313.

Sand, A. (1937). The mechanism of lateral sense organs of fishes. *Proc. Roy. Soc. (London)* B123, 477.

Sato, M. (1962). Studies on the pit organs of fishes V. The structure and polysaccharide histochemistry of the cupula of the pit organ. *Ann. Zool. Japan.* 35, 80.

Schmidt, R. (1965). Amphibian acoustico-lateralis efferents. *J. Cellular Comp. Physiol.* 65, 155.

Schulze, F. E. (1861). Über die Nervenendigung in den sogenannten Schleimkanälen der Fische und über entsprechende Organe der durch Kiemen athmenden Amphibien. *Arch. Anat. Physiol. Leipzig* 759.

Steinhausen, W. (1933). Über die Beobachtung der Cupula in den Bogengangs ampullen des Labyrinths des lebenden Hechts. *Pfluegers Arch. Ges. Physiol.* 232, 500.

Steno, N. (1964). *De muscalis et glandulis observationum specimen cum duabus epistelis quarum una ad Guil.* Pisonum de Rajae etc. Halniae.

Tanaka, Y., and Y. Katsuki (1966). Pharmacological investigations of cochlear responses and of olivocochlear inhibition. *J. Neurophysiol.* 29, 94.

Tasaki, J., and C. Fernández (1952). Modification of cochlear microphonics and action potentials by KCl solution and by direct currents. *J. Neurophysiol.* 15, 497.

Thomopolous, A. (1957). Sur la ligne latérale des Téléostiéns. II. La cupule et les neuromasts chez des embryons et des larves planctoniques d'espéces marines. *Bull. Soc. Zool. France* 82, 437.

Trincker, D. (1957). Permanent potentials in the semicircular canal system of the guinea pig and their changes in experimental cupula leads. *Arch. Ges. Physiol.* 264, 351.

Vinnikov, J. A., J. V. Osipova, L. K. Titova, and V. J. Govardovski (1965). Electron microscopy of Corti's organ of birds. *Zh. Obshch. Biol.* 26, 138.

de Vries, H. (1948). Die Reizschwelle des Sinnesorgane als physikalisches Problem. *Experientia* 4, 205.

——— (1956). Physical aspects of the sense organs. *Progr. Biophys. Biophys. Chem.* 6, 207.

——— and J. D. Bleeker (1949). The microphonic activity of the labyrinth of the pigeon. *Acta Oto-Laryngol.* 37, 289.

Waltman, B. (1966). Electrical properties and fine structure of the ampullary canals of Lorenzini. *Acta Physiol. Scand. Suppl.* 264, 1.

Wedenberg, F., and J. Wersäll (1965). Personal communication.

Wersäll, J., and A. Flock (1964). Suppression and restoration of the microphonic output from the lateral line organ after local application of streptomycin. *Life Sci.* 3, 1151.

——— (1966). Morphological aspects of cochlear hair cell physiology, in *Henry Ford Hospital International Symposia on Sensorineural Hearing Processes and Disorders, Detroit.* Academic Press, New York.

LATERAL LINE DETECTORS (P. Cahn, ed.), 199–214, © 1967 Indiana University Press

# 13 INDEPENDENCE OF AFFERENT ACTIVITY FROM EFFERENT ACTIVITY IN THE LATERAL LINE ORGAN OF *XENOPUS LAEVIS* DAUDIN

PETER GÖRNER

Zoological Institute
Free University
Berlin, Germany

The lateral line organ, like many other sense organs, has a double innervation. Besides the thick afferent fibers, there are one or several thin efferent fibers, which accompany the afferents to the basal membrane of each neuromast (Murray, 1955; Dijkgraaf, 1956; Katsuki et al., 1951). After they penetrate the basal membrane, both thick and thin fibers lose their myelin sheaths. The further course of the fibers in the lateral line organ of fishes has been studied by electron miscroscopy by Hama (1962) in *Rhynchocymba* and by Flock (1965) in *Lota*. (See also Flock, Chap. 12 of this volume.) Both authors describe two types of nerve endings: nongranulated nerve endings, which probably are afferent sensory terminals; and granulated nerve endings, which probably are efferent terminals. Besides these myelinated fibers, a bundle of unmyelinated fibers penetrates the basal membrane. The further course of the unmyelinated fibers is not known.

All unit recordings from the lateral line nerves showed a similar impulse pattern. The pattern changed in a characteristic manner when the organ was mechanically stimulated (Hoagland, 1933a,b, 1934a,b; Schriever, 1935; Sand, 1937; Suckling and Suckling, 1951; Katsuki et al., 1951; Dijkgraaf, 1956; Görner, 1961, 1963). All impulses recorded can be attributed to one group of afferent fibers, which most likely are the thick fibers. This suggestion can be confirmed for *Xenopus*. From each group of neuromasts, two types of spikes were recorded. The response pattern of each of the two types was affected in an opposite manner when the organ was stimulated by water currents in one direction (Görner, 1961, 1963): The rate of one unit was increased, while that of the other one was inhibited. By stimulation in the opposite direction, the response pattern of the two types was changed in a contrary manner. Corresponding to these two types of receptor response, there are two types of sense cells, which are distinguished by an opposite insertion of the kinocilium at the apical end of the cells (Flock and Wersäll, 1962; Kalmijn, cited by Dijkgraaf, 1963; Flock, 1965). In fish and *Xenopus* nothing is known about the functional significance of the thin fibers. Schmidt (1965) reported that in *Necturus* efferent activity could be recorded from the distal end of an isolated lateral line nerve or facial nerve, respectively, when the animal was rotated or when it was touched. Schmidt did not find any effect of the efferent activity on the spontaneous afferent activity. In these experiments, however, nerve impulses were recorded from neuromasts outside the water. By this procedure the neuromasts might have become insensitive to adequate mechanical stimulation. Under these conditions the finding that efferent activity did not influence afferent activity may be explained as an experimental artifact.

In comparison with the efferent inhibition in the vestibular organ (Galambos, 1956; Desmedt and La Grutta, 1963; Sala, 1963), the efferent innervation of the lateral line organ suggests a similar inhibitory mechanism. The vestibular receptors are phylogenetically developed from the lateral line organ.

In the experiments described in this paper it is shown, first, that the thin fibers are of the efferent type. Then, it is demonstrated what effect on receptor sensitivity is elicited by stimulation of these efferent fibers.

## METHODS

Most experiments were carried out on the South African toad, *Xenopus laevis* Daudin. The animals were anesthetized with a solution of 3% urethan or by cooling to about 0°C in the refrigerator. Brain and spinal cord were destroyed by means of a steel wire inserted through one nostril. The animals were thoroughly washed with Ringer solution before preparation. The experiments were performed at room temperature (18 to 22°C). The Ringer solution was prepared after Stieve (1958): NaCl, 6.47 g/liter; KCl, 0.14 g/liter; CaCl$_2$, 0.12 g/liter; NaHCO$_3$, 0.2 g/liter. In some cases, the solution was buffered with Tris to pH 7.4. For curarizing, 1 ml of a 0.3% solution of curare was injected into the ventral lymph sac of an anesthetized toad with undamaged brain and spinal cord. The toad was fastened on the wax layer of the bottom of a glass vessel filled with Ringer solution (Fig. 1). Close to the toad a cork was fixed to the wax layer. On one side

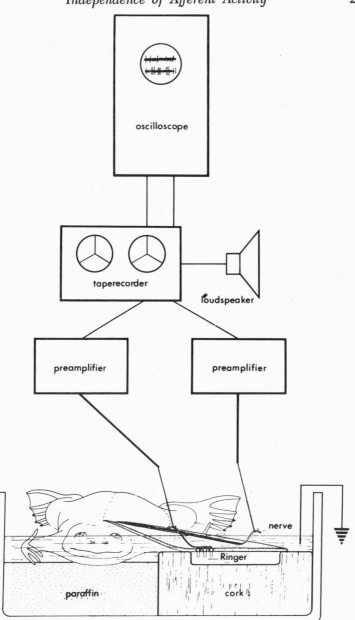

Fig. 1. Experimental arrangement for recordings from the partially dissected skin of a curarized *Xenopus*.

the dorsal skin was prepared off from caudal to frontal, up to the forelegs. Care was taken that neither the lateral nerve nor the main vessels of the arteria and vena cutanea magna were damaged. The isolated part of the skin was pinned upside down on the flat side of the cork, which was hollowed at its center. The hollow was filled with Ringer solution; the cupulae, therefore, could move freely within the Ringer solution. The distal end of the middle lateral line nerve was dissected for a few millimeters. One of the small side branches supplying one group of neuromasts was exposed carefully as far as possible. Then the Ringer level was lowered until the inner side of the isolated skin was just covered with a thin layer of solution. Ringer solution and the toad were connected to ground potential. Unipolar recordings were made from the distal nerve and from the small side branch by means of single silver-wire electrodes. The impulses were preamplified and fed to a double-beam oscilloscope, audiomonitor, and tape recorder. The neuromasts were mechanically stimulated by water currents from a pipette or by water waves initiated by touching the surface of the Ringer solution with a glass rod. Some groups of neuromasts were extremely sensitive. These responded to continuous vibrations of the institute building itself, caused by the traffic nearby.

For electrical stimulation of the lateral nerve, the skin of the right or left half of *Xenopus* was dissected. The skin was fixed upside down to the wax layer of a petri dish filled with Ringer solution (Fig. 2). The center of the petri dish was free of wax, so that, as in organs of a curarized *Xenopus*, the cupulae could move freely within the Ringer solution. The proximal nerve end and one of the small side branches supplying one group of neuromasts were exposed, as described above. The proximal end was taken up by the stimulating electrode, which consisted of two hooked silver wires. The small side branch was taken up by the recording electrode, which was a single hooked silver wire. Ringer solution and skin were connected to ground potential. The stimulation device consisted of an impulse generator and a transformer. Nerve impulses were recorded as described above.

A few experiments were carried out on the larvae of several *Urodela:* namely, *Ambystoma mexicanum, Triturus cristatus* Laur., and *T. vulgaris* L. Their length varied between 25 and 60 mm, head to tail. After being anesthetized with 3% urethan, the brain and spinal cord were destroyed, as described for *Xenopus*. The animals were fastened on the wax layer of a petri dish filled with Ringer solution. The skin caudal to the gills was dissected off for a few millimeters. The lateral nerve was cut proximally. Impulses of several groups of neuromasts were recorded from the proximal nerve end with silver-wire electrodes.

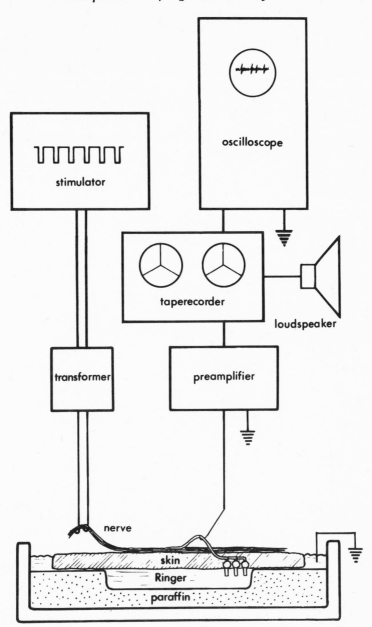

FIG. 2. Experimental arrangement for stimulation and recording from the isolated skin of *Xenopus*.

Under oscillographic and auditory control, groups of neuromasts were disconnected one after the other by cutting of the skin and of the lateral line nerve. The procedure was continued from distal to proximal until only one group of neuromasts remained active. The neuromasts were stimulated by water currents from a pipette or by bending the cupulae with an insect needle. Bending of a cupula was carried out by means of a micromanipulator under microscopic control.

## RESULTS

**Simultaneously Recorded Units in *Urodela.*** As in the small side branches of the *Xenopus* lateral line nerve, the thick fibers spike amplitudes of the lateral line nerve in *Urodela* reached about 1 mV. Therefore in *Urodela* activity from thin fibers should be recognized.

The impulse pattern evoked by mechanical stimulation of the neuromasts did not differ principally from that of *Xenopus*. As in *Xenopus*, in one group of neuromasts mostly two afferent units were recorded simultaneously (26 of 36 recordings). By adequate stimulation of the organ, the spontaneous impulse rate of one fiber was raised, and that of the other inhibited. On stimulation in the opposite direction, the impulse rates of the two fibers behaved contrarily. There were several (10) recordings with more (3 to 4) or less (1) active units, respectively. The origin of the third and the fourth unit could not be determined; these probably belonged to a second group of neuromasts.

In one *Axolotl* the number of fibers supplying one group of neuromasts was controlled by microscopic technique. In 18 of 24 side branches two nerve fibers were detected; in two cases, one fiber; and in 4 side branches, three fibers. In the *Axolotl* no significant difference in fiber diameters (33 $\mu$) was found.

**Physiological Evidence of Efferent Impulses in *Xenopus.*** Experiments with curarized animals: without stimulation from a side branch, two classes of impulse pattern were recorded. Both had a random spontaneous activity and were either activated or inhibited by stimulation of the neuromasts with water currents. When the skin of the toad was touched with a needle, one or a few small units appeared significantly different in amplitude from the units responding to water currents. These small impulses obviously were generated in efferent axons. Simultaneously with these low-amplitude impulses in the side branch, bursts of impulses at the distal nerve were recorded. In several preparations, small impulses were discovered in the distal nerve end but not in the side branches.

Efferent impulses also were evoked by stimulation of the neuromasts

a)

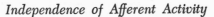
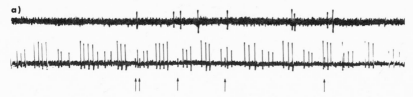

b)

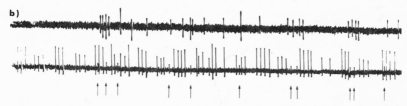

FIG. 3. (a) Afferent impulse volleys (lower record) and single efferent impulses (upper record), the latter evoked by mechanical stimuli of the skin. (b) Afferent impulse volleys and the beginning of a burst of spontaneous efferent impulses. Upper records: Efferent impulses, recorded from the distal nerve end. Lower records: Volleys of impulses of the large and the small afferent unit, recorded from a small side branch. (Arrows indicate efferent impulses.)

of the undamaged contralateral side of *Xenopus*. This corresponds to the observation of Schmidt (1965), who reported efferent impulses in *Urodela* by contralateral stimulation of the neuromasts. In *Xenopus*, however, it cannot be excluded that, by the stimulation with water currents, the toad or a part of it was moved slightly and, therefore, that the skin was stimulated mechanically. After repeated mechanical stimulation of the skin, the toad sometimes tried to move, if the curarization was incomplete. Immediately before and during those slight movements, a series of efferent impulses was recorded from the distal nerve end. At the same time several impulses of low amplitude were picked up from the side branch (Fig. 3b).

A few preparations were so sensitive as to respond with volleys of impulses to the continuous vibrations of the laboratory (Fig. 3). In Fig. 3 two different groups of volleys can be distinguished, corresponding to the two different impulse units. Each group appeared with a repetition rate of 16.5 per sec. In the whole record, the number of spikes per volley varied between 1 and 4 in the small afferent unit and between 2 and 6 in the large afferent unit. The distribution of afferent impulses of volleys without efferent impulses was compared with volleys including efferent impulses (Fig. 4). This was done separately for units of the large type and for units of the small type. From the similarity of the distributions, it may be concluded that the occurrence

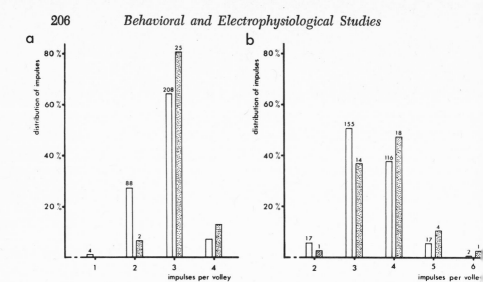

FIG. 4. Distribution of afferent impulses per volley, including an efferent spike (dotted column) and volleys without efferent spikes (blank column). (a) Small efferent unit. (b) Large afferent unit. Above the columns: number of values.

of efferent impulses in a volley did not alter the number of afferent spikes within the volley.

The next problem was to prove or disprove the existence of a delay effect of the efferent impulses to the afferent impulses generated in the neuromasts. No significant difference (chi-square test) between interval distributions of afferent unit activity was found whether there was an efferent activity or not (Fig. 5).

**Periodic Stimulation of Efferent and Afferent Units.** To evoke a series of efferent impulses, the proximal nerve end of an isolated skin preparation was stimulated electrically with a pulse frequency between 10 and 100 cps. As expected from the fiber diameters, the thresholds of the fibers of the afferent units were lower than those of the efferent units. Therefore, when the stimulation threshold of the efferent fibers was reached, the afferent fibers were always stimulated simultaneously. Attempts to block the afferent impulses at the anode of the bipolar stimulating electrode, as described by Kuffler and Williams (1953), were unsuccessful. Therefore the efferent influence on afferent activity was controlled indirectly. Electrical stimulation was started with a low stimulus strength, eliciting discharges in afferent fibers only. Then the stimulus amplitude was raised above the threshold of the efferent fibers. The responses of afferent fiber activity were compared for both types of electrical stimulation.

After strong electrical stimuli were applied to the proximal nerve

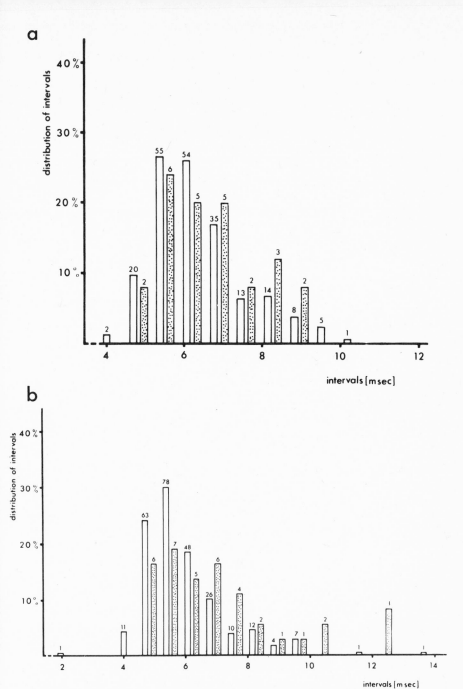

Fig. 5. Distribution of intervals of afferent impulses within a volley. Dotted columns: afferent intervals including an efferent impulse. Blank columns: afferent intervals without efferent impulse. (a) Small afferent units. (b) Large afferent units.

207

ending, two different groups of impulses were recorded at the distal side branch: these were one to three impulses of higher amplitude and zero to two impulses of about one-third the amplitude of the larger ones. In 56 recordings, one large impulse was found 6 times, two large impulses were found 40 times, and three large impulses were found 10 times. No small impulses were found 22 times, and one small impulse was found 25 times. Two small impulses were found 9 times. The most characteristic difference between the two impulse groups was their different conduction velocity. The conduction velocity of 24 nerve preparations between 8 and 40 mm in length (mean length, $21 \pm 2$ mm) was measured. The mean conduction velocity of the large units was $17.4 \pm 0.6$ m per sec; that of the small units, $6.8 \pm 0.5$ m per sec. Because of their different amplitudes and different conduction velocities, it is very probable that the large impulses were generated in the thick fibers, and the small impulses in the thin fibers. By comparison with the height of the units responding to receptor stimulation, the large units could be identified as recordings from afferent fibers. Therefore it is very probable that the small impulses were identical with the efferent units activated by skin stimulation in curarized animals.

The influence of evoked antidromic afferent and orthodromic efferent impulses was studied in 56 neuromast groups of 11 toads. A stimulation frequency between 10 and 50 cps had either no or only a small inhibitory effect on the afferent spontaneous activity. In all preparations there was no difference in the inhibitory effect with subthreshold and suprathreshold stimuli for the efferent fibers. Inhibition therefore was not due to efferent activity.

The inhibition was more pronounced at stimulation frequencies of 100 cps (Fig. 6a). At this frequency there were no longer found any afferent orthodromic impulses between the afferent antidromic impulses. When the antidromic stimulation ceased, the afferent spontaneous discharge of the two afferent fibers was markedly lower compared with the impulse rate before stimulation. The discharge rate increased to its original value after several seconds. The impulse pattern of the two afferent units after stimulation was equal for subthreshold or suprathreshold stimuli for the efferent fibers (Fig. 6a and b). This again implies that inhibition is not evoked by efferent activity.

In one preparation the afferent fibers became inactive at the proximal nerve ending. They could no longer be stimulated by electrical impulses. The efferent fibers, however, were still sensitive to electrical stimuli and could be controlled at the distal nerve branch. Stimulation

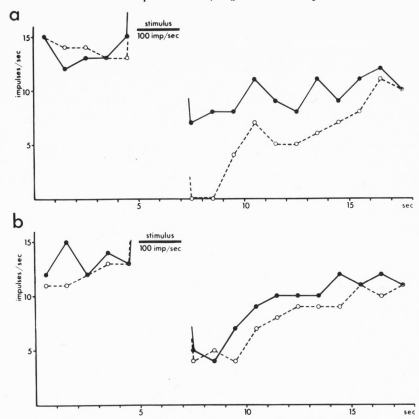

FIG. 6. Spontaneous impulse rate recorded from the two afferent fibers (heavy and broken lines). After the 4th second, the proximal nerve end is stimulated with 100 cps for 2 sec. In (a), only the afferent fibers are stimulated; in (b), both afferent and efferent fibers are stimulated.

of the efferent fibers with 100 cps had in one case a small but insignificant influence on the spontaneous afferent activity (Fig. 7). This result confirms the conclusion that evoked efferent activity does not influence spontaneous afferent activity. The same result was obtained when efferent impulses were evoked while the organ was stimulated by water currents.

It might be that repeated stimulation quickly exhausts the efferent inhibitory substance released at the efferent synapse with the sense cell. In this case, an inhibitory effect would be evident only in the first stimulation of a nerve preparation. Therefore, in several neuromast groups, care was taken to record the first stimulation after preparation

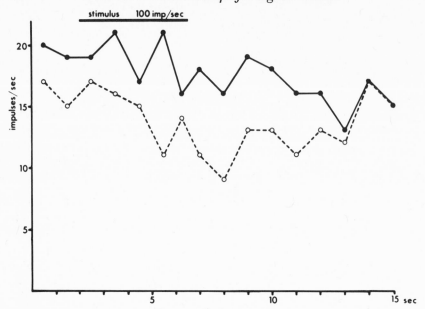

FIG. 7. Spontaneous impulse rate of the two afferent fibers (heavy and broken lines). From the 2d to the 7th second, only the efferent fibers are stimulated.

of the lateral line nerve. In these records, however, efferent stimulation had no inhibitory effect on the afferent activity.

## DISCUSSION

There is no doubt that neuromasts have an afferent and an efferent innervation. This was demonstrated by both the electrophysiological results and by the electron microscopy findings of Flock (see Chap. 12 of this volume). The impulse pattern elicited by a strong mechanical stimulus to the hair cells is similar to the impulse pattern elicited by high-frequency antidromic electrical stimulation of the nerve: after stimulation the impulses are inhibited. The impulse rate reaches its original value after several seconds (Görner, 1963). Therefore it is suggested that inhibition of the afferent activity after high-frequency stimulation depends on accommodation or fatigue of the afferent nerve endings or of the first node of Ranvier, respectively.

One may conclude from these experiments in which no efferent fibers were found by microscopic and physiological methods that not all groups of neuromasts have an efferent innervation. It is possible, however, that thin fibers were overlooked in microscopic examination and that, by preparation of the small side branches, the efferent nerve fibers were damaged. The efferent fibers were very sensitive to rough mechanical handling (e.g., stretch). Stretching, however, could not be avoided when the nerve branch was taken up by the recording electrode. In a great number of preparations, the efferent units disappeared irrecoverably after a few recordings. The afferent fibers, on the contrary, were less sensitive to stretching and often remained active for several hours. It cannot be decided whether a group of neuromasts is normally innervated by one, two, or more efferent fibers, because of their fragile structure. This should be clarified by histological or electron microscopic examination.

The observation that the efferent fibers may be easily damaged leads to another question: May the fact that efferent stimulation did not effect afferent activity be explained by the assumption that in all preparations examined the efferent fibers had been damaged? One may assume that all efferent impulses are blocked at the recording electrode. This explanation cannot be ruled out, but it does not seem very plausible. It is unlikely that the effect occurred in all 34 successful recordings of efferent fiber activity.

But if efferent impulses were conducted up to the groups of neuromasts, why did they effect the afferent activity? This question is indeed difficult to answer. There are at least two apparent possibilities: (1) The neuromast organs were damaged in some way by the preparation. This assumption is not very likely. Many of the preparations were extremely sensitive to mechanical stimulation. The conclusion seems justified that the neuromasts were in good physiological condition. (2) Even under natural conditions, efferent activity does not influence afferent activity. As long as there is no evidence to the contrary, this possibility cannot be rejected; but it is unsatisfying. The CNS generates a series of efferent impulses when the toad intends to move. This is expected if there is some prevention of the strong stimulation of the neuromasts by water currents due to movement of the toad. Then the afferent activity would be inhibited, e.g., by hyperpolarizing of the hair cells. An adequate external stimulus may then fall to the normal working range of the organ.

One alternative hypothesis remains: (3) Efferent activity does not inhibit afferent activity but has a quite different effect. It is difficult to say what this effect might be. Possibly, efferent activity may release secretion of the hair cells or supporting cells. No attempt was made in this investigation to clarify this question.

Two explanations of the experimental results may be realized: (1)

There is an inhibitory effect of efferent activity on afferent activity. This effect is difficult to demonstrate. Failure to demonstrate the inhibitory effect may be explained by faults in the experimental arrangement. (2) Efferent activity does not influence afferent activity but has a quite different effect. Which of the two possibilities is realized, or whether or not there is a third alternative, cannot be decided.

## SUMMARY

In *Urodela,* each group of neuromasts gives two types of afferent units that can be recorded. By adequate stimulation, the impulse patterns of these two types change in the same manner as is known from the *Xenopus* lateral line organs. Depending on the direction of the stimulating water current, one unit is activated and the other inhibited during stimulation.

In the lateral line nerve of a curarized *Xenopus,* efferent unit activity can be evoked by mechanical stimuli of the skin. When the toad intends to move, bursts of efferent impulses appear in the distal lateral line nerve and in small side branches innervating the neuromasts. The evoked efferent impulses do not influence the afferent unit activity.

Afferent and efferent impulses may be generated by electrical stimulation of the proximal end of the lateral line nerve. During a stimulation frequency of 100 cps, the afferent orthodromic impulses are inhibited. After stimulation, the inhibited afferent activity slowly reaches its original level of activity. This corresponds to the time course of the impulse rate after excitation elicited by mechanical stimuli of the neuromast organs. The time course of afferent activity during and after electrical stimulation is identical for the case that only afferent fibers are stimulated and for the case that both types (afferent and efferent) of fibers are stimulated. Electrical stimulation of the efferent fibers only has no effect on afferent activity.

The experimental results imply that periodical efferent stimulation does not influence afferent activity. Therefore inhibition of the spontaneous impulse rate after electrical stimulation at the proximal nerve end must be attributed to accommodation or fatigue of the distal afferent nerve terminals.

*Acknowledgments:* I am gratefully indebted to Dr. O. J. Grüsser for help in preparation of the English manuscript. My thanks are due also to Miss F. Eckert, Mrs. S. Friedemann, and to Mr. P. Moller for their assistance in evaluation of the film records and in drawing the illustrations.

## REFERENCES

Desmedt, J. E. (1962). Auditory-evoked potentials from cochlea to cortex as influenced by activation of the efferent olivo-cochlear bundle. *J. Acoust. Soc. Am.* 34, 1478-1496.

―――― and V. La Grutta (1963). Function of the uncrossed efferent cochlear fibers in the cat. *Nature (London)* 200, 427-474.

Dijkgraaf, S. (1956). Elektrophysiologische Untersuchungen an der Seitenlinie von *Xenopus laevis. Experientia* 12, 276-278.

―――― (1963). The functioning and significance of the lateral-line organs. *Biol. Rev.* 38, 51-105.

Flock, A. (1965). Electron microscopic and electrophysiological studies on the lateral line canal organ. *Acta Oto-Laryngol. Suppl.* 199, 1-90.

―――― and J. Wersäll (1962). A study of the orientation of the sensory hairs of cells in the lateral line organ of fish, with special reference to the function of the receptors. *J. Cell. Biol.* 15, 19-27.

Galambos, R. (1956). Suppression of auditory fibers by stimulation of efferent fibers to cochlea. *J. Neurophysiol.* 19, 424-437.

Görner, P. (1961). Beitrag zum Bau und zur Arbeitsweise des Seitenorgans von *Xenopus laevis. Verhandl. Deut. Zool. Ges. Saarbrücken,* 193-198.

―――― (1963). Untersuchungen zur Morphologie und Elektrophysiologie des Seitenlinienorgans vom Krallenfrosch (*Xenopus laevis* Daudin). *Z. Vergleich. Physiol.* 47, 316-338.

Hama, K. (1962). Fine structure of the lateral line organ of the Japanese sea eel. *Electron Microscopy. Vth Intern. Congr. Electron Microscopy,* Philadelphia, Vol. II, N-4.

Hoagland, H. (1933a). Electrical responses from the lateral-line nerves of catfish. I. *J. Gen. Physiol.* 16, 695-714.

―――― (1933b). Quantitative analysis of responses from lateral-line nerves of fishes. II. *J. Gen. Physiol.* 16, 715-732.

―――― (1934a). Electrical responses from lateral-line nerves of fishes. III. *J. Gen. Physiol.* 17, 77-82.

―――― (1934b). Electrical responses from the lateral-line nerves of fishes. IV. The repetitive discharge. *J. Gen. Physiol.* 17, 195-209.

Katsuki, Y., X. Yoshino, and J. Chen (1951). Neural mechanism of the lateral-line organ of fish. (Fundamental neural mechanism of sensory organs in general). *Japan. J. Physiol.* 1, 164-168.

Kuffler, S. W., and E. M. V. Williams (1953). Small-nerve junctional potentials. The distribution of small motor nerves to frog skeletal muscle, and the membrane characteristics of the fibers they innervate. *J. Physiol. (London)* 121, 289-317.

Murray, R. W. (1955). The lateralis organs and their innervation in *Xenopus laevis. Quart. J. Microscop. Sci.* 96, 351-361.

Sala, O. (1963). Modifications of the vestibular nerve activity by stimulation of the efferent vestibular system. *Experientia* 19, 39.

Sand, A. (1937). The mechanism of the lateral sense organs of fishes. *Proc. Roy. Soc. (London)* B123, 472-495.

Schriever, H. (1935). Aktionspotentiale des N. lateralis bei Reizung der Seitenorgane von Fischen. *Arch. Ges. Physiol.* 235, 771-784.

Schmidt, R. S. (1965). Amphibian acoustico-lateralis efferents. *J. Cellular Comp. Physiol.* 65, 155-162.

Stieve, H. (1958). Die Abhängigkeit der Schwelle und des Aktionsstroms isolierter markhaltiger Nervenfasern von Temperatur und Stoffwechsel. *Z. Naturforsch.* 13b, 96-108.

Suckling, E. E., and J. A. Suckling (1951). The electrical response of the lateral line system of fish to tone and other stimuli. *J. Gen. Physiol.* 34, 1-8.

## COMMENTS

Lowenstein: You got inhibition when you stimulated the afferent nerve with a-c impulses. Did you ever apply a d-c potential on the afferent nerve? According to the direction of the potential, you can increase and decrease or inhibit the spontaneous activity.

Görner: I did not try any experiments with d-c potentials applied to the afferent nerves. But the effect (excitation, inhibition) elicited by d-c potentials should be a local one and should last only as long as the stimulus is applied. The inhibitory effect on a-c stimuli, however, lasts several seconds after stimulation has ceased (compare Fig. 6). Therefore it is suggested that inhibition by afferent antidromic stimulation depends rather on an effect on the distal nerve terminals than on an effect on the proximal part of the nerve fibers.

Lowenstein: The inhibitory synapse might have been blocked by curare. Therefore efferent impulses coming there were not affecting the receptor cells.

Görner: This is possible. The example in Fig. 3, however, refers to a toad that recovered from anesthesia before the curare was fully effective. In all experiments carried out with an isolated skin, the toads were anesthetized by cooling to about 0°C. In this case, blocking of the inhibitory synapse by anesthesia is ruled out.

# III THE LATERAL LINE AND HEARING

LATERAL LINE DETECTORS (P. Cahn, ed.), 217–237, © 1967 Indiana University Press

# 14 THEORETICAL ANALYSIS OF THE ROLE OF THE LATERAL LINE IN DIRECTIONAL HEARING

TOSHIRO KUROKI

Faculty of Fisheries
Hokkaido University
Hakodate, Japan

For some years past, the author has studied the relation between the hearing capability of fishes and underwater sound (Kuroki, 1957a and b; 1959, 1960). It was recognized that the results of experiments on audibility were very complex and variable (Kleerekoper and Chagnon, 1954). To understand and evaluate these phenomena, it was necessary to develop a systematic theory of hearing in fishes.

The fundamental ideas described in this paper may be applicable, as far as two receptors in a nervous system are concerned, not only to directional hearing in fishes but also to directional receptivity in other senses of other animals.

## THEORETICAL CONSIDERATIONS

In the consideration of directional hearing in fishes, we must clear up the matter of the interference that may be present when two or more receptors are located near each other. Let us explain the relationships between two such receptors in regard to the following three conditions: spatial relations; nerve-transmission relations; and sound-pressure relations.

**Spatial Relations (Fig. 1).** Let us consider two receptors, $R_1$ (1st) and $R_2$ (2nd), on the same lateral line sensory row, with $S$ as a sound source. According to the notations in Fig. 1,

$$D_2^2 = D_1^2 + l^2 - 2D_1 l \cos (\pi - \theta)$$

$$d = D_2 - D_1 = D_1 \left( \sqrt{1 + \frac{l^2 + 2D_1 l \cos \theta}{D_1^2}} - 1 \right)$$

217

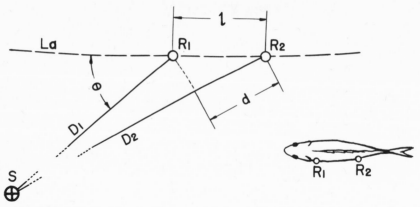

FIG. 1. Spatial relations: $R_1$, $R_2$, 1st and 2nd receptors ($R_2$ is farther from S than $R_1$); $D_1$, $D_2$, distances between S and $R_1$, $R_2$, respectively; $d = D_1 - D_2$, differential length of two paths of sound, from S to $R_1$ and to $R_2$; $\theta$, directional angle of the lateral line (at $R_1$) against S; $l$, distance in length from $R_1$ to $R_2$ along the lateral line (nerves); $La$, lateral line (nervous system); S, sound source.

Here,

$$\frac{l^2 + 2D_1 l \cos \theta}{D_1^2} \ll 1$$

Then, from the development of two terms,

$$\left(\frac{1 + l^2 + 2D_1 l \cos \theta}{D_1^2}\right)^{1/2} \approx 1 + \frac{l^2 + 2D_1 l \cos \theta}{2D_1^2}$$

$$d \approx l \cos \theta + \frac{l^2}{2D_1} \tag{1}$$

Thus, we can obtain formula (1).

**Nerve Transmission Relations (Fig. 2).** In Fig. 2 the sound stimulus should reach the second receptor ($R_2$) later than the first receptor ($R_1$). This differential time is $d/V$. Furthermore, the time in which the excitation from $R_2$ reaches the nerve center should be later by a value of $l/v$ than the time from $R_1$.

Total time lag, then, is shown as follows:

$$\bar{t} = \frac{d}{V} + \frac{l}{v} \tag{2}$$

For recognizing two stimuli from $R_2$ and $R_1$ at the nerve center,

$$\tau \lesseqgtr \bar{t} \tag{3}$$

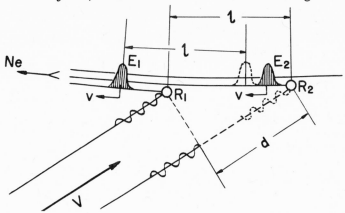

FIG. 2. Nerve transmission relations: $R_1$, $R_2$, 1st and 2nd receptors; $E_1$, $E_2$, excitations from $R_1$ and $R_2$, respectively; $l$, distance in length from $R_1$ to $R_2$ along the lateral line (nerve fibers) ($l$ is not equal to the distance between the positions of two excitations $E_1$, $E_2$); $Ne$, (to) nerve center (along nerve fibers); $V$, sound velocity (1500 m/sec); $v$, transmitting velocity of an excitation along nerve fibers; $d$, differential length of two paths of sound, from S to $R_1$ and to $R_2$.

Generally,

$$V \ (\approx 1500 \text{ m/sec}) \gg v \ (\approx 10 \sim 30 \text{ m/sec})$$

and

$$d < l$$

from Eq. (1); then, from Eq. (2),

$$\tau \lessgtr \frac{l}{v} \qquad \tau \cdot v \lessgtr l \qquad (\text{set } \tau \cdot v = l^*) \qquad (4)$$

**Sound-Pressure Relations.** When we examine one pored scale and its neighbors in a lateral line series (Fig. 3), we should keep in mind

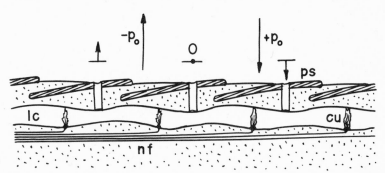

FIG. 3. Sectional schema of sound stimuli: *ps*, pored scale; *cu*, cupula; *lc*, lateral canal; *nf*, nerve fiber; $+p_0$, $-p_0$, threshold values of (positive and negative) sound pressure for receiving; 0, nonpressure.

the following: When a sound wave reaches the pore, the liquid in the canal may press against or move a cupula under the scale. It is uncertain if pressure or movement of liquid will stimulate the cupula. It is probably correct that the following consideration about the audibility may be applied to the receptors on the lateral line, because there is only a half phase difference between pressure and movement of the cupula.

In Fig. 4, the decrease in sound pressure is shown. The path length of sound $(V \times t)$ is written on the abscissa. From the notations, two equations at $R_1$ and $R_2$ are obtained. At $R_1$,

$$\sin (2\pi f t^*) = \frac{1}{n \cdot 10^{Vt^*/k}} \tag{5}†$$

At $R_2$,

$$\sin \left[ 2\pi f \left( t^* + \frac{d}{V} \right) \right] = \frac{10^{V(t^*+d/V)/k}}{n} \tag{6}†$$

From Eqs. (5) and (6),

$$\cos \left( \frac{2\pi f d}{V} \right) + \sqrt{n^2 \cdot 10^{2Vt^*/k} - 1} \times \sin \left( \frac{2\pi f d}{V} \right) = 10^{(2Vt^*+d)/k} \tag{7}$$

For the threshold of audible sound (minimum pressure), one-quarter of the wavelength should be equal to the length of the sound path during the time $(t^* + d/V)$.

$$\frac{V}{4f} = V \cdot t^* + d \qquad t^* = \frac{1}{4f} - \frac{d}{V} \tag{8}$$

† Let

$$\overline{P} \sin (2\pi f t) = 0$$

at $R_1$, when $t = 0$. Under the threshold conditions at $R_1$:

$$-p_0 = \overline{P} \cdot 10^{(-V)(-t^*)/k} \sin [2\pi f(-t^*)]$$
$$\overline{P} = P_0 \cdot 10^{-D/k} = np_0$$
$$\therefore -p_0 = -np_0 \cdot 10^{V \cdot t^*/k} \sin (2\pi f t^*)$$

or

$$\sin (2\pi f t^*) = \frac{1}{n \cdot 10^{V \cdot t^*/k}} \qquad ft < 1$$

At $R_2$,

$$+p_0 = \overline{P} \cdot 10^{-V(t^*+d/V)/k} \sin [2\pi f(t^* + d/V)]$$
$$\sin [2\pi f(t^* + d/V)] = \frac{10^{V(t^*+d/V)/k}}{n} \qquad 2\pi f(t + d/V) < 1$$

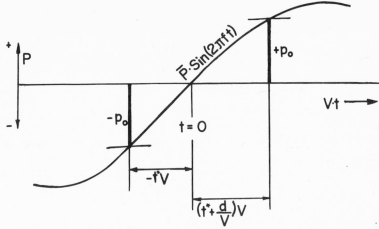

FIG. 4. Decreasing of sound pressure: $P_0$, maximum sound pressure at $S$ (sound source); $\bar{P}$, sound pressure on $R_1$ at distance $D_1$ from $S$; $\pm p_0$, threshold value of sound pressure on every receptor ($P = np_0$, where $n$ is a multiplier); $k$, distance in which sound pressure is reduced to $\frac{1}{10}$ [cf. Eq. (5)] (sound pressure $P$ at distance $D$ meters from $S$ is $P_0 \times 10^{-D/k}$); $f$, frequency of sound vibration (cps) [cf. Eq. (5)]; $t^*$, time elapsed since $P = -p_0$ to $P = 0$ ("minus" means time before $t = 0$).

By substitution of $t^*$ from Eq. (8) into (7),

$$\cos\left(\frac{2\pi f d}{V}\right) + \sqrt{n^2 \cdot 10^{(V/2kf - 2d/k)} - 1}$$

$$\times \sin\left(\frac{2\pi f d}{V}\right) = 10^{(V/2kf - d/k)} \quad (9)$$

$V$ and $k$ are constant values in a certain water mass, and Eq. (9) shows the relation between $f$ (frequency), $n$ (intensity, in decibels), and $d$ (path difference) under the most sensitive condition. That is, Eq. (9) shows the sensitivity curve of $n$ vs. $f$ for a constant value of $d$.

### RESULTS CALCULATED FROM ACTUAL VALUES

Actual values may be substituted for the above-mentioned notations. By using the actual values for a typical fish under normal conditions, we can find the inclinations of "fish hearing" and obtain other information about it as is discussed below.

**Relation between $d$ and $\theta$.** When $D_1 = 1$ m, the curves at $l_1 = 100$, 80, 40, 20, 4, 1, and 0.4 cm, from Eq. (1), are shown by the solid lines in Fig. 5. For example, at $l_1$ (distance between two receptors $R_1$,

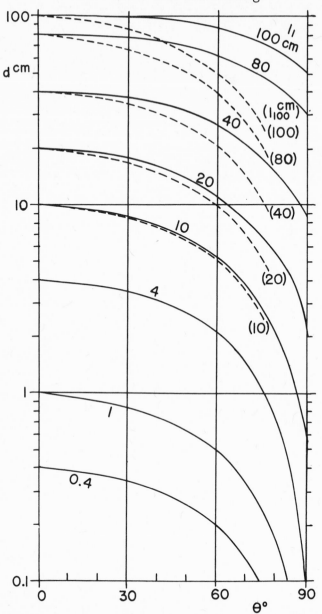

FIG. 5. Relation between $d$ and $\theta$ at various values of $l$: Ordinate, path difference $d$ (cm; logarithmic scale); abscissa, directional angle $\theta$ (deg); solid lines, $l_1 =$ 100, 80, 40, 20, 10, 4, 1, 0.4 cm at $D_1 = 1$ m; broken lines, $(l_{100}) = (100)$, $(80)$, $(40)$, $(20)$, $(10)$, cm at $D_1 = 100$ m.

$R_2$) $= 20$ cm, $d$ (sound-path difference) changes from 20 cm ($\theta = 0°$) to 2 cm ($\theta = 90°$). For $D_1 = 100$ m, the curves are shown by broken lines.

**Length of $l^*$ in the Biological Meaning.** The data for silver carp, *Carassius auratus,* are shown in Table 1. That is, in order to have di-

TABLE 1. ELECTROPHYSIOLOGICAL DATA ON THE LATERAL LINE
NERVES OF SILVER CARP (BODY LENGTH, 20 cm)
*(after Ogawa, 1956)*

|  | A neuron | B neuron | Remarks |
|---|---|---|---|
| Transmitting velocity of stimulation (m/sec) | 28.9 | 6.5 | Experiment at 9°C |
| Absolute refractory period (sec) | $3 \times 10^{-3}$ | $11 \times 10^{-3}$ | |
| Chronaxe (sec) | $0.47 \times 10^{-3}$ | $1.4 \times 10^{-3}$ | |
| Diameter of neuron ($\mu$) | 17–18 | 9–11 | total neurons, 929 (1–25 $\mu$) at 12th scale |
| Number of neurons | 76 | 213 | |
| Values of $l^*$ (cm) | 8.7 | 7.1 | From Eq. (4) |

rectional hearing, the biological distance $l$ from receptor $R_1$ to receptor $R_2$ should be longer than 8 to 9 cm ($l^*$ value) in the lateral line of silver carp (body length, 20 cm) at a water temperature of 9°C. The value of $l^*$ will be increased; then $l$ must be increased as water temperature and, perhaps, as body length increase.

**Sensitivity Curve.** Modifying Eq. (9),

$$\sqrt{n^2 \cdot 10^{(V/2kf-2d/k)} - 1} = \frac{10^{(V/2kf-d/k)} - \cos{(2\pi fd/V)}}{\sin{(2\pi fd/V)}} \qquad (10)$$

Squaring both sides,

$$n^2 \cdot 10^{(V/2kf-2d/k)} - 1$$
$$= \frac{10^{(V/kf-2d/k)} - 2 \cdot 10^{(V/2kf-d/k)} \cos{(2\pi fd/V)} + \cos^2{(2\pi fd/V)}}{\sin^2{(2\pi fd/V)}}$$

Then, we have

$$n^2 = \frac{10^{V/2kf} - 2 \cdot 10^{d/k} \cos{(2\pi fd/V)} + 10^{(2d/k-V/2kf)}}{1 - \cos^2{(2\pi fd/V)}} \qquad (11)$$

Generally, $V \approx 150{,}000$ cm per sec. Some examples of sensitivity curves under the conditions combining various values of $k$ and $d$ are shown in Fig. 6.

As you see, the longer that $k$ (1/10 decreasing length) becomes, the

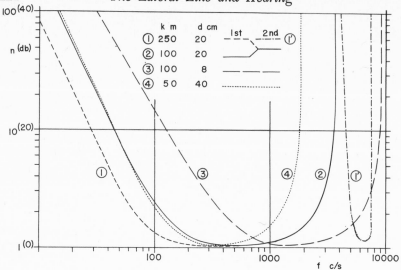

FIG. 6. Examples of sensitivity curve at $V = 1500$ m/sec: Ordinate, relative pressure $n$ (dB); abscissa, frequency (cps).

| | $k$(cm) | $d$(cm) |
|---|---|---|
| 1. Dashed line | 250 | 20 |
| 2. Solid line | 100 | 20 |
| 3. Broken line | 100 | 8 |
| 4. Dotted line | 50 | 40 |

*Note:* Dashed line (1) and solid line (2) join with each other at the range of higher frequency, more than 600 cps. Dash-dot line (1′) is the second-order ($\cos \pi \sim \cos 2\pi$) curve at $k = 250$ m, $d = 20$ cm.

left portion of the curve is shifted to the lower-frequency side. And the longer that $d$ (path difference) becomes, the curve itself is shifted to the lower-frequency side, too.

Here, it may be pointed out that the theoretical data could predict the experimental results as follows (Fig. 7a). The points shown in this illustration are taken from an imaginary experiment. If the points are plotted on the right side of the theoretical curve, the higher-frequency side, the experimenter may get the points by measuring the shorter $d$ (or larger $\theta$). On the other hand, if the points of an experiment are plotted on the left side of the theoretical curve, the lower-frequency side, the points may be measured by the longer $k$ (in purer water) or by the longer $d$ (narrower $\theta$); or by the effects of the sound reflections, interferences, etc.

In Fig. 7b and c, some examples of actual threshold curves of fish hearing are shown (Iversen, 1966; Tavolga and Wodinsky, 1963; Wodinsky and Tavolga, 1964).

## CALCULATIONS ON DIRECTIONAL AUDIBILITY

**Directional Audibility by Two Receptors.** Under conditions of weakest sound (with the most sensitive audibility), the value of Eq. (6), at the second receptor $R_2$, should be equal to 1.

From the left side of Eq. (6),

$$\sin [2\pi f(t^* + d/V)] = 1 \qquad \text{or} \qquad 2\pi f(t^* + d/V) = \pi/2 \qquad (12)$$

$$t^* = \frac{1}{4f} - \frac{d}{V} \tag{8}$$

From the right side of Eq. (6),

$$10^{V(t^*+d/V)/k} = n$$

$$t^* = (k \log_{10} n - d)/V \tag{13}$$

Setting Eq. (12) equal to (13),

$$n = 10^{V/4fk} \tag{14}$$

Substituting Eq. (12) for $t^*$ in the left side of Eq. (5), and Eq. (13) into the right side of Eq. (5),

$$\sin \left[ 2\pi f \left( \frac{1}{4f} - \frac{d}{V} \right) \right] = \frac{1}{n \cdot 10^{(\log_{10} n - d/k)}}$$

or
$$\cos (2\pi fd/V) = 10^{d/k}/n^2 \tag{15}$$

Substituting Eq. (14) for $n$ in Eq. (15),

$$\cos (2\pi fd/V) = 10^{(d/k - V/2fk)} \tag{16}$$

The relations between $\theta$ and $d$ and $D_1$ are decided from Eqs. (16) and (1) under the conditions of Eq. (4).

For example, when $V = 1500$ m per sec, $k = 250$ m and $l = 20$ cm. The directional audibility for the couple $R_1$ and $R_2$ is shown in Fig. 8. Clearly, in the direction of the body axis the most sensitive frequency is relatively low; in the direction of the body side it is very high.

**Directional Localization of Lateral Lines of Different Shapes.** Against the weakest sound (at sensitive audibility), $t^*$ in Eq. (12) should be equal to $\tau$ in Eq. (4). Then, we have

$$\frac{1}{4f} - \frac{d}{V} \lessgtr \frac{l}{v} \qquad (17)$$

$$\frac{l}{v} \gg \frac{d}{V} \qquad f \lessgtr \frac{v}{4l} \qquad (17')$$

On the carp lateral line, $v_B = 6.5$ m per sec from Table 1, and the

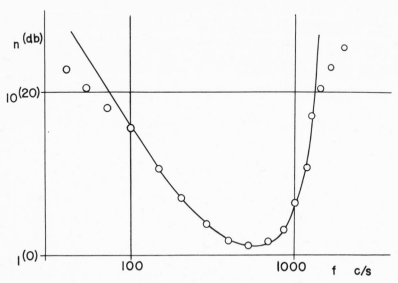

Fig. 7a. Model points, beside the theoretical curve: Ordinate, relative pressure $n$ (dB); abscissa, frequency of sound $f$ (cps).

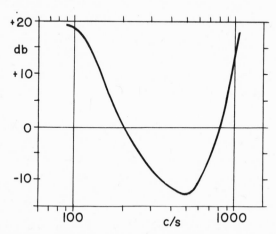

Fig. 7b. Threshold curve of yellowfin (tuna) hearing (*from Iversen, 1966*): Ordinate, relative pressure (dB; to 1 dyne/cm²); abscissa, frequency (cps).

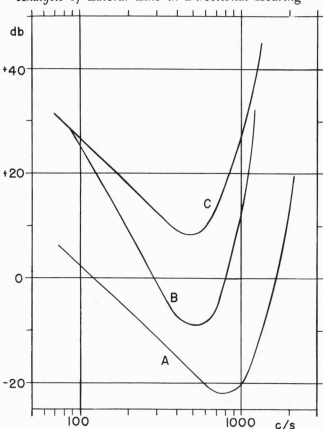

Fig. 7c. Threshold curves of three kinds of fish (*after Tavolga and Wodinsky, 1963*): Ordinate, relative pressure (dB; to 1 dyne/cm$^2$); abscissa, frequency (cps). A, squirrelfish (*Holocentrus ascensionis*); B, beau gregory (*Eupomacentrus leucostictus*); C, blue-head wrasse (*Thalassoma bifasciatum*).

line length (from the nasal pit organ to the caudal end of the lateral line) is about 18 cm. Then, the lower limit $f_{min}$ is, from Eq. (17'),

$$f_{min} \lessgtr \frac{650}{4 \times 18} = 9 \text{ cycles/sec}$$

From Eqs. (16) and (17), Table 2 is obtained by calculating certain characteristics.

Using the values in Table 2, the characteristic curves of directional audibility are obtained by a diagrammatic method (cf. Fig. 9). In the illustration, two angles (upper and lower) of the audible zone for 600 cps sound are shown at an optional point of $R_2$. The wave front

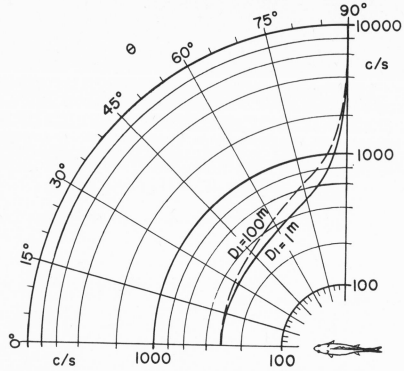

Fɪɢ. 8. Sample curves of the relation between direction of sound source and frequency of sound, heard most sensitively ($V = 1500$ m/sec, $k = 250$ m, $d = 20$ cm). $\theta$, direction angle, from 0° at front to 90° at right side; $f$, sound frequency (cps; $10^2$-$10^4$, logarithmic scale). Solid line, at $D_1 = 1$ m (cf. Fig. 1 about $D_1$); broken line, at $D_1 = 100$ m.

of the sound in the direction $S_0 \rightarrow R_2$ is shown by the line $R_0T_0$, and the front of the sound on $S_1 \rightarrow R_2$ is shown by $R_1T_1$. When $R_1$ is shifted from $R_0$ to the aft side, a normal line $S_0T_0R_2$ is shifted to the position of $S_1T_1R_2$. That is, $\angle S_0R_2S_1$ means the angle of an audible zone at $R_2$.

By shifting $R_1$ and $R_2$ on a lateral line under the conditions of Eqs. (16) and (17), it is possible to show the angle ranges of the audible zones for various frequencies of sound on a certain shape of lateral line. Some examples of curves (under the most sensitive conditions) are shown for various shapes of the lateral line in Fig. 10a, b, and c. We know that, for example, fish with this general shape of lateral line must be able to hear the weak sound of 300 to 800 cps in the direction of +47° (upper front), as shown by a dotted line in Fig. 10b. With a linear-shaped lateral line, as shown in Figs. 8 and 10a, it is clear

TABLE 2. VALUES OF $f$ AND $d$ UNDER THE CORRELATIVE RELATIONS
(AT $k = 250$ m, $V = 1500$ m/sec)

| Spatial difference between sound-wave paths, $d$ (cm) | Best audible frequency, $f$ (cps) | Lower limit‡ of length along the nerve fibers, $l$ (cm) |
|---|---|---|
| (100)† | 80 | 7.8 |
| (73)† | 100 | 6.4 |
| 28 | 200 | 3.4 |
| 10.4 | 400 | 1.8 |
| 5.7 | 600 | 1.2 |
| 3.8 | 800 | 0.9 |
| 2.7 | 1000 | 0.72 |
| 1.45 | 1500 | 0.48 |
| 0.88 | 2000 | 0.37 |
| 0.18 | 4000 | 0.18 |
| 0.04 | 6000 | 0.12 |

† Too long.
‡ All values ($< 8$ cm) are satisfied.

that the fish cannot hear any higher-frequency sound ($>4000$ cps) except at a sharp angle (only 2 to 3°) at right angles to the body axis.

## PREDICTIONS

The sensitivity curves of the relationship between two adjoining receptors on a lateral line system were resolved mathematically, and they are very similar to the threshold curves obtained experimentally. This indicates that the "two-receptor theory" is a proper hypothesis to consider the directional hearing of fish.

Based on these theoretical analyses some qualitative predictions may be proposed as follows:

1. When $S$ (sound source) is in the direction of the body axis of the fish, the threshold of hearing is shifted to the lower-frequency side; conversely, when the sound source is in the direction of the body side of the fish, the threshold for the same strength of sound pressure is on the higher-frequency side.

2. When the value of $k$ is relatively greater (which means that the water surrounding the fish is purer), the lower-frequency portion of the threshold curve is shifted to the lower-frequency side. That is, a lower-frequency sound is audible for fish in purer water.

3. As the upper limit of audible frequency is decided by the value of $d$ (sound-path difference), we must know $\theta$ (directional angle of

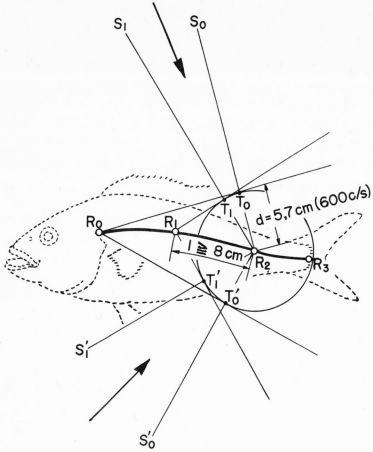

FIG. 9. Illustration of diagrammatic method to seek localization zones: $R_0$, $R_3$, front and aft ends on a lateral line (about 18 cm length); $R_1$, 1st receptor, selected as a movable point shifted from $R_0$ to aft side; $R_2$, 2nd receptor, selected as a movable point shifted from $R_3$ to front side. Distance between $R_1$ and $R_2$ must be longer than $l^*$ ( $= 8$ cm in this case). About the sound wave that comes from lower (front) side, the labeling symbols are shown with primes ($'$); and about the sound wave from upper (front) side, these symbols are shown without primes. $T_1$, $T_0$, tangential points of lines drawn from $R_0$, $R_1$ to the circle of radius $d = 5.7$ cm (at 600 cps).

body axis against sound source) and $l$ (especially, biological length $l^*$ of the distance between two receptors) for calculation of the upper limit of audibility. Furthermore, it is necessary to know the value of $\tau$ (refractory period of the lateral line system) and $v$ (transmitting velocity of the excitation by sound stimuli along the nerve fibers of the lateral line system) to decide on the $l^*$ value.

4. It seems that the stronger the sound pressure becomes, the lower is the audible frequency on the left side (low-frequency side) of the threshold curve; but in the most sensitive condition for a weak sound, there is a lower limit of audibility, based on the biological condition (of $l^*$ and $v$).

## REFERENCES

Iversen, R. T. B. (by T. A. Manar) (1966). *Progress in 1964-1965 at the Bureau of Commercial Fisheries Biological Laboratory,* Honolulu, 6-7.

Kleerekoper, H., and E. C. Chagnon (1954). Hearing in fish, with special reference to *Semotilus a. atromaculatus* (Mitchel). *J. Fisheries Res. Board Can.* 11(2), 130-152.

Kuroki, T. (1957a). Sound from rope in water. *Mem. Fac. Fisheries Kagoshima Univ.* 6, 89-94.

—— (1957b). Biophysical studies on the auditory characteristic of fish (I). *Bull. Japan. Soc. Sci. Fisheries* 23(748), 400-404.

—— (1959). Echoless-wall of aquarium, *Mem. Fac. Fisheries Kagoshima Univ.* 7, 102-105.

—— (1960). Biophysical studies on the auditory characteristic of fish (II). *Mem. Fac. Fisheries Kagoshima Univ.* 8, 89-100.

Ogawa, H. (1956). On the stimulation of lateral nerve (*Carrasius auratus*). *Elect.-Physiol. Showa Med. Univ.* 10, 143-158.

Tavolga, W. N., and J. Wodinsky (1963). Auditory capacities in fishes. *Bull. Am. Museum Nat. Hist.* 126, 179-239.

Wodinsky, J., and W. N. Tavolga (1964). Sound detection in teleost fishes, in *Marine Bio-Acoustics* (W. N. Tavolga, ed.). Pergamon Press, Oxford, pp. 252-280.

## COMMENTS

These comments are based on a lengthy correspondence between Dr. Kuroki and Dr. Harris that occurred following the Conference.

HARRIS: As I understand your paper, the basic idea is to treat the lateral line organ as a time-difference or phase-difference detector. Next you assume a pressure difference at threshold and then calculate the pattern of directional sensitivity of the fish from the geometrical shape of the lateral line organ. I would like to question the basic assumption that the lateral line organ is sensitive to time differences.

It is true that human beings make use of the difference in time of arrival between the two ears in order to localize a sound source. It is important to note in this respect that the path length in the nervous system is not impor-

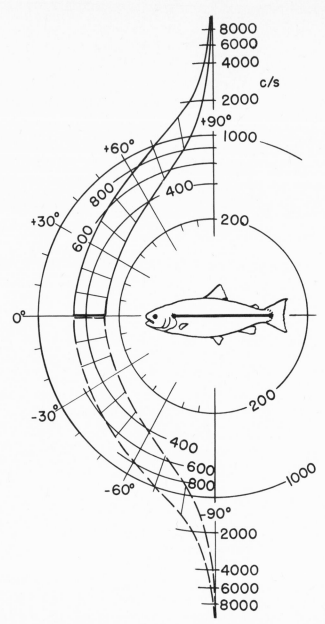

FIG. 10a. Characteristic curve of directional localization by the linear type of lateral line: examples of *Oncorhynchus keta* (Walbaum), *O. masu* (Brevoort), *Cyprinus carpio* (Linne), and *Carassius carassius* (Linne). Circles = frequency of sound in (cps, logarithmic scale of radius length); Solid line = characteristic curve for the sound wave on the upper-frontal direction; Broken line = characteristic curve for the sound wave on the lower-frontal direction.

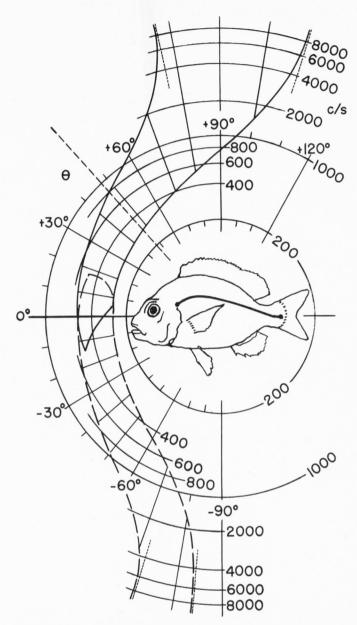

Fig. 10b. Characteristic curve of directional localization by the general type of lateral line: examples of *Chrysophrys major* (Temminck and Schlegel) and many other kinds. Circles = frequency of sound (cps, logarithmic scale of radius length); solid line = characteristic curve for the sound wave on the upper-frontal direction; broken line = characteristic curve for the sound wave on the lower-frontal direction.

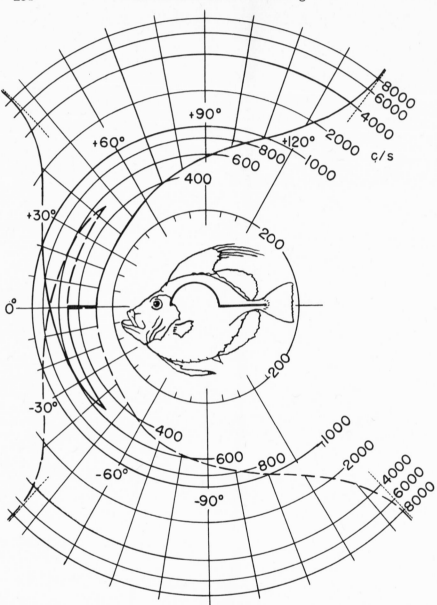

Fɪɢ. 10c. Characteristic curve of directional localization by the semicircular and linear type of lateral line: examples of *Zenopsis nebulosa* (Temminck and Schlegel), etc. Circles = frequency of sound (cps, logarithmic scale of radius length); solid line = characteristic curve for the sound wave on the upper-frontal direction; broken line = characteristic curve for the sound wave on the lower-frontal direction.

tant. Any differences in path length of the nerve from the right ear and from the left ear can be compensated in the nervous system, and the quantities limiting the accuracy of localization are the time difference between the two ears and the accuracy with which this time difference can be represented in the nervous system. All nerve impulses show timing error. The standard deviation of the timing error for the ear is about ¼ msec, and in order to achieve accuracy of less than 50 $\mu$sec it is necessary to average over many nerves.

It is an interesting question whether the bat uses timing information in echo location. Because of the small size of the bat head, the time difference between the ears is about ten times smaller than for human ears. Therefore, in order for the bat to use interaural time differences, either the nerves must have a more precise timing or an average must be taken over many more nerves. Perhaps the bat makes more use of interaural intensity differences than interaural time differences.

It is also an interesting question whether dolphins and other marine mammals that use echo location use time difference as a means of sound location. Because of their large size, the time difference may be large enough even though the velocity of sound in water is about four times faster than in air. I have heard of evidence that dolphins use time difference information, but it is still in question.

Do fish use time information from the lateral line organ? I don't think they do. Both small and large fish have well-developed lateral line organs. In small fish the time differences are much too small to be useful. Fish are cold-blooded, and thus their nerves do not respond so fast as the nerves of warm-blooded animals. I would also expect that any error in timing would be much greater. Moreover, the acoustical part of the nervous system of fish is less complex than even that in the amphibians. For instance, fish have two Mauthner cells. Frog tadpoles have these cells also. When they metamorphose and develop terrestrial ears, they lose these cells and develop a superior olive. (The superior olive is one of the centers where binaural timing interaction takes place.) I don't know if there are any neural centers in fish where timing interaction could take place. None of these reasons is conclusive, but they are strongly suggestive that timing information is not used in fish.

I know more about the toad *Xenopus laevis*, which I have worked with. In this animal the lateral line organ remains well-developed after metamorphosis, since the toad remains underwater. The nerve is not able to follow a sine-wave stimulus whose frequency is above 60 cps, and so this organ is not a good time-difference detector. The small size of the toad means that the maximum time difference is less than 60 $\mu$sec from head to tail. It is extremely unlikely that this animal uses time-difference information to locate external objects. Yet he has a well-developed lateral line organ. What does it detect? I think that it detects intensity gradients of water-velocity displacements.

Görner has done some interesting experiments on the ability of a blinded toad to orient to an object moving in the water. The toad can do this with considerable accuracy. The toad can even do this with only two groups of sensory organs (what I call "stitches"), one in the upper lateral row and the other in the middle lateral row. These two groups are only a few millimeters apart, so that timing information is certainly not used. Of course, large fish could have time differences large enough to use, but I don't think it could be a primary stimulus.

You will see from the above remarks why I question whether the lateral line organ of fish is sensitive to time differences. For the sake of discussion, let us assume that the lateral line organ is sensitive to time differences, then I would like to question some specific points in your paper. With reference to Fig. 2 on the nerve transmission relations, it does not seem to me that the travel time in the nerve is important. This time does not contain any information about the stimulus and can, so to speak, be cancelled out by the nervous system. This is true in the superior olive of the cat, where the nerves from the ears are of different length, but the travel time is somehow compensated for. It is also true that in this organ it is not the refractory period of the nerve which is the limiting factor. The limiting factor is much smaller. Thus, in the cat the nerves that act as coincidence detectors can be sensitive to time differences which are only a fraction of a millisecond.

In referring to Fig. 4, the decreasing of sound pressure, it is not clear to me what your assumptions are here. Do you assume a constant threshold pressure $p_0$ independent of frequency? Why do you need a time difference $t^*$ between the two receptor points? It is also not clear why $t^* + d/v$ should be a quarter wavelength? Why not $2t^* + d/v$? Why do you assume an exponential decrease of intensity with distance?

Of the above points, the first is the most serious. I believe that you assume a constant threshold pressure $p_0$ as a function of frequency; you then calculate Eq. (11), whose important part is

$$n^2 \approx [1 - \cos^2{\left(\frac{2\pi f d}{V}\right)}]^{-1}$$

This is the interference term between two receivers with a path difference $d$ and is the term which gives the shape to the curve in Fig. 6. I believe the fact that this curve is similar to the hearing threshold curve for fish is fortuitous. The threshold curve for hearing is how $p_0$ varies with frequency for the ear, and is not due to any interference effect but is due more to the mechanical construction of the ear. The actual sensitivity of the lateral line organ would be the product of your Eq. (11) with the variation of $p_0$ with frequency. For *Xenopus*, $p_0$ increases very rapidly with a frequency above 100 cps. In other words, the lateral line organ of *Xenopus* acts as a low-pass filter and is not sensitive to frequencies above 100 cps.

I wish to return again to the main point of my comments, which is to encourage you to look at the theoretical consequences of considering the lateral line organ as a spatial gradient detector.

KUROKI: I believe that basically your opinion is understandable. In small fish, time differences are too small to be useful.

Your excellent work with amphibians is very interesting. I think that the lateral line of a slow-swimming animal may as you say "detect intensity gradients of water velocity displacements," and this may also be true in the ampullary type of lateral line. In the ordinary type of lateral line organ, where the neuromast and associated cupula are located in a canal and are covered by skin and scales, the sensory cells are protected from water displacements or currents. It is true that there are pores in the scales, open to the exterior, but often these holes are separated from the outside water by a thin membrane. It is my suggestion that the neuromasts in a canal are sensitive to pressure differences, not to water displacements, and that the hard scales which cover the neuromasts and cupula have an amplifying function for sound pressure.

In reference to Fig. 4 of my paper, $p_0$ is the minimal value of sound pressure in a certain threshold curve in a fish of a specific kind and of a specific body length. Thus,

$$p_0 = \text{const} \times 1 \ \mu\text{bar}$$

That is, $n$ depends on frequency, but $p_0$ is independent of frequency. $p = np_0$ is action pressure.

I therefore consider that the lateral line is a spatial gradient detector, but at the same time I believe that the spatial difference between two receptors is transformed into a time difference at the central nervous system. Fish can then localize the direction of a sound source by sensing the time difference between the two receptors.

SUCKLING: Dr. Kuroki's treatment is a useful addition to the theory of lateral line functioning. It should be pointed out, however, that (1) his conclusions are based on the assumption that a simple mechanism of sequential nerve impulses is involved in the timing mechanism used by the fish. Dr. Kuroki thus uses the refractory period of the nerve as a basic parameter in his calculation. In actuality, it is possible that either more subtle mechanisms permit the fish to discriminate or measure times with greater precision than this parameter would allow or, alternatively, that the variations of peripheral nerve conduction velocities or other factors make less favorable conditions for central nervous system timing. (2) Moreover, Dr. Kuroki extends his calculations and curves to frequencies far beyond the 200- or 300-cycle limit that experimenters believe the lateral line capable of responding to.

LATERAL LINE DETECTORS (P. Cahn, ed.), 239–248, © 1967 Indiana University Press

# 15 EFFECT OF THE ACOUSTIC NEAR FIELD ON THE SOUND THRESHOLD IN FISHES †

PER S. ENGER

Institute of Physiology
University of Oslo
Oslo, Norway

In studies of sound perception by the fish ear, little attention has been paid to the possible significance of the distance between the experimental fish and the sound source. On the other hand, it has long been recognized that, in order to stimulate the lateral line organ, the stimulus must be presented fairly close to the fish. There is probably no disagreement that this is because local water displacements stimulate the lateral line organ and free neuromasts (Dijkgraaf, 1963). Auditory stimuli also excite lateral line receptors (Suckling and Suckling, 1950), provided that the fish is in the acoustic near field, as was shown quantitatively by Harris and van Bergeijk (1962), who also gave a theoretical treatment of the physical characteristics of the underwater sound stimulus. Their considerations are highly appropriate to the acousticolateral system in general, and they pointed out that the acoustic near field might very well stimulate also the labyrinth in a perhaps unpredictable manner.

If one considers the particle displacement ($d$) associated with underwater sound, this can be expressed as a function of sound pressure ($p$) and distance ($r$) from a spherical, pulsating sound source (Harris, 1964):

$$d = \frac{p}{2\pi f \rho c}\left(i - \frac{\lambda}{2\pi r}\right)$$

† Supported by P.H.S. Research Grant NB-03405 from National Institute of Neurological Diseases and Blindness, U.S. Public Health Service. The electrophysiological part of this study was made possible by the provision of laboratory space and a supply of herring by the Institute of Marine Research, Bergen, and a supply of sculpins by the Biological Station of the University of Bergen, Espegrend, Norway.

where $f$ = sound frequency, $\rho$ = density of water, $c$ = sound velocity, and $i = \sqrt{-1}$ (meaning a 90° phase difference between the first and second term). In this expression the first term represents displacement due to the sound pressure wave, and the second term is the correction for particle displacement in the near field. For a given pressure, only the latter is dependent upon the distance from the sound source. With decreasing distance, the second term would represent a larger and larger part of the total displacement. Sound pressure is what is usually measured, and if this is the actual and only physical stimulus, the sound threshold should be independent of distance; whereas if, for example, displacement is the physical stimulus, the sensitivity should be highly dependent upon distance.

According to Parvulescu (1964), there is only one way of avoiding the near-field effect for low frequencies in small tanks, namely, by producing the sound in air. Consequently, to get information about the importance of the near-field effect in determinations of sound threshold in fish, it seemed necessary to perform experiments in which the distance between fish and sound source varied and, also, to stimulate with a loudspeaker hanging in air above the water.

The present paper deals with the results of experiments in which (1) the sound pressure threshold has been determined for goldfish (in conditioning experiments) stimulated with an underwater loudspeaker at various distances, as well as an air loudspeaker [these experiments have been reported elsewhere in greater detail (Enger, 1966)] and where (2) thresholds have been determined for a number of single units of the medulla oblongata (electrophysiological experiments) in herring and sculpin stimulated with underwater and air loudspeakers.

## CONDITIONING EXPERIMENTS ON GOLDFISH (*CARASSIUS AURATUS*)

The experimental setup consisted of a plastic trough 5 m long, 30 cm wide, 15 cm deep. In one end was hung a J9 underwater sound projector (Chesapeake Instrument Corp., Shadyside, Md.), and in the other end the last 2 m were packed with rock wool. The air loudspeaker was hanging some 15 to 20 cm above the container, and the fish was placed in a small cage of gauze. Positive-reward conditioning technique was used, in which the fish was fed a tiny piece of meat 5 to 10 sec after the onset of the sinusoidal tone. The fish cage was usually kept at distances of 2, 1, 0.2, and 0.1 m from the underwater loudspeaker in most tests for acoustic threshold as a function of

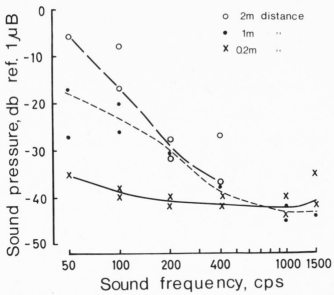

Fig. 1. Sound pressure thresholds in goldfish for frequencies of 50 to 1500 cps, determined for distances of 0.2, 1, and 2 m between fish and underwater loudspeaker. [Figures 1 and 2 reprinted with permission of *Comp. Biochem. Physiol.* (Enger, 1966)].

frequency and distance. Sound pressures were measured with a calibrated hydrophone (LC 34, Atlantic Research Corp.) placed in the fish cage.

The results from one of six successfully trained specimens are shown in Figs. 1 and 2. The general trend in the results was the same in all these fish, although the absolute threshold values were up to 6 db higher (in the specimen with the highest threshold). For low frequencies (below 400 cps), the effect of distance on threshold was very marked indeed (Fig. 1). For frequencies above 600 to 700 cps, there seems to be no significant distance dependence in the 0.2 to 2 m range, at least not for frequencies up to 1500 cps, which was the highest tested in this series.

A complete audiogram for the goldfish in the frequency range between 50 and 5000 cps is shown in Fig. 2. The lower curve represents the threshold as determined by using the water loudspeaker at a distance of 10 cm, and the upper curve is the threshold as determined by the use of the air loudspeaker.

For frequencies above 1500 cps, there is a sharp increase in threshold and no significant difference between the values obtained by

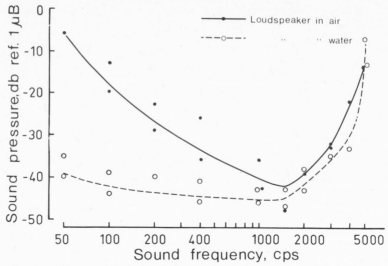

Fɪɢ. 2. Goldfish audiogram for frequencies of 50 to 5000 cps, obtained from tests with water loudspeaker and air loudspeaker.

using the underwater versus the air loudspeaker. For lower frequencies, the curve representing the air loudspeaker audiogram is similar to that for the underwater speaker at 2 m distance (Fig. 1), whereas the audiogram at 10 cm distance is 3 to 4 dB below that at 20 cm distance.

It is quite clear that the distance between fish and sound source is a very important parameter in determination of acoustic threshold; and the question arises as to which physical parameter can be the actual stimulus. Harris and Van Bergeijk (1962) found that lateral line receptors are responding to water displacements rather than to particle velocity or particle acceleration. The particle displacements have been calculated for the present results, using Harris's (1964) formula for the total displacement magnitude:

$$d = \frac{p}{2\pi f \rho c} \sqrt{1 + \left(\frac{\lambda}{2\pi r}\right)^2}$$

Points closer to the sound source than a distance equal to $\lambda/2\pi$ are said to lie in the near field; points lying at greater distances are in the far field (Van Bergeijk, 1964). This formula is valid for a sound source that is a pulsating sphere. The present sound source was a vibrating diaphragm, and also other conditions for which the formula was developed are not fulfilled (container walls will be forced to vibrate and consequently produce "secondary," local near-field effects; shape of tank will channel the sound; water surface and bottom will reflect sound, etc.). Nevertheless, calculation of displacement from this formula might give a rough first-hand approximation of the total displacement magnitude. Table 1 gives the actual values calculated.

TABLE 1. CALCULATED DISPLACEMENT AMPLITUDES (IN ÅNGSTRÖMS) AT
SOUND PRESSURE THRESHOLDS FOR GOLDFISH OBTAINED FROM
STIMULATION WITH AIR AND UNDERWATER LOUDSPEAKERS
(at 0.1 to 2 m distance).

| Frequency (cps) | Distance | | | | |
|---|---|---|---|---|---|
| | 10 cm | 20 cm | 1 m | 2 m | Air |
| 50 | 1.03 | 0.63 | 1.22 | 2.58 | 1.00 |
| 100 | 0.18 | 0.13 | 0.18 | 0.21 | 0.13 |
| 200 | 0.039 | 0.025 | 0.024 | 0.020 | 0.025 |
| 400 | 0.0089 | 0.0059 | 0.0031 | 0.0035 | 0.0037 |
| 1000 | 0.0013 | 0.0011 | 0.0009 | | 0.0009 |
| | Near field | | Far field | | |

At threshold, the particle displacement for any given frequency is rather constant and independent of distance between fish and sound source. For the higher frequencies (above 200 cps), far-field effects have predominated as the acoustic stimulus at 1- and 2-m distances, and the calculated displacement threshold is practically equal to that obtained by using the air loudspeaker. For frequencies of 50 and 100 cps, stimulation with the water loudspeaker produced mainly near-field effects, even at the greatest distance tested. Even so, the average displacement magnitude calculated from thresholds for the water loudspeaker did not differ widely from the value for the air loudspeaker. In conclusion, particle displacement seems to be a better parameter for determinations of acoustic threshold than is sound pressure.

## ELECTROPHYSIOLOGICAL EXPERIMENTS ON HERRING (*CLUPEA HARENGUS*) AND SCULPIN (*COTTUS SCORPIUS*)

The experiments on goldfish demonstrate the importance of taking into account the distance between the fish and the underwater sound source in determination of acoustic threshold. This is not to say that the acoustic near field will always stimulate auditory receptors. In fact, some evidence to the contrary is presented below, based on experiments on herring.

Clupeoids have long been suspected of possessing a well-developed sense of hearing—a suspicion that is based on the anatomical structure of the swim bladder–labyrinth connection and the presence of air-filled cavities in close contact with the labyrinth. The swim bladder extends rostrally in the form of a thin duct that divides just behind the two labyrinths and expands on both sides into two air-filled bony cavities, one extending dorsally (bulla squamosa), which is embraced by the horizontal semicircular canal, and the other anteriorly (bulla prootica). The latter is divided by an elastic membrane into a lower air-filled and an upper perilymphatic compartment connecting closely with the macula utriculi (de Burlet, 1935; Wohlfahrt, 1936).

In the present experiments, extracellular single-unit nervous activity has been recorded by glass micropipettes from the auditory area in the medulla oblongata of 24 specimens of herring. In specimens 11 to 12 cm long, this area was about 800 $\mu$ long, 800 to 1000 $\mu$ high, and 1200 to 1500 $\mu$ wide, located 1.5 to 2.5 mm below the cerebellar surface at the level of the entrance of the eighth nerve. The area corresponds to the central acoustic lobe described by Evans (1932), but it extends further ventrally, comprising also the region where at least some primary eight-nerve fibers apparently terminate.

The fish was kept in a plastic trough and held 1 to 2 cm below the water surface in a special holder, as shown schematically in Fig. 3. In this holder the fish was clamped by adjustable steel rods above the eyes and at a few points along the dorsal part of the back. After the brain was exposed, the steel rods clamping the head were loosened

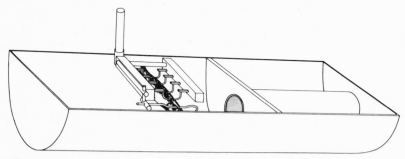

Fig. 3. Experimental tank (80 × 30 cm, 15 cm deep) and fish holder for recording nervous activity in herring brain. Tank divided by a perspex wall, through which frontpiece and diaphragm of a J9 underwater sound projector were fitted. Projector rested on rock wool and was covered with fine iron mesh (not shown) as an electric shield (to make recording of nervous activity possible).

in order not to interfere with the vibrations of the skull produced by sound stimulation.

The underwater loudspeaker was placed in one end of this container, and the distance between the loudspeaker membrane and the fish was about 15 cm. An air loudspeaker was hung above the container, and the acoustic pressure was measured after the fish was taken out.

The nervous activity recorded was from second-order (or higher) neurons, and the response to acoustic stimulation consisted of a decrease or an increase in the "spontaneous" level of neural discharges. The acoustic threshold for single units was taken as the lowest sound pressure producing a change in discharge frequency. Threshold values obtained by stimulation with underwater and air loudspeakers, respectively, are plotted in Fig. 4A. As is seen, no threshold differences were obtained. The values for two different units are plotted in this graph, and only low frequencies (below 400 cps), which are of particular interest for the present discussion, are included. Thus, the near-field effect does not seem to stimulate auditory receptors in herring. This result was at first rather surprising and puzzling, in view of what was found from training experiments in goldfish.

In order to test the validity of this finding, the same type of experiments were therefore performed on sculpins (seven specimens). (As

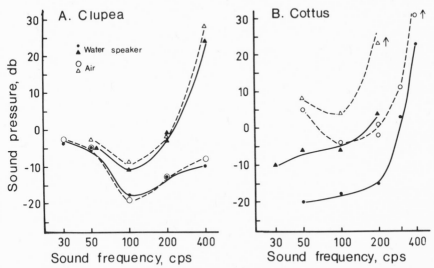

Fig. 4. Sound-pressure thresholds of two neural units (triangles and circles, respectively) in herring (A) and sculpin (B). Acoustic stimulation at 15 cm distance with water loudspeaker and air loudspeaker.

far as hearing is concerned, the sculpin should be the extreme opposite of the herring, since the former lacks a swim bladder altogether.) Fig. 4B shows the results. In this case, there is a marked difference in thresholds determined from tests with water and air loudspeakers, respectively. Taking the lower pair of curves (open and filled circles, respectively), at 200 and 100 cps, the air loudspeaker gave a threshold some 15 dB higher than that determined by the water loudspeaker. At 50 cps this difference is 25 dB, and for higher frequencies—at which one would expect this difference to be smaller—the difference is 5 to 10 dB. The top pair of curves (open and filled circles, respectively) illustrate the same phenomenon, although not quite so marked. In other words, the near-field effects do stimulate auditory receptors in the sculpin.

DISCUSSION

The response to acoustic near-field effects has been found to be different in goldfish and sculpin, on the one hand, and in herring, on the other. In spite of differences in experimental technique, it appears that the ear of the first two species reacts to near-field water displacements, whereas this is not so for the herring. An attempt to give a possible explanation of how this is brought about is given in the following discussion.

In *Ostariophysi* (to which the goldfish belongs), the swim bladder can be regarded as a pressure receptor (Van Bergeijk, 1964), but it will also react to near-field water displacements due to the elastic properties of the swim-bladder wall. Vibrations of the swim bladder, produced in either way, will be transmitted through the Weberian ossicles to the labyrinth. The labyrinth as such has no way of distinguishing whether the vibrations received are produced by a far-field pressure wave or near-field water displacement.

In species lacking a swim bladder (such as sculpin), the sensory cells of the ear will respond directly to the acoustic near field.

In the clupeids (such as herring), the swim bladder is probably of little importance in hearing because the swim-bladder–labyrinth canal is very thin, and rapid pressure changes produced by sound probably will be strongly damped in this canal. On the other hand, pressure changes in the water will produce pressure changes in the air-filled capsules (bullae) in contact with the labyrinth and thereby initiate vibrations of the membrane separating the air from the perilymph in the bulla prooticum. The end result, of course, is a displacement of the sensory cells. Near-field water displacements certainly will cause the rigid bony capsules to vibrate, but this produces little or no change in pressure within the capsules. Consequently—or at least this is my interpretation of the finding—no stimulation of the sensory cells occurs.

This explanation implies that the ear of the herring is a true pressure-sensing device, insensitive to other vibrational stimuli. In this respect, the clupeoids must be regarded as an exception rather than as the rule, as far as the sense of hearing is concerned. Mormyrids are probably the only other group of fishes that may possess similar properties. The rule would be that the fish labyrinth, whether the swim bladder plays a role in hearing or not, is influenced by the acoustic near field, and this must be considered in determinations of acoustic thresholds.

REFERENCES

Bergeijk, W. A. van (1964). Directional and nondirectional hearing in fish, in *Marine Bio-Acoustics* (W. N. Tavolga, ed.). Pergamon Press, Oxford, pp. 269-288.

de Burlet, H. M. (1935). Vergleichend Anatomisches über endolymphatische und perilymphatische Sinnesendstellen des Labyrinthes. *Acta Oto-Laryngol.* 22, 287-305.

Dijkgraaf, S. (1963). The functioning and significance of the lateral-line organs. *Biol. Rev.* 38, 51-105.

Enger, P. S. (1966). Acoustic threshold in goldfish and its relation to the sound source distance. *Comp. Biochem. Physiol.* 18, 859-868.

Evans, H. M. (1932). Further observations on the medulla oblongata of Cyprinoids, and a comparative study of the medulla of Clupeoids and Cyprinoids with special reference to the acoustic tubercles. *Proc. Roy. Soc. (London).* B111, 247-280.

Harris, G. G. (1964). Considerations on the physics of sound production by fishes, in *Marine Bio-Acoustics* (W. N. Tavolga, ed.). Pergamon Press, Oxford, pp. 233-247.

———— and W. A. van Bergeijk (1962). Evidence that the lateral-line organ responds to near-field displacements of sound sources in water. *J. Acoust. Soc. Am.* 34, 1831-1841.

Parvulescu, A. (1964). Problems of propagation and processing, in *Marine Bio-Acoustics* (W. N. Tavolga, ed.). Pergamon Press, Oxford, pp. 87-100.

Suckling, E. E., and J. A. Suckling (1950). The electrical response of the lateral line system of fish to tone and other stimuli. *J. Gen. Physiol.* 34, 1-18.

Wohlfahrt, T. A. (1936). Das Ohrlabyrinth der Sardine (*Clupea pilchardus* Walb.) und seine Beziehungen zur Schwimmblase und Seitenlinie. *Z. Morph. Okol. Tiere* 31, 371-410.

COMMENTS

TAVOLGA: In our work we have started to get some curves on auditory thresholds of goldfish, and they don't quite match yours. This might simply reflect a difference in technique. What I'm curious about particularly is your criterion for a positive response. This can be perplexing, because when you're dealing with a threshold, the response of the organism becomes rather vague. The animal appears "uncertain" of whether he's getting the signal or not, and so the observer becomes a bit unsure if it's a positive response.

ENGER: We've been rather conservative about calling it a positive response. The fish in the confined test chamber showed a reaction to the sound somewhat like a snapping reaction toward some food that was not present, and then a sudden stopping, or something of the sort. I started out by going down in 6-dB steps, and then in 3, in determining a criteria for threshold.

TAVOLGA: Did you therefore use a 50% criteria for threshold?

ENGER: No, I couldn't tell the precise response level in those terms, but each point on the curves gives three positive responses.

MURRAY: In this formula of Harris and Van Bergeijk's, there's a trap that I think I fell into, and that is in regard to the value of $\rho c$. If you assume this to be 150,000 for water, this is all right. For a free field out in the middle of the Pacific Ocean, at a depth of 6,000 m, there is no problem. In a small tank, I think that Dr. Parvulescu has shown that this value comes very close to that of air, and that is going to raise the value of your displacements by several orders of magnitude.

ENGER: Does it vary with frequency?

MURRAY: Perhaps Dr. Parvulescu could answer that, but before he does I just want to make one more comment. Your data, especially that on the goldfish, made me very happy because it gives me a little support for the idea presented in 1963 as to the existence of two thresholds, one for the inner ear or something, and one for the lateral line, or something else—thus a bimodal threshold at low frequencies. This looks very good to me.

PARVULESCU: I'd like to defer until after Mr. Banner's paper to comment on the above. My question at this time is: Is the position of the electrode in the brain sufficiently localized so that one can say that the results can discriminate between the overall response of the fish and the response of a hearing mechanism? Can we be certain that we are actually getting an acoustic response, or a response from the lateral line, or from a higher level of neural organization?

ENGER. It may well be that these results were caused by many different responses, in addition to that of low-frequency vibrations.

MURRAY: How close was your air loudspeaker to the water surface?

ENGER: 15 cm.

MURRAY: It occurred to me that even at that distance, there might be some near field in the air created by the air loudspeaker, which could cause a concavity in the water that could spread out, which would again give you some displacement and still show a difference in the pressure-displacement relation. I don't think you could call it just pressure alone.

LATERAL LINE DETECTORS (P. Cahn, ed.), 249–264, © 1967 Indiana University Press

# 16 SONIC SENSITIVITY IN THE GOLDFISH (*CARASSIUS AURATUS*)†

BURTON A. WEISS ‡

Auditory Research Laboratory
Princeton University
Princeton, New Jersey

The present study, though concerned with auditory sensitivity in the goldfish (*Carassius auratus*), has significance for the study of the lateral line because behavioral separation of the two senses was obtained. The main difficulty in studying sonic sensitivity in fishes is the specification of the sound stimulus. Sound in water has different characteristics, including a 35.5-dB difference in impedance, as Fig. 1 shows by comparing air and water characteristics as calculated in MKS units from the information provided by Albers (1960, 1965).

In addition, Harris and van Bergeijk (1962) indicated that near field may be stimulating the lateral line in hearing studies. The purpose of this study was, therefore, to design and attempt to construct a reliably calibrated tank, to determine behavioral thresholds for the entire sensitivity range of a species of fish, and to consider the problem of isolating auditory sensitivity in the fish from the senses of the closely related lateral line organs.

† This investigation was supported in part by the National Institute of Neurological Diseases and Blindness, Public Health Service, and was aided by a contract with the Office of Naval Research and by Higgins funds alloted to Princeton University. During this study the author held Public Health Service fellowship 5 F1 MH-20, 901-02 from the National Institute of Mental Health. Permission is given for reproduction and use by the United States Government. In addition, gratitude is expressed to Drs. E. G. Wever and G. von Békésy for their suggestions on the design of the experimental tank. Acknowledgment is also given to the Office of Naval Research, Underwater Sound Reference Laboratory, Orlando, Florida, for the loan of underwater projectors.

‡ Present address: Department of Psychology, University of South Florida, Tampa, Florida.

| | Air (20°C) | Water sea (13°C) | Water distilled (20°C) | Difference Factor |
|---|---|---|---|---|
| Density (kg per cubic meter) | 1.21 | 1026 | 998 | 1000× |
| Sound Velocity (meters per second) | 343 | 1500 | 1481 | Over 4× |
| Wave Length at 100 cps ($\lambda = v/f$) | 3.43m | 15m | 14.81m | Over 4× |
| Impedance (MKS rayls) (density × sound velocity) | 415 | $1.54 \times 10^6$ | $1.48 \times 10^6$ | 3600× |
| Acoustic Intensity (watts per square meter) At 0.1 Newton per square meter (1 dyne per square centimeter) At 0.00002 Newton per square meter (0.0002 dyne per square centimeter) [(Newton per square meter)$^2$/rayls] | $2.41 \times 10^{-5}$ $9.64 \times 10^{-13}$ | $6.43 \times 10^{-5}$ $2.6 \times 10^{-16}$ | $6.75 \times 10^{-9}$ $2.7 \times 10^{-16}$ | For two acoustic waves with the same frequency and amplitude (particle displacement): 3600× Air power = Water power, means that 60× Air pressure = Water pressure |
| db at 0.1 Newton per square meter (1 dyne per square centimeter) | 0 | 35.5 | 35.5 | 35.5 db |
| db at 0.00002 Newton per square meter (0.0002 dyne per square centimeter) | -74 | -38.5 | -38.5 | 35.5 db |

FIG. 1. Comparative acoustic characteristics for air and water.

PROCEDURE

Six goldfish (*C. auratus*) were individually trained by a shock-avoidance technique to cross a barrier in an aquatic shuttle box in response to a tonal stimulus. The goldfish was chosen because it is one of the *Ostariophysi*. Poggendorf (1952), Kleerekoper and Roggenkamp (1959), and many others indicated that the *Ostariophysi*, with their swim bladder and Weberian ossicles, are the most sensitive to auditory stimuli.

Tonal stimuli were generated by a Hewlett-Packard oscillator (Model 200CD) and monitored for frequency with a Hewlett-Packard electronic counter (5532A). Amplitude was monitored with a Hewlett-Packard vacuum-tube voltmeter (Model 400D). An onset switch designed and built in our laboratory by Dr. J. F. Crump set the rise and fall time of the tonal stimuli at 0.2 sec. The signal intensity was controlled by a Daven-type attenuator (T-693), amplified by a McIntosh 30-watt audioamplifier (MC-30), and presented by two United States Navy J-9 projectors.

The unconditioned shock stimulus was provided by the 110-V a-c line stepped down through an isolation transformer and a variable autotransformer switch operated to give 0 to 24 V of alternating current across the right or left sides of the tank between screen electrodes. The shock level was found to be most effective at 20 V.

The intertrial interval was timed by a Standard Electric Time Company clock (S-60), while the trial duration and conditioned-unconditioned stimulus interval were measured by a Standard Electric clock (S-1) operated in conjunction with the tonal-stimulus onset switch.

A block diagram of the apparatus is presented in Fig. 2.

The experimental tank was a Plexiglas aquatic shuttle box. The tank dimensions were small ($4 \times 4 \times 8$ in.) in order to restrict the water mass to a minimum. A diaphragm of rho-c rubber, which has a density near that of the water, was used to ensure sonic transparency and to divide the tank into two equal cubes. A small passage hole was cut in the diaphragm to give the subjects free access to either side of the tank. Each half of the tank had screen electrodes on the side walls, wired in parallel with the other half to provide a shock system that could be switched to either the right or left half of the tank, depending on where the subject was at the onset of the unconditioned stimulus. To escape or avoid the shock, the subject had to cross through the hole in the barrier to the opposite half of the tank. The ends of the tank were composed of the speaker faces of the projectors. The two projectors were driven 180° out of phase to maintain a push-pull system, thereby giving a uniform sound field. The ambient noise level and both the magnitude and harmonic content of the tonal stimuli were determined with a Chesapeake Instrument Corporation Model BD-120 calibrated hydrophone operating into a Chesapeake Model FE-40A preamplifier and finally into a Hewlett-Packard Model 302A wave analyzer.

The six subjects were separately conditioned according to the method of Tavolga and Wodinsky (1963). The work was done in a

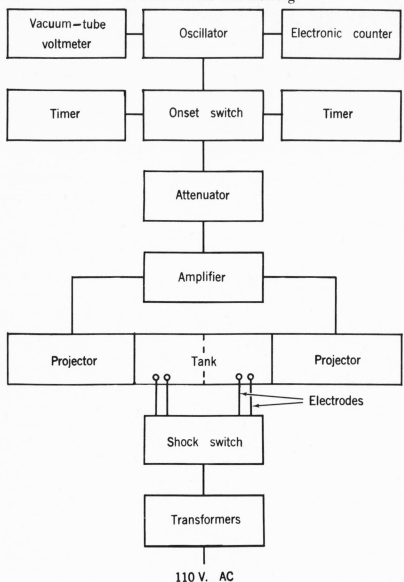

Fig. 2. Block diagram of apparatus.

soundproof room. Each subject was placed in the experimental tank, and the subjects were acclimated for several minutes under dim lighting. The tonal stimulus to be conditioned (500 cps at 25 dB above 1 dyne per sq cm) was then turned on, and 10 sec later the unconditioned shock stimulus of 1 pulse per sec was presented until the fish crossed the barrier, or until one minute of shocking elapsed, after which the subject was pushed through the barrier with a fish net. As soon as the subject's body, excluding the tail fin, had passed through the barrier, all stimuli were terminated. After an intertrial interval varied systematically among 45-sec, 60-sec, and 75-sec periods (average 60 sec), another training trial was started, and so on, until 25 trials had been completed. The subject was then removed from the tank, thus ending the session. Training at the rate of one session per day generally lasted for 25 days. Although an escape response was quickly acquired, great difficulty was experienced with avoidance conditioning by this training method until a light was employed in conjunction with the sound stimulus. Avoidance conditioning to light and sound was more rapid. After acquisition, the light was dimmed by a rheostat at the rate of 25% each day and finally turned off, so that only sound conditioning remained. The goldfish seemed especially sensitive to visual cues; therefore, care was taken that their view of the experimenter was blocked by a screen.

After the acquisition of an avoidance response to over 80% of the trials, thresholds were obtained for the range of frequencies to which the subjects would respond. At the start of a threshold-determination session, 5 to 10 reinforced trials were run in the same manner as in acquisition training. Following these initial trials, 30 nonreinforced trials were run without shock. A positive response to the sound stimulus was recorded if the subject had crossed the barrier or was part way through and moving to complete the crossing within 10 sec after the onset of the tonal stimulus. At that time the shock ordinarily would have been presented. Shock was not employed in the threshold determination trials because of the danger of experimental neurosis near and below threshold intensities. When a positive response was observed, the sound intensity was decreased by 5 dB. When no positive response was observed, the sound intensity was increased by 5 dB. This "up-and-down" or "staircase" method of threshold determination devised by the Statistical Research Group at Princeton University during World War II has been described by McCarthy (1949). The "staircase method" was used because the technique allows rapid measurement of threshold values. The threshold could then be calculated as the average of values lying midway between positive and negative responses. Usually five or six up-and-down sweeps were required to bracket the threshold, and the average of the midpoints of these sweeps was taken to be the threshold value. Cornsweet (1962) discussed this technique in a recent work.

After determination of the threshold for the training frequency, another adjacent frequency threshold was evaluated. By testing frequencies farther and farther from the training tone, the entire range of the subject above and below the training tone was determined. Reinforced trials were used after each change of frequency to decrease any effect of generalization gradient. These reinforced trials were at an intensity well above the previous threshold determination at a neighboring frequency to ensure being above the threshold intensity of the new frequency. All threshold values were determined at least twice, and some as many as ten times on different days, sometimes as far as three weeks apart to reduce any error or change with time or experience. The separate threshold determinations seldom varied as much as 15 dB and were almost consistently within 5 to 10 dB of the previous values at the same frequency. An average of the separate threshold determinations was used at the final threshold value.

Difficulty with spontaneous crossing responses was experienced until an optimum barrier-hole size and a suitable intertrial interval were found. The intertrial interval was critical, and after it was determined, the spontaneous crossings were reduced to the category of rare events. The repetitions involved in the "staircase" method of threshold determination and the replicated threshold values also controlled for spontaneous crossing errors.

RESULTS

Of the six subjects, five acquired avoidance behavior in response to tonal stimuli. Subject 1 never reached a reliable frequency of avoidance response, because of the irregularity of the initial conditioning attempts. No difficulty in training occurred with the other subjects. However, subject 4 became ill and died before thresholds could be tested. Subject 2 accidently received a dosage of quinine sulfate that was contained in a commercial preparation used to treat an infection in a nonsubject fish. Quinine, among other drugs, such as streptomycin and neomycin, is known to have a deleterious effect on the auditory sensitivity of many organisms. Results for this fish are presented in Fig. 3 because of their incidental interest. As may be seen, the curve of intensity thresholds plotted against frequency for this subject is similar in shape to the threshold functions for subjects 3, 5, and 6, but shows an average of 22 dB less sensitivity and a reduced upper range. Since these drugs are readily available in forms used to treat disorders in fishes and other aquatic animals, systematic study of their effects on auditory sensitivity in these animals would be desirable.

Figure 3 also presents the curve of intensity thresholds as a function

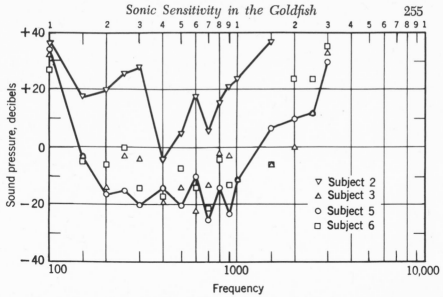

Fɪɢ. 3. Curve of intensity thresholds as a function of frequency for subjects 2 and 5, with threshold values for subjects 3 and 6 (0 dB is 1 dyne per sq cm).

of frequency for subject 5, with the points only for subjects 3 and 6. The range of responses for these subjects is between 100 and 3000 cps. The most sensitive point for subject 5 was at 25 dB below 1 dyne per sq cm, and for subject 6 was 21 dB below this level for 700 cps; subject 3 showed a maximum sensitivity at 22 dB below this level for 600 cps.

The ambient noise level in the tank was fairly uniform in the frequency range of the subjects and was 37 dB below 1 dyne per sq cm. Thus the ambient noise level is at least 12 dB below any subject threshold. Harmonic analysis indicated all overtones were 30 to 60 dB below the fundamental frequency and were below the threshold level of the subjects.

DISCUSSION

The range of the curves of intensity thresholds as a function of frequency for subject 5 and the range of the threshold values for subjects 3 and 6 in Fig. 3 was from 100 to 3000 cps. This range is in good agreement with previous work with the goldfish (*C. auratus*). Stetter (1929) found the upper limit of sensitivity of the goldfish to be 3480 cps, whereas Manning (1924) reported a range from 43 to over 2752 cps. Responses below 100 cps were also obtained for the four goldfish included in Fig. 3 of this study; however, the responses to 70, 50, and 20 cps were clearly startle reactions, such as a quick motion of the fins and body and immediate changes in orientation. Crossing behavior rarely occurred even at intensities from 35 to 60 dB above 1 dyne per sq cm. Apparently the fish were responding to tones below 100 cps, as if these low tones were a different order of stimuli, to which the crossing response was not generalized. Perhaps another sensory system, such as the lateral line organs, had become the primary receptor organs at these low frequencies. Lateral line activity in this region is expected from the studies of Jielof, Spoor, and de Vries (1952), who found that the resonant frequency of the lateral line cupular organ was about 100 cps, and from the work of Kuiper (1956), who noted that the highest microphonic output of a single cupula was about 75 to 100 cps. Tavolga and Wodinsky (1963) and Wodinsky and Tavolga (1964) reported a similar duplex behavior at the low frequencies. They found that with experience the response curves of the fishes shifted to a level about 20 dB more sensitive than their initial curves below 500 cps. The shift was attributed to a switch from the use of the inner ear to the lateral line as the primary receptor. Tavolga and Wodinsky (1965) repeated their previous studies using instead 18 blue-striped grunts (*Haemulon sciurus*) and found less-pronounced threshold shifts with experience.

The shift may not at first seem logical, because such a shift would indicate that the fishes were using their least-sensitive receptors for initial detection instead of their most-sensitive organs. However, consideration of the training procedure used in the Tavolga-Wodinsky studies and in the present experiment leads to the conclusion that training was conducted in a range where the inner ear was most sensitive. When low tones were subsequently tested, the generalization across sensory modalities to the lateral line did not immediately occur. The phenomenon of threshold shift below 500 cps was not found in the present study, and the duplex behavior reported in the present study was not evidenced in the work of Tavolga and Wodinsky. Tavolga and Wodinsky did not explore the threshold range below 100 cps, probably because their transducer was not reliable at this low range. The J-9 projectors used in the present study were electrodynamic speakers rather than crystal transducers and permitted exploration of threshold ranges below 100 cps. Manning (1924) used an unconditioned startle response instead of a conditioned crossing response, and his work was therefore unaffected by generalization difficulties when he reported a range of 43 to over 2752 cps.

The region of maximum sensitivity at 600 and 700 cps shown in Fig. 3 for subjects 3, 5, and 6 compares with the studies of Tavolga and

Wodinsky (1963) and Wodinsky and Tavolga (1964), in which an optimum sensitivity between 300 to 800 cps was reported for nine species of marine fishes, and with the findings of Poggendorf (1952), who noted an optimum swim-bladder resonance at 800 cps for the bullhead catfish (*Ameiurus nebulosus*). Tavolga (1965) also reported a frequency range of 50 to 500 cps in the swim-bladder vibrations of sound-producing fishes. Hence the goldfish region of maximum sensitivity lies near the region of swim-bladder resonance in sound-producing fishes and has adaptive significance.

The level of sensitivity of 21 to 25 dB below 1 dyne per sq cm for subjects 3, 5, and 6 of Fig. 3 compares with the Tavolga and Wodinsky (1963) and Wodinsky and Tavolga (1964) studies, in which peak sensitivity levels of 40 dB below to 10 dB above 1 dyne per sq cm were reported for nine species of marine fishes. A human air threshold of 74 dB below 1 dyne per sq cm is equivalent in intensity to an aquatic sound pressure of about 38.5 dB below 1 dyne per sq cm, as Fig. 1 shows. Thus the sensitivity values for the goldfish are near those of the human ear. Lower thresholds, 57 dB below 1 dyne per sq cm, reported by Autrum and Poggendorf (1951) for the catfish (*A. nebulosus*) were challenged by Albers (1960) and by Tavolga and Wodinsky (1963, 1965) because these are equivalent in intensity to air sound pressures of 92.5 dB below 1 dyne per sq cm, which is well below the ambient noise level of the sea (15 dB below 1 dyne per sq cm at dead calm, with no vessels or sound-producing animals in the area). Such a low threshold would seem to make the organism overly sensitive to noise. Figure 4 presents the threshold curve for subject 5 superimposed on the curves of background noise as given by Albers (1960, 1965). The sensitivity of goldfish as determined in this research would seem adequate for the aquatic environment.

Lowenstein and Roberts (1951) noted that elasmobranchs are not known to discriminate pitch above 800 cps and that they do not appear to have a morphologically obvious frequency analyzer. However, elasmobranchs are not alone in lacking such a frequency analyzer. The sensory maculae of all the fishes do not appear to be frequency analyzers. Probably fish perceive sound by synchronization of impulse and stimulus frequencies, as formulated in the frequency theory of auditory perception. To reach the 800-cps limit of discrimination in the elasmobranchs or the 3000-cps limit of the goldfish in impulse rate would require the alternation of neuron activity, as conceived by Wever (1949) in the volley principle of auditory perception, in addition to the frequency-matching response. Indeed, considering the ap-

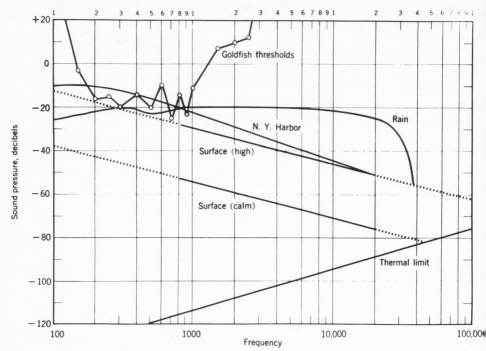

Fig. 4. Goldfish threshold curve compared with aquatic background noise (0 dB is 1 dyne per sq cm).

parent upper limit of fish hearing, fishes may not have evolved the morphological analyzer required for place perception of the higher frequencies.

The range and sensitivity of fishes, especially the goldfish of this study, are similar to the corresponding values for frogs as reported by Strother (1959, 1962) for the bullfrog (*Rana catesbeiana*) and by Weiss and Strother (1965) for the green tree frog (*Hyla cinerea*), in which galvanic skin responses to sound stimuli were recorded. The frogs, however, showed a clear tuned point of sensitivity, which was at 1400 cps for the bullfrog and at 2000 cps for the tree frog. Frishkopf and Goldstein (1963), recording from single neurons within the frog's eighth nerve, found two distinct classes of auditory units, one of which was attributed to the amphibian papilla and the other to the basilar papilla. Frishkopf and Geisler (1966) also found that neurons innervating the basilar papilla responded to a rather narrow band of frequencies centered about 1400 cps for the bullfrog. Thus the basilar papilla is clearly responsible for the tuned sensitivity peak discovered in frogs by Strother, Weiss, Frishkopf, Goldstein, and Geisler. This sensitivity peak is apparently the first development of a place-frequency analyzer in the vertebrates. The basilar papilla subsequently evolved into the cochlea of higher vertebrates. This development to more morphologically complex place-frequency analyzers was traced by Wever (1965) for the lizards. However, Moulton (1963) stated that fishes have no homolog to the basilar papilla. Thus fishes may very well perceive sound only by means of the frequency and volley principles of direct-impulse following of stimulus frequency.

Studies with the bullhead catfish, such as those of Stetter (1929), Autrum and Poggendorf (1951), and Kleerekoper and Roggenkamp (1959) previously discussed, indicate an exceptionally high upper limit of frequency perception. Stetter (1929) reported an upper limit of 13,139 cps. Such a high upper limit would seem to require a morphological analyzer for perception through the place principle. However, the accuracy of these studies can be questioned because of the subsequent work of Albers (1960), Tavolga and Wodinsky (1963), and Tavolga (1965), as already noted. Another effort at determining the auditory sensitivity curve for the bullhead catfish seems highly desirable and will be attempted by this author.

The study of Harris and van Bergeijk (1962), as already noted, and much of their subsequent work raised the problem of near-field contamination. Lowenstein (1957) stated that physiological (and here "physical" and "mathematical" should be added) data indicate only what stimuli are possible and that only behavioral data indicate what stimuli are effective. When a behavioral separation of middle ear and lateral line perception is demonstrated, as in the present study, then this evidence is primary in finding effective stimuli. If the near-field and far-field constructs do not correspond to behavioral evidence, then they must be irrelevant to the organism and should be abandoned. The main utility of the near-field and far-field constructs seems to have been for localization. Van Bergeijk (1964) claimed that fishes could not localize in the far field, because they had essentially only one receptor and did not possess two isolated ears. This claim applies for instantaneous localization but neglects the fact that, with rotation or motion, a fish or a human could localize readily with only one effective ear. Thus studies such as that of Nelson, presented at this lateral line conference, clearly indicate the phenomenon of localization but not the mechanism so long as movement of the fish is not controlled. The best method for studying the auditory or vibration sensitivity of fish is still to develop a tank with a uniform sound field and proceed behaviorally, in spite of the presence of the near field.

The tank developed in this study was an improvement over other tanks used to date. However, a 10-dB attenuation of sound was measured from the speaker faces to the barrier, and about 8 dB of this attenuation occurred within a few centimeters of the speaker face. From 2- to 5-dB changes in sound level were detected near the side walls, top, and bottom of the tank. The subjects did not swim close to the speaker faces or tank boundaries in any systematic manner but generally remained near the center of the two halves of the tank except when crossing the barrier. Thus the sound field about the fish was reasonably uniform.

No attempt was made in this study to separate surgically the lateral line function from that of the inner ear. Some behavioral isolation of these two senses occurred below 100 cps, as was previously noted. However, independent study of the relative role of these two senses is highly desirable, and this author intends to pursue this line of investigation by conditioning a crossing response to tones below 100 cps in the region of lateral line sensitivity of goldfish and obtaining a lateral line threshold curve.

REFERENCES

Albers, V. M. (1960). *Underwater Acoustics Handbook*. Pennsylvania State University Press, University Park.

────── (1965). *Underwater Acoustics Handbook* II. Pennsylvania State University Press, University Park.

Autrum, H., and D. Poggendorf (1951). Messung der absoluten Horschwelle bei Fischen (*Amiurus nebulosus*). *Naturwiss*. 38, 434-435.

Bergeijk, W. A. van (1964). Directional and nondirectional hearing in fish, in *Marine Bio-Acoustics* (W. N. Tavolga, ed.). Permagon Press, Oxford, pp. 281-299.

Cornsweet, T. N. (1962). The staircase method in psychophysics. *Am. J. Psychol.* 75, 485-491.

Fletcher, H. (1940). Auditory patterns. *Rev. Mod. Phys.* 12, 47-65.

Frishkopf, L. S., and D. C. Geisler (1966). Peripheral origin of auditory responses recorded from the eighth nerve of the bullfrog. *J. Acoust. Soc. Am.* 40, 469.

────── and M. H. Goldstein, Jr. (1963). Responses to acoustic stimuli from single units in the eighth nerve of the bullfrog. *J. Acoust. Soc. Am.* 35, 1219-1228.

Harris, G. G., and W. A. van Bergeijk (1962). Evidence that the lateral line organ responds to near-field displacements of sound sources in water. *J. Acoust. Soc. Am.* 34, 1831-1841.

Jielof, R., A. Spoor, and H. de Vries (1952). The microphonic activity of the lateral line. *J. Physiol.* (*London*), 116, 137-157.

Kleerekoper, H., and P. A. Roggenkamp (1959). An experimental study on the effect of the swimbladder on hearing sensitivity in *Ameiurus nebulosus nebulosus* (Lesueur). *Can. J. Zool.* 37, 1-8.

Kuiper, J. W. (1956). The microphonic effect of the lateral line organ. *Publication*

Biophysical Group Natuurkundig Laboratory, Groningen, Netherlands, 1-159.
Lowenstein, O. E. (1957). The sense organs: the acousticolateralis system, in *The Physiology of Fishes*, Vol. 2 (M. E. Brown, ed.). Academic Press, New York, pp. 155-186.

—— and T. D. M. Roberts (1951). The localization and analysis of the responses to vibration from the isolated elasmobranch labyrinth. A contribution to the problem of the evolution of hearing in vertebrates. *J. Physiol. (London)*, 114, 471-489.

McCarthy, P. J. (1949). A class of methods for estimating reaction to stimuli of varying severity. *J. Educ. Psychol.* 40, 143-156.

Manning, F. B. (1924). Hearing in the goldfish in relation to the structure of its ear. *J. Exptl. Zool.* 41, 5-20.

Moulton, J. M. (1963). Acoustic behaviour of fishes, in *Acoustic Behaviour of Animals* (R. G. Busnel, ed.). Elsevier, Amsterdam, pp. 655-693.

Poggendorf, D. (1952). Die absoluten Hörschwellen des Zwergwelses (*Amiurus nebulosus*) und Beiträge zur Physik des Weberschen Apparatus der Ostariophysen. *Z. Vergleich. Physiol.* 34, 222-257.

Stetter, H. (1929). Untersuchungen über den Gehörsinn der Fische, besonders von *Phoxinus laevis* L. und *Amiurus nebulosus* Raf. *Z. Vergleich. Physiol.* 9, 339-447.

Strother, W. F. (1959). The electrical activity of the auditory mechanism in the bullfrog (*Rana catesbeiana*). *J. Comp. Physiol. Psych.* 52, 157-167.

—— (1962). Hearing in frogs. *J. Audit. Res.* 2, 279-286.

Tavolga, W. N. (1965). Review of Marine Bio-Acoustics. Tech. Rept. NAVTRADEVCEN-1212-1.

—— (ed.) (1967). *Marine Bio-Acoustics.* Pergamon Press, Oxford.

—— and J. Wodinsky (1963). Auditory capacities in fishes. Pure tone thresholds in nine species of marine teleosts. *Bull. Am. Museum Nat. Hist.* 126, 179-239.

—— and J. Wodinsky (1965). Auditory capacities in fishes: threshold variability in the blue-striped grunt, *Haemulon sciurus. Animal Behavior* 13, 301-311.

Weiss, B. A., and W. F. Strother (1965). Hearing in the green treefrog (*Hyla cinerea cinerea*). *J. Audit. Res.* 5, 297-305.

Wever, E. G. (1949). *Theory of Hearing.* Wiley, New York.

—— (1965). Structure and function of the lizard ear. *J. Audit. Res.,* 5, 331-371.

Wodinsky, J., and W. N. Tavolga (1964). Sound detection in teleost fishes, in *Marine Bio-Acoustics* (W. N. Tavolga, ed.). Permagon Press, Oxford, pp. 269-280.

## COMMENTS

ENGER: About how young were the goldfish?

WEISS: They were very young, and about 1½ in. long.

ENGER: The reason I asked this was that I obtained a similar threshold curve for goldfish with the higher-frequency cutoff also at 3 kc, rather than at 5 kc as Tavolga did. I was trying to find some correlation between results of the perhaps three or four experimenters with threshold curves for goldfish.

WEISS: Did you use a behavioral technique?

ENGER: I used a classical conditioning technique with shock and startle. The upper frequencies were about the same as yours, but at lower frequencies the threshold curve had much less of a slope, with the level at 40 cps about the same as your level at 100 cps. The goldfish, however, were about 13 to 15 cm in length.

Just one other comment—in investigating the higher frequencies a bit further at a little higher intensity than what you have, the threshold curve levels off up to 20 kc.

WEISS: Well, the reason for that leveling off might be that you reached some sort of pain threshold or a damage area.

ENGER: I am sure that is the reason, or something analogous. You can hear all the sounds if you put your ear in the water.

WEISS: Do you mean that there is some sort of rectifier device?

ENGER: There is apparently no sense of frequency, just a general sensing of high pitch, and I would imagine that an analogous situation exists for the goldfish.

Perhaps size could have something to do with our different results at the low frequencies. In doing this work, it might be well to note the size and age of the animal we are working with. We may find some differences in response with size and age.

WEISS: It seems to me that the low-frequency difference can be attributed to use of the essentially unconditioned startle response, enhanced by association with shock. As noted, Manning (1924) also did a study using startle responses, in which he found responses from 43 to over 2752 cps. A startle response automatically generalizes across modalities and so occurs throughout the sonic range of the goldfish. I think you can get the differentiation between lateral line and inner ear sensory responses only with conditioning in one modality and the resulting lack of generalization for the other modality.

TAVOLGA: I am working on this now, too. I am only half through, but my thresholds run about 30 dB below yours, using an enclosed speaker on the order of that which Dr. Parvulescu suggested and similar to the one Dr. Enger used. I also wonder whether you got thresholds that were masked by a considerable amount of ambient noise, which could effect the threshold substantially.

Now, you mentioned the startle response at low frequencies—that you did not get avoidance but got a startle response. I am curious about how you turned on the sound. What was the mechanism?

WEISS: In the first place, I worry about your intensity level being much below mine, for the reason I stated—the 35.5-dB difference in impedance between air and water. If you are getting thresholds quite a bit below the level of the goldfish curves just presented, the fish will be sensitive to pressure levels much lower than our own ears can detect, and our own ear is much more developed than the ear of the fish.

However, there are some discrepancies, which are no doubt due to a difference in technique. Ambient noise is not a problem, because the tank was in a soundproof room and had an ambient noise level at least 12 dB below the most-sensitive thresholds. Harmonics were down 30 to 60 dB and were well below the threshold levels at their frequencies. I think the problem is in the use of shock. I used shock only during reinforcement trials during conditioning and the beginning of testing at a new frequency, while well above threshold intensity. The shock is then stopped. This is done because, when the subliminal level is reached and the tone is turned on, the fish does not perceive the tone. Thus, to the fish this is essentially an intertrial interval, not a trial, and the correct response is not crossing. However, if the shock is continued during threshold determinations as Dr. Tavolga does, then the fish will be shocked for that correct response. The situation of pushing the organism beyond its capabilities may be created much as Pavlov did in his work on experimental neurosis. The tones were turned on by an electronic switch which was built in the laboratory and which had a rise and fall time of 0.2 sec.

MYRBERG: A startle response can be conditioned, and you can get the same threshold. Therefore, I am not sure if this generalization or lack of generalization fits specifically with regard to the startle response and the delay that you have. The animal might just be starting to receive that stimulus, and now it might be an unconditioned stimulus.

WEISS: The startle response can be conditioned as any physiological response can. However, there is also an unconditioned element involved in the startle response to tones. The fish were not conditioned to startle but to cross from one side of the tank to the other through a hole in the barrier within 10 sec, the elapsed time from the onset of the tone to the onset of the shock. At the lower frequencies, below 100 cps, no crossing responses occurred, but only startle behavior. Startle behavior is very clear; there is no question about it. The fish changes the direction in which it was swimming, fin motions change, depth of swimming changes, etc. The crossing response, which is also very clear and extinction-resistant, was conditioned to occur within the same 10 sec; therefore the time delay was long enough. No doubt the fish's startle reaction was unconditioned. The point is that the conditioned response was not evidenced below 100 cps, but the startle response indicated that the fish perceived the tones as different stimuli, probably because of a switch to a new modality—namely, the lateral line system.

VAN BERGEIJK: Did I hear you say that the frog is the first animal in which the place mechanism appears?

WEISS: I am attributing the evolution of a place mechanism of hearing to the amphibians as a whole. The frog is the one we have investigated, but there may be other such amphibians.

VAN BERGEIJK: The point is that this is a bit unlikely—although I still maintain it is so. But Tavolga's results demonstrate critical bands in fish. You must have a place principle in fish to account for critical bands. I explained how it could be done (by differential vibration of the otolith) in fishes. The evolving of the place principle is a lot older than the amphibians, I believe.

WEISS: The attempt by Tavolga (1967) to demonstrate critical bands in fish was not conclusive. He demonstrated that narrow and broad bands did not have different masking effects, thus concluding that a critical band of 200 cps or less existed. However, his evidence might also indicate that no critical bands existed at all. The existence of critical bands in fish would still not indicate a place mechanism of hearing. Fletcher's (1940) use of critical bands to calculate the place location on the basilar membrane already assumed the existence of the place mechanism, and thus his findings cannot be used to show that where critical bands are present a place mechanism exists. In addition, a place mechanism based on differential vibration of the solid otolith to stimulate separately the hair cells embedded in the otolith does not seem reasonably possible.

ENGER: It seems to me that there must be zero displacement all the time, making threshold measurements more meaningless than they have been for the rest of us. Furthermore, you are worried about the energy in fish thresholds as compared with that of man. Well, as far as I know, you must go down to 76 dB below a microbar to approach the human threshold. Is this right?

WEISS: The difference in density between the fish's swim bladder and bones and the water, as well as the inertia of the fish, prevents a zero displacement because of the fish's being moved with the water. The goldfish thresholds are actually about 25 dB below 1 dyne per sq cm. Add to that 35.5 dB, because of the different impedance of water, and that gives 60.5 dB below 1 dyne per sq cm, which is close to the human air threshold.

HARRIS: I am wondering about the quality of your stimulus. You have the two diaphragms of the speakers 180° out of phase. It seems to me that what you are getting is almost a perfect near field.

WEISS: You said "perfect." I do not like the word "perfect." There is also far field present, although I am not sure these terms are apropos in a push-pull system. Near field and far field are good problems for acousticians, but these concepts have unnecessarily intimidated many behaviorists. When the question of what the fish is perceiving is raised, then behavioral evidence is primary. At lower frequencies, the fish are perceiving by a different modality; they are not generalizing. The upper frequencies are probably perceived by the inner ear, whereas the lower frequencies are sensed by the lateral line system. Now, if you want to argue that one system is sensitive to near field and the other to far field, then these concepts must conform to the behavioral differentiation. If they do not, then *they* must be changed or abandoned—not the fish.

LATERAL LINE DETECTORS (P. Cahn, ed.), 265–273, © 1967 Indiana University Press

# 17 EVIDENCE OF SENSITIVITY TO ACOUSTIC DISPLACEMENTS IN THE LEMON SHARK, *NEGAPRION BREVIROSTRIS* (POEY)†

ARNOLD BANNER

Institute of Marine Science
University of Miami
Miami, Florida

In recent years interest in the capabilities and mechanics of elasmo-branch hearing has increased (see Wisby et al., in Tavolga, 1964). Sharks have been found to be capable of orienting toward a sound source from distances of up to 200 m (Wisby and Nelson, 1964). Also, audiograms have been obtained for the bull shark, *Carcharinus leucas* (Kritzler and Wood, 1961); the hammerhead shark, *Sphyrna lewini* (Olla, 1962); and the lemon shark, *Negaprion brevirostris* (Nelson, 1965).

In all previous studies, sound intensities have been measured as pressures, not as displacements, although the significance of each parameter has not yet been determined. Unfortunately, it is not practical to calculate displacement from pressure measurements made under laboratory conditions. Therefore, if sharks are not pressure-sensitive, such measurements are of little value.

Actually, displacement sensitivity seems probable. Lowenstein and Roberts (1951) demonstrated a sensitivity to vibrations of the inner ear of an elasmobranch, *Raja clavata*. Such vibrations could be caused by water-borne displacements. In addition, sharks possess well-developed lateral line systems; these systems have been found to be displacement-sensitive in those bony fishes thus far studied (Harris and van Bergeijk, 1962; Suckling and Suckling, 1964). Also, there is a notice-

† Contribution No. 807 from the Institute of Marine Science, University of Miami. This paper constitutes a report of research done with financial support from the U.S. Office of Naval Research, Contract NONR 4008(10). The author gratefully acknowledges the advice and criticism offered by Drs. Arthur A. Myrberg, Jr., and Warren J. Wisby, and technical assistance by Mr. Joseph D. Richard.

able lack of evidence of an acoustic-pressure receptor in elasmobranchs.

A study was designed, therefore, to determine whether auditory thresholds of the lemon shark, *N. brevirostris,* when measured under laboratory conditions, were a result of pressure or displacement (i.e., displacement, velocity, or acceleration) sensitivity.

MATERIALS

The sound-producing equipment (see Fig. 1) consisted of a Hewlett-Packard audiofrequency oscillator (Model 200 CD) connected through

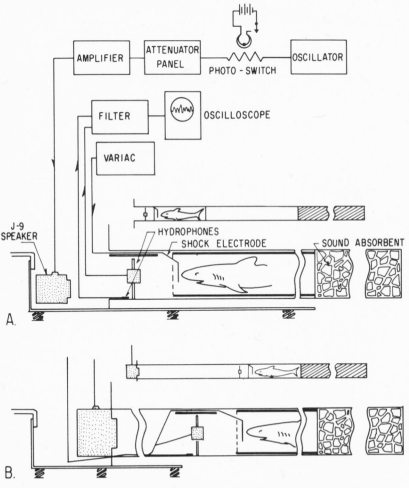

Fɪɢ. 1. Audiometric apparatus: arrangements A (transducer not attached to tube) and B (transducer attached to tube); shark-speaker distance constant.

a photoswitch to an attenuator panel. The signal was then passed through a Heathkit amplifier (W-5M) with fixed gain. The equipment was placed in this order to maintain electrical noise constant over trial and intertrial periods. The amplifier drove a grounded J-9 underwater speaker.

The quality and intensity of the sine-wave signal and ambient noise levels were monitored in both the pressure and displacement parameters. Outputs from both the pressure hydrophone and the acceleration transducer (see below) were passed through a Krohn-Hite Model 330M bandpass filter. The signal and filtered noise were observed and measured on a Tektronix Type 502 dual-beam oscilloscope.

Two calibrated pressure hydrophones were used (Atlantic Research Corporation, BC32C; Gulton Industries, SSQ23). The acceleration transducer (Fig. 2) consisted of a Hall-Sears Model HS-1 seismic accelerometer, rigidly mounted in a Plexiglas disc. The disc was suspended from three lengths of thin nylon line, within a Plexiglas tube, so that it moved freely in the indicated direction of sensitivity. Accelerations of the disc were transformed into voltage output from which displacements were calculated. These values were corrected after provisional calibration of the device. Since only relative values of pressure and displacement were required, absolute calibration was not attempted.

The sound tunnel consisted of Pyrex glass tubing with an inside diameter of 15 cm and a total length of 6.5 m. Sound absorbent (sponges) filled one end of the tunnel for a length of 4 m. The speaker was

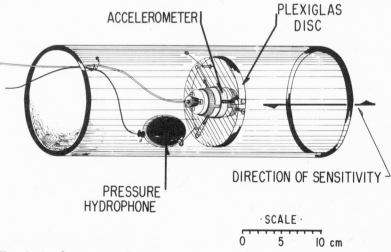

FIG. 2. Acceleration transducer.

mounted at the opposite end; the test subject and monitoring transducers were situated about 1.5 m from the speaker. A gradual flow of
seawater was maintained through the tunnel during the experiments.

METHODS

The relationship of displacement to pressure was found to vary with
changes in the arrangement of the subject and the sound source within
the experimental apparatus. Two such arrangements were chosen in
which the displacement-pressure ratios were found to be distinctly
different (Fig. 1, A and B). In arrangement A the speaker was not
sealed to the mouth of the tunnel, and the animal and hydrophones
were positioned near the tunnel mouth; in B the speaker was sealed to
the tunnel mouth, and the animal and hydrophones were moved back
toward the sound absorbent. Corresponding to these two arrangements,
I expected to find two thresholds when monitoring the nonsignificant
parameter but only one relatively constant threshold for the significant
parameter.

All the test subjects, 8 females and 11 males, were collected from the
Florida Keys. They ranged from 40 to 65 cm in total length. Each subject was tested several times, in both arrangements of the apparatus
and at several frequencies. The experiments covered a period of six
months and were conducted at virtually all times of day.

The test frequencies chosen (20, 320, 640, and 1000 cps) were considered representative of the auditory range of the lemon shark as
determined by previous experiments.

A behavioral response, sudden shutting of the jaws and brief cessation of respiration, was used in the determination of auditory sensitivity. This response could be elicited by high-intensity sound prior to
any training. To attain threshold levels, however, it was necessary to
negatively reinforce absence of this response to the stimulus situation
with an electric shock. Determinations made using this technique are
in agreement with those made using a conditioned heart-rate response
(see Wisby et al., 1964).

Testing was conducted as follows: sound intensity at any test frequency was attenuated in 2 dB steps until the animal no longer responded to the stimulus, even after reinforcement with shock. The
sound intensity was then increased to a level at which the animal did
respond, then once again attenuated to the level of no response. The
lowest level at which the animal responded was considered its threshold.

Potential secondary cues were controlled by having the observer and all read-out equipment in an adjoining room. The reflection of the animal was observed through binoculars focused onto a mirror located in the test room. All electrical leads around and in contact with the test apparatus were grounded. The problem of vibration as a source of stimulation is discussed below.

RESULTS

Threshold values obtained from both arrangements of the test apparatus were plotted both as displacements and as pressures (Figs. 3-6). Two distinct groups of pressure values can be seen at both 20 and 320 cps, while displacement values from both arrangements form essentially one group at each frequency. At 640 and 1000 cps, increased overlap of pressure values is seen. Therefore, the significance of the difference between the mean pressures from arrangements A and B, and of the difference between the mean displacements from these arrangements, were statistically analyzed. Results of a Student's *t*-test

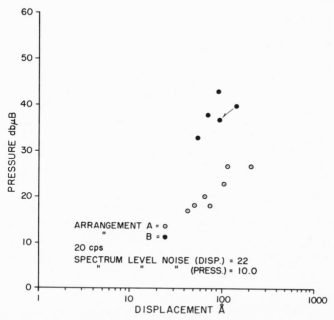

FIG. 3. Threshold values for lemon sharks tested in arrangements A and B.

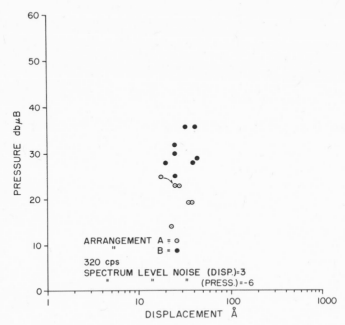

FIG. 4. Threshold values for lemon sharks tested in arrangements A and B.

(Fig. 7) show that the difference between the mean pressures is significant (5% level) at all frequencies, whereas the difference between the mean displacements is not significant. From this I conclude that the sharks responded to displacements; pressure values did not reflect true thresholds but were simply levels associated with displacement thresholds.

Vibration of the sound tunnel was considered a possible interfering stimulus. A series of experiments was therefore conducted in which the ratio of vibration to displacement magnitudes was altered and thresholds in each parameter were observed. As with the previously described experiment, I expected two groups of threshold values in the nonsignificant parameter but only one group in the significant parameter. Results of a *t*-test analysis of differences between mean vibration values from arrangements A and B and of differences between the corresponding mean displacement values are summarized in Fig. 8. Again, displacements formed one group of values, while there were two groups of

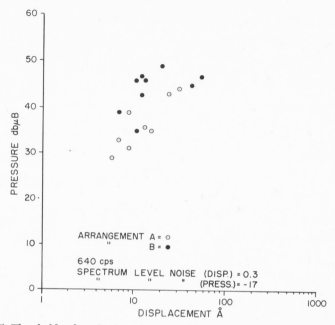

F<small>IG</small>. 5. Threshold values for lemon sharks tested in arrangements A and B.

vibration values at both test frequencies. This indicates response to the displacement rather than the vibration stimulus.

The displacement thresholds obtained were higher than those one might expect from an animal capable of homing in on a sound source from 200 m. Nelson (1965) found that increases in ambient noise level masked auditory stimuli, thereby effectively raising thresholds in the lemon shark. Masking may have been responsible for the unexpectedly high displacement thresholds, since laboratory ambient noise levels (see Figs. 3-6) were higher than those normally occurring in the open ocean (Wenz, 1962).

CONCLUSIONS

Evidence has been obtained that young lemon sharks respond either to acoustic displacements or to associated functions at frequencies between 20 and 1000 cps. This alone does not eliminate the possibility of

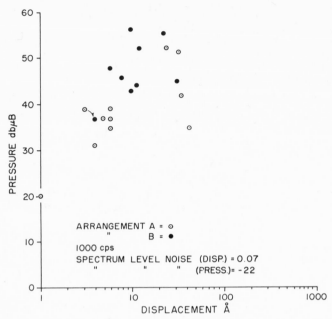

FIG. 6. Threshold values for lemon sharks tested in arrangements A and B.

| FREQUENCY | ARRANGEMENT | N | X̄ DISPLACEMENT * | X̄ PRESSURE * | s X̄ DISPLACEMENT | s X̄ PRESSURE | t DISPLACEMENT | t PRESSURE | p DISPLACEMENT | p PRESSURE |
|---|---|---|---|---|---|---|---|---|---|---|
| 20 cps | A | 7 | .40 | .90 | .093 | .16 | .53 | 5.3 | >.5 | <.05 |
|  | B | 5 | .34 | 5.9 | .022 | 1.1 |  |  |  |  |
| 320 cps | A | 6 | .26 | .04 | .020 | .006 | .98 | 1.8 | >.3 | <.001 |
|  | B | 9 | .30 | .21 | .033 | .076 |  |  |  |  |
| 640 cps | A | 8 | .21 | .22 | .050 | .050 | .94 | 3.3 | >.3 | <.01 |
|  | B | 9 | .30 | .52 | .081 | .075 |  |  |  |  |
| 1000 cps | A | 9 | .19 | .36 | .12 | .20 | .099 | 2.2 | >.9 | <.05 |
|  | B | 11 | .20 | .84 | .073 | .11 |  |  |  |  |

**✱ IN MILLIVOLTS HYDROPHONE OUTPUT**

FIG. 7. Student's *t*-test of threshold values: displacement and pressure.

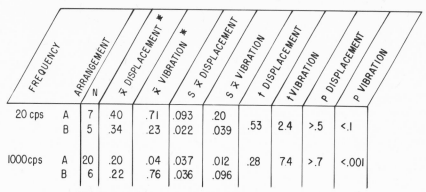

| FREQUENCY | ARRANGEMENT | N | X̄ DISPLACEMENT* | X̄ VIBRATION* | s X̄ DISPLACEMENT | s X̄ VIBRATION | t DISPLACEMENT | t VIBRATION | P DISPLACEMENT | P VIBRATION |
|---|---|---|---|---|---|---|---|---|---|---|
| 20 cps | A | 7 | .40 | .71 | .093 | .20 | .53 | 2.4 | >.5 | <.1 |
|  | B | 5 | .34 | .23 | .022 | .039 |  |  |  |  |
| 1000 cps | A | 20 | .20 | .04 | .037 | .012 | .28 | 7.4 | >.7 | <.001 |
|  | B | 6 | .22 | .76 | .036 | .096 |  |  |  |  |

✳IN MILLIVOLTS  HYDROPHONE OUTPUT

FIG. 8. Student's *t*-test of threshold values: displacement and vibration.

sensitivity to acoustic pressures. The displacement thresholds presented are representative of signal-to-noise sensitivity and probably are not indicative of absolute sensory thresholds. It is suggested that future marine bioacoustic studies record sound intensities as displacements as well as pressures.

## REFERENCES

Harris, G. G., and W. A. van Bergeijk (1962). Evidence that the lateral-line organ responds to near-field displacements of sound sources in water. *J. Acoust. Soc. Am.* 34(12), 1831-1841.

Kritzler, H., and L. Wood (1961). Provisional audiogram for the shark, *Carcharhinus leucas. Science* 133(3463), 1480-1482.

Lowenstein, O. E., and T. D. M. Roberts (1951). The localization and analysis of the responses to vibration from the isolated elasmobranch labyrinth. Contribution to the problem of the evolution of hearing in vertebrates. *J. Physiol.* (*London*) 1144(4), 471-489.

Nelson, D. R. (1965). Hearing and acoustic orientation in the lemon shark, *Negaprion brevirostris* (Poey), and other large sharks. Doctoral Dissertation, Library, University of Miami, Miami, Fla., 150 p.

Olla, B. (1962). The perception of sound in small hammerhead sharks, *Sphyrna lewini.* Masters Thesis, Library, University of Hawaii, Honolulu.

Suckling, E. E., and J. A. Suckling (1964). Lateral line as a vibration receptor. *J. Acoust. Soc. Am.* 36(11), 2214-2216.

Wenz, G. M. (1962). Acoustic ambient noise in the ocean: spectra and sources. *J. Acoust. Soc. Am.* 34(12), 1936-1956.

Wisby, W. J., and D. R. Nelson (1964). Airplane observations of acoustic orientation in sharks. Abstract distributed at A.F.S. Conference, Sept. 1964.

———, J. D. Richard, D. R. Nelson, and S. H. Gruber (1964). Sound perception in elasmobranchs, in *Marine Bio-acoustics* (W. N. Tavolga, ed.). Pergamon Press, Oxford, pp. 255-266.

# IV THE LATERAL LINE AND ELECTRORECEPTION

LATERAL LINE DETECTORS (P. Cahn, ed.), 277–293, © 1967 Indiana University Press

# 18 THE FUNCTION OF THE AMPULLAE OF LORENZINI OF ELASMOBRANCHS

RICHARD W. MURRAY

Department of Zoology and Comparative Physiology
University of Birmingham
Birmingham, England

More than seventy years ago, Fuchs (1895) applied the then novel technique of galvanometric recording to the trigeminal nerves of *Torpedo* in an attempt to determine the function of the lateral line canals and the ampullae of Lorenzini. To the lateral line and to Savi's vesicles he rightly attributed an adapting mechanical sensitivity, but he concluded that the ampullae could not be sense organs after all and were probably secretory. For many years after that time, little new information emerged, and it is only quite recently that a satisfactory picture of the function of the ampullae has begun to form, mainly as a result of the work of Dijkgraaf and Kalmijn (1963; as well as Chapter 7 in the present volume). In behavioral experiments the sensitivity of dogfish (*Scyliorhinus canicula*) to weak electrical stimuli has been clearly shown, together with the role of the ampullae in mediating this response. In the first series of experiments, unconditioned responses (eye movements) were elicited with artificial square-wave electrical stimuli at 5 per sec, with a whole-fish threshold gradient in the water of 0.1 $\mu$V per cm and a local threshold (the area affected was a few square centimeters) of 3 $\mu$V per cm. Further experiments involving slowing of heartbeat showed that the absolute sensitivity was to stimuli as small as 0.01 $\mu$V per cm. However, an obvious biological function has only been suggested by the results of their latest experiments, in which food-searching and digging have been elicited in swimming dogfish by means of a stimulus current passed between electrodes buried in the sandy floor of the aquarium tank.

In order to understand the functioning and usefulness of a sense organ, behavioral observations can be supplemented by anatomical and physiological studies, and it is these which will be further examined here.

MORPHOLOGY

The distribution of the ampullae over the body of representatives of the two main groups of the cartilaginous fish (rays and sharks) is illustrated in Fig. 1A and B. Since the direction and length of the tubes are important, as will be shown below, the distribution for the two examples has been redrawn in Fig. 2 with the projection onto the horizontal plane of the tube openings shown relative to the ampullae —the latter all being superimposed at the center of the diagram. Only those tubes facing to one side have been drawn, which, as Fig. 1 shows, is not the same thing as the tubes lying on one side of the body.

In both groups the ampullae themselves are located in the head

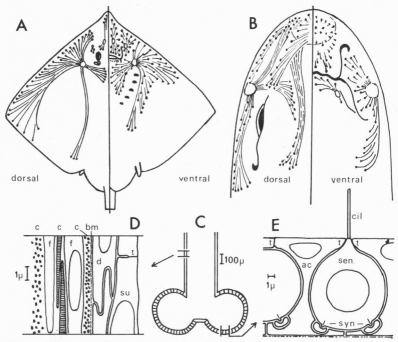

Fɪɢ. 1. Aspects of the anatomy of the ampullae of Lorenzini. (A) Dorsal and ventral view of the system in *Raja clavata*. (B) Dorsal and ventral view in *Scyliorhinus canicula*. (C) Diagrammatic L.S. of an ampulla and its adjacent tube to provide the location of D and E. (D) Ultrastructure of the tube wall. (E) Ultrastructure of the sensory epithelium. ac, accessory or supporting cell; bm, basement membrane; c, collagen fibers; cil, cilium; d, deep epithelial cell; f, fibroblast; sen, sensory cell; su, superficial epithelial cell; syn, synaptic apparatus; t, "tight junctions." (A, after Murray, 1960; B, after Dijkgraaf and Kalmijn, 1963; D, E, after Waltman, 1966.)

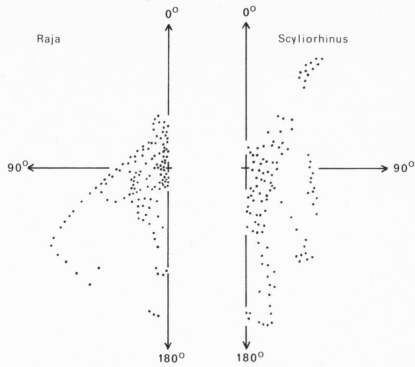

Fig. 2. The distribution of tube openings plotted relative to the position of the ampulla, to illustrate their "all-round cover." 0° represents anteriorly and 180° posteriorly directed tubes. For a ray and a dogfish, both dorsal and ventral tubes are shown, but only those pointing to one side (redrawn from data of Fig. 1, A and B).

region, so that the nerve pathways are all of approximately equal length, and "all-round cover" is provided, although the distribution of the longer tubes is more limited. The restriction to the head of the tubes and openings also in dogfish, together with their different body shape, results in the all-round cover being obtained by overlap and crossing of tubes, whereas in the rays most of the tubes radiate from the head in a simpler fashion.

Some of the detail of the tube wall and ampulla (where the sensory epithelium is located) is illustrated in Fig. 1C, D, and E. The tube wall has a very high electrical resistance (Waltman, 1966), as will be detailed later, and probably responsible for this are the "tight junctions" or regions of membrane fusion between the superficial epithelial cells of the wall and between the apical margins of the sensory and supporting cells of the sensory epithelium. The sensory epithelium itself is clearly very unlike that of typical lateral line organs (Flock, Chap. 12 of this volume). The main points of difference are that the sensory cells are rounded and lie almost entirely within the epithelium, surrounded by the supporting cells; the apex of the sensory cell reaches the surface only at one point where·a single cilium protrudes into the jelly. [This has been seen in *Raja* by Waltman (1966), but not in *Torpedo* by Barets and Szabo (1962).] The cilium has an $8 + 1$ or $9 + 0$ pattern of fibrils; there is a complex synaptic apparatus of ribbon, vesicles, and gutter (Barets and Szabo, 1962; Waltman, 1966). Finally, no efferent fibers or nerve endings have been found.

The ionic composition of the jelly is very approximately equal to that of seawater (Murray and Potts, 1961) and is therefore about twice as concentrated as that of the body fluids. Isotonicity of the latter is, of course, maintained with urea (Smith, 1929). Including a separate estimate of $Ca^{++} + Mg^{++}$ made in *Raja ocellata* (Murray, unpublished), the jelly composition per kg of water is approximately: $Na^+$, 445 m$M$; $K^+$, 12.5 m$M$; $Ca^{++} + Mg^{++}$, 50 m$M$; $Cl^-$, 580 m$M$; urea, 75 m$M$. The jelly itself is mucopolysaccharide in nature (Doyle, 1963), with only small amounts of protein.

### ELECTRICAL PROPERTIES

The passive electrical properties of the tubes are described by Waltman (1966), together with the conclusions to be drawn from these. Essentially, the tube wall and sensory epithelium have such a high resistance that a d-c voltage applied to the end of the tube relative to the body tissues is not attenuated significantly and appears virtually unchanged as a potential difference across the sensory epithelium: for example, the space constant of large tubes in *R. clavata* is 50 to 100 cm, i.e., several times the tube length. Moreover, skin resistance is relatively low compared with tissue resistances (see Table 1), so that a fish placed in a potential gradient in seawater will experience a comparable potential gradient through its tissues. This is completely unlike the situation in mormyrid fishes (Bennett, Chap. 20 in this volume), where the inside of the fish is approximately equipotential. The result of these two facts is that in a uniform external gradient it is the length and direction of a tube that determines the stimulus intensity at the sensory epithelium, rather than the position of the opening on the surface of the fish, as is the case in the mormyrids. The receptor threshold, for example, will therefore be given by the threshold external potential gradient multiplied by the length of the tube in line with the gradient.

TABLE 1. TISSUE RESISTANCES IN ELASMOBRANCHS

| Genus | Tissue | Resistivity ($\Omega \cdot$cm) | Specific resistance ($\Omega \cdot$cm$^2$) | References |
|---|---|---|---|---|
| | Seawater, 33.2% | 22 | | Thomas, Thompson, and Utterback, 1934 |
| *Raja* | Ampulla jelly | 24–25 | | Murray and Potts, 1961; Wattman, 1966 |
| *Raja* | Body fluids | 48 | | Murray and Potts, 1961 |
| *Raja* | Cartilage | 47–66 | | Murray, unpublished |
| *Raja* | Muscle | | | |
| | longitudinal | 110–200[a] | | Murray, unpublished |
| | transverse | 250–800[a] | | Murray, unpublished |
| *Raja* | Skin | | | |
| | dorsal | | 75–125[b] | Murray, unpublished |
| | ventral | | 75–150[b] | Murray, unpublished |
| | Skin | | 400–2800 | Waltman, 1966 |
| *Torpedo* | Skin | | | |
| | dorsal | | 1430–2440[c] | Bennett, 1961 |
| | | | 148–193[d] | Bennett, 1961 |
| | ventral | | 490–1150[c] | Bennett, 1961 |
| | | | 60–64[d] | Bennett, 1961 |
| *Squalus* | Skin | | 370 | Bennett, 1961 |
| *Raja* | Ampulla tube wall[e] | | 6 × 10$^6$ | Waltman, 1966 |

[a] Low values, fish span 30 cm; high values, fish span 22 cm.
[b] Low values, fish span 22 cm; high values, fish span 30 cm.
[c] Skin not covering electric organ.
[d] Skin covering electric organ.
[e] Specific capacity, 0.4 $\mu$F per sq cm.

The second main property of the tube is the capacity of the wall, and this, in conjunction with the longitudinal resistance of the jelly in the tube and the other tissue resistances that make up the effective source impedance of the stimulus, determines the a-c response of the system. As Waltman has shown, the time constants are relatively high, especially those of the larger tubes; therefore high frequencies and transients are much attenuated and square stimuli are rounded off. For example, a 3-dB attenuation would occur in 20-cm tubes at 3 cps, and in 1-cm tubes at 300 cps; or in a 10-cm tube, the effective potential across the receptors following a 10-msec pulse would be reduced to one-third and its peak delayed by 16 msec. It may therefore be useful to the fish to have long tubes for detecting relatively long stimuli with a very low threshold, and to have short tubes for detecting transients.

ELECTROPHYSIOLOGY

One puzzling feature of the ampullae has been the variety of stimuli to which sensitive impulse-discharge responses are given. It is this variety which has made the study of behavioral responses so important,

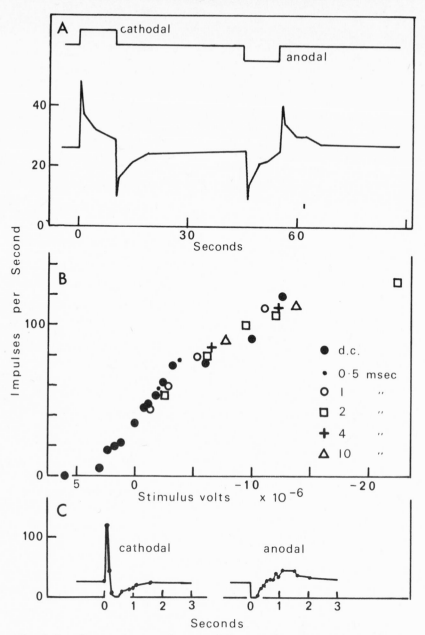

FIG. 3. Impulse activity in single units of the ampullae of Lorenzini in response to electrical stimulation. (A) With maintained stimulation, showing adaptation and rebound; the upper record indicates the duration and polarity of the stimulating voltage applied to the tube opening relative to an electrode elsewhere on the fish. (B) Stimulus-response curve with d-c and repeated pulses; the abscissa represents the mean stimulus voltage. (C) Responses to 5-msec single pulses (stimulus voltage approximately 5 mV). (A, from Murray, 1962; B, C, from Murray, 1965a.)

for each of several modalities could be usefully detected by the fish on the basis of the electrophysiological evidence.

The responses to electrical stimuli are summarized in Fig. 3. With maintained direct current, a cathode applied to the end of a tube, with the anode anywhere else on the fish (outward current relative to the fish), causes an adapting increase in the frequency of the resting discharge, with inhibition at break; whereas an anode on the opening inhibits, with a rebound at break (Fig. 3A; Murray, 1962). The threshold for this response in the most sensitive of the mandibular tubes is about 2 $\mu$V, that is, 1 $\mu$V per cm gradient $\times$ 2-cm tube, under seawater, or in air with a fine insulated wire electrode on the opening. The latter threshold was previously reported as $5 \times 10^{-11}$ A (Murray, 1965a), but the voltage figure is more meaningful, and the conversion has been checked with a microelectrode inserted beneath a current-passing electrode of the same dimensions as was previously employed (Murray, unpublished).

The impulse frequency can be increased or decreased along an approximately linear "characteristic" curve of frequency against stimulus (Fig. 3B) over a range from 0 impulses per sec to approximately 80 impulses per sec, at which point the curve begins to flatten out. When monophasic pulsed stimuli are employed, they are as effective as direct current of equivalent charge per second (Fig. 3B). Only when the stimulus frequency falls below 5 to 10 per sec does the impulse discharge in the nerve become grouped following each stimulus pulse. This is in keeping with the time course of responses to single brief stimulus pulses (Fig. 3C).

When a d-c stimulus is used, the maximal change of impulse frequency is not reached until 100 to 200 msec, in tubes 2 to 4 cm long. This is in fair agreement with Waltman's figures for rounding-off of square stimuli in longer tubes (10 to 20 cm). It certainly does not exclude the hypothesis that the electrical properties of the tube account for the smoothing of the pulses. Trains of brief pulses must also continue for this minimum time of about 100 msec if the smoothing is to result in the lowest threshold.

The ampullae are also sensitive to salinity changes in the water (Fig. 4; Murray, 1962; Loewenstein and Ishiko, 1962). The mechanism involved is probably the above-mentioned electrical sensitivity responding to the junction potentials either at water-water, water-jelly, or water-skin interfaces (Murray, 1965b). Unfortunately, as far as a possible function is concerned, although the sensitivity to change of concentration is very great (e.g., threshold impulse-frequency changes were given to a change from 33‰ to 32‰ salinity and back), adapta-

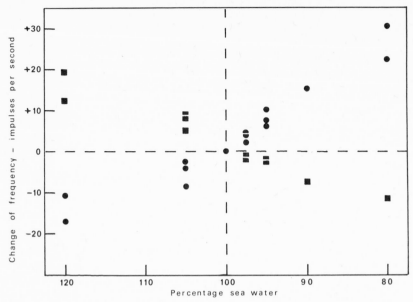

FIG. 4. Response of a single unit to change in salinity of the water at the tube opening. (100% represents normal seawater.) The impulse frequency plotted is the mean of the first 3 sec after a change, expressed as an increase or decrease over the previous frequency. This was necessary because the resting frequency varied between 30 and 40 impulses per sec during the course of the experiment. ●, after application of the test solution; ■, after return to normal seawater. The half-circles and half-squares are meant to represent two almost coincident circles or squares, respectively. "Dilute" solutions were kept isotonic to normal seawater with sucrose, and all test solutions were applied for 15 sec (from Murray, 1962).

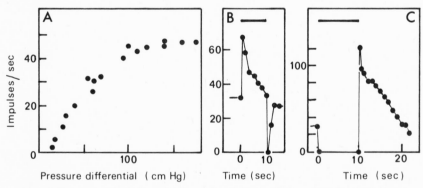

FIG. 5. Responses of single units to mechanical stimulation. (A) Tonic frequency in response to maintained pressure differentials in a cannulated, isolated ampulla. (B,C) Phasic responses to light touch on the tube opening in different units. (A, from Loewenstein, 1960; B,C, from Murray, 1960.)

tion is almost complete within a few seconds, so that the ampullae cannot be effective as absolute salinity detectors, and changes must be sudden.

Mechanical stimuli are effective in causing changes of impulse frequency. The exciting stimulus is one that tends to force the jelly down the tube so as to distend the ampulla. This is clear both from indirect evidence in relatively intact preparations (Murray, 1960) and from direct pressure-differential measurements in isolated, cannulated single ampullae (Loewenstein, 1960). Both phasic and tonic response components are present, but the latter are much less marked (Fig. 5A). The phasic component, on the other hand, is much more sensitive, and impulse-frequency changes occur with less than a 1-mg pressure on a tube opening (Murray, 1960) or with a change of differential pressure of a few centimeters of water. (The figure stated in Loewenstein, 1960, viz., meters of water, is apparently a misprint for centimeters; Loewenstein, personal communication.) In a few units, touch at one tube opening excites, whereas touch at another inhibits (Fig. 5C).

Slight distortion of the skin is effective, with stretching along the line of the tube inhibiting and compression increasing the resting frequency, with adaptation as usual. Two further functional points should be noted: first, that uniform hydrostatic pressure is ineffective and, second, that even the greatest recorded sensitivity is much less than that of the adjacent lateral line organs and is approximately equal to that of the cutaneous nerve endings (Murray, 1961). For example, the 1-mg touch must be on the jelly itself for stimulation of the ampullae, whereas the lateral line will respond to the same touch several millimeters away.

The temperature sensitivity of the ampullae (Fig. 6), although it was the first to be described electrophysiologically (Sand, 1938), appears to be unconnected with their biological function, chiefly because the sensitive region is the sensory epithelium and nerve endings, and there is no specific thermal conducting property of the jelly. The fact that the ampullae have many points of resemblance with the cold fibers of the mammalian tongue (Hensel, 1955) and are the most-sensitive cold-responding sense organs known electrophysiologically must presumably be explained away by saying that adequate thermal stimulation does not normally reach the ampullae, or that the CNS can recognize and ignore impulse responses due to temperature changes. The latter is more probable, for at least the more superficially located ampullae would respond if the fish swam into water differing in temperature by 1°C, and many elasmobranchs must do this from time to time.

Responses to changed $CO_2$ concentrations in the air surrounding an

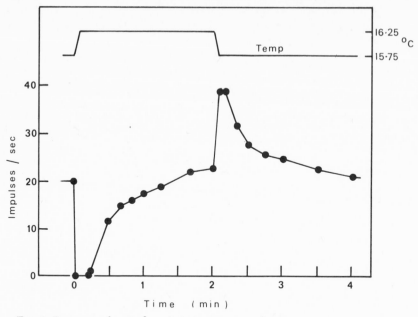

Fɪɢ. 6. Response of a single unit to temperature change.

isolated preparation have been recorded, e.g., with 2 to 10% $CO_2$ (Hensel, 1957). There was inhibition, often with some transient speeding of the discharge at first.

## DISCUSSION

The ampullae, like the lateral line organs and the cutaneous nerves, serve wide regions of the body surface, especially in rays; yet their pattern of accessory structures and innervation is very different. The distinction between the cranial and segmental innervation can probably be associated with the phylogenetic and embryological origins of the acousticolateral organs, and their function in detecting and locating objects at a distance (which requires central computing), but the characteristically short, equal-length nerve pathways in the ampullae merit further discussion.

One straightforward reason for the equal-length nerve pathways would be that accurate time comparisons are important, which would not be possible if there were different delays in the nerve conduction pathway to the CNS from stimuli affecting widely different parts of the body. Unfortunately, this explanation cannot apply to weak electrical stimuli because of the calculated (and recorded) rounding-off at the ampullae of the onset of square stimuli; the onset of stimuli many times threshold could be compared satisfactorily, however, but such stimuli are synchronous anyhow.

Such an explanation is more meaningful for mechanical stimuli, as long as the transmission properties of the jelly are suitable (they are not in fact known). The detection of the time relations of mechanical stimuli could also provide an explanation for the existence of the ampullae, for it would be a function not covered by the lateral line organs or the cutaneous receptors.

Another type of explanation for the tube system of the ampullae depends on the fact that the inside of the fish is not equipotential when in an external voltage gradient. A length of tube in the appropriate direction is essential in order to detect voltage gradients in the water (contrast the mormyrids; see Bennett, Chap. 20 in this volume). The all-round radiating pattern of the tubes (Fig. 2) would therefore provide all-round sensitivity, and the different lengths would give the possibility of both high d-c sensitivity and detection of transients.

A related question concerns the different anatomical distribution of the ampullae in the rays and dogfish, for in the latter fish not only the ampullae but also the tubes and openings are restricted to the head. It is true, in general, that the body of a shark undergoes more movement and distortion than does the body of a ray; but the latter's wings move during locomotion, and the head of the shark has jaw and gill movements that might be expected to stimulate the ampullae mechanically (apparently the dorsally situated ampullae in dogfish are not so stimulated; see remarks of Dijkgraaf in the discussion following this paper). But even if this direct mechanical stimulation is not effective, the location of distant electrical sources must be made more difficult by the movement of the electroreceptors relative to one another (especially since body-position receptors are not known in fish).

One of the characteristic features of the electrical sensitivity of the ampullae is the shape of the stimulus-impulse-frequency curve (Fig. 7A), for it is very different from that of the electroreceptors in *Hypopomus* (Fig. 7B; Hagiwara, Kusano, and Negishi, 1962), although essentially similar to that of *Sternarchus* (Fig. 7C; Hagiwara, Szabo, and Enger, 1965). From an inspection of the curves, it seems reasonable that the *Hypopomus* receptor is designed to detect small changes in a relatively intense stimulus pulse (i.e., the effect of field distortion due to objects in the vicinity), whereas the ampullae seem fitted to detect externally originating stimuli of small absolute magnitude. In keeping with these two biological functions and the two physiological types, one might also expect to find anatomical differences, such as

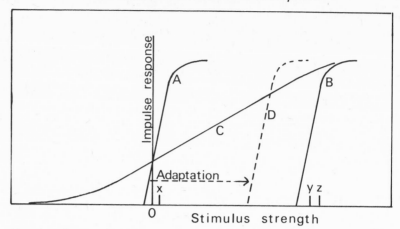

Fig. 7. Different types of response curve of electroreceptors. (A) Ampullae of Lorenzini. (B) In *Hypopomus*. (C) In *Sternarchus*. (D) As A, but after adaptation to a constant strong stimulus. x, strength of an externally generated stimulus; y, strength of the fish's own electric-organ pulse; z, electric-organ pulse distorted by an external object. For full description, see text. (B, after Hagiwara, Kusano, and Negishi, 1962; C, after Hagiwara, Szabo, and Enger, 1965; D, after Murray, 1965b.)

those between the tuberous and ampullary receptors described by Szabo (1965). Unfortunately, the anatomical distinction does not as yet appear to be involved in this functional duality. Moreover, the division of electroreceptors into two distinct types, specialized for either pulse-modulation detection or for external-signal detection, is not necessarily the only way in which they have evolved in those fish which are known to have an electrical navigation system as well as to be sensitive to weak external fields.

Other methods are possible. For example, in many fish the electric-organ output is at a high frequency, and smoothing (or integration) occurs in the receptors, with previous rectification where appropriate. In this case, a weak external stimulus could summate directly with the smoothed pulses and produce just the same effect as the distortion of the electric-organ field. Thus the two types of stimulus situation are not so very different, and the problem is for the receptor to detect small changes in a strong stimulus. Apart from having a receptor with a response curve similar to type B in Fig. 7, there are two special mechanisms that can help to give greater sensitivity. The first is adaptation (Fig. 7D). This mechanism is, of course, commonly found in many sense organs, with just this function of allowing sensitive responses over a wide dynamic range. It has been described in the electroreceptors of *Eigenmannia* (Hagiwara and Morita, 1963) and *Sternarchus* (Hagiwara, Szabo, and Enger, 1965), both of which are high-frequency fish. Adaptation normally occurs in response to maintained, not to pulsed, stimuli—which is indeed the situation in a high-frequency fish with smoothing. In low-frequency fish, any adaptation would have to be of the rarer, repeated-stimulus type, but in fact in *Hypopomus* it has not been described.

Another type of explanation arises from work on the mechanism of object location in *Gymnarchus* (Lissmann and Machin, 1958; Machin, 1962). It is suggested that the effective stimulus for the receptor is not dependent on the potential at the point in the water above it but, rather, on the second spatial derivative of the potential. This means that a uniform potential gradient in the water will not stimulate, however strong it may be. Therefore, insofar as the pulses emitted by the electric organ produce a uniform spatial gradient over the surface of the fish and insofar as weak external stimuli and distorting objects nearby do not produce such a uniform spatial gradient, the receptor can be highly sensitive to modulation of the fish's own pulses and to weak, externally originated stimuli, and yet not be "deafened" by the pulses themselves.

Two final points should be noted in connection with the receptor mechanisms involved in the electrical sensitivity of the ampullae of Lorenzini. Potential differences across the sensory epithelium of as little as 1 $\mu V$ are clearly effective, and there must be statistically detectable changes in impulse frequency caused by potential differences as small as 0.01 $\mu V$. These values are so low that no reasonable mechanism based on membrane properties has yet been proposed. The concept of statistical detection by the CNS of meaningful signals in sensory fibers is not a new one, but it obviously occurs in an acute form in the ampullary system. It is particularly so because, in addition to the random element involved in the irregularity of the resting discharge, there are the externally initiated responses to mechanical or thermal stimuli, which presumably have to be discounted in some way.

The possibility of a mechanoreceptive function must still remain open in spite of Dijkgraaf's strong evidence for the electroreceptive, for not only is the electrophysiological sensitivity suggestive, but also there are indications that not all ampullae of one fish—let alone of all species—have the same function. For example, *N. brevirostris* is sensitive to weak external fields, but only between the eye and gills, whereas other sharks are completely insensitive (quoted by E. Agalides in a discussion at this conference). Now, although behavioral differences of this kind can be explained more easily by response differences rather than by sensitivity differences, it is possible that differences in the function of the ampullae are involved as well.

In summary, it seems clear that the thermal and $CO_2$ sensitivities of the ampullae are unlikely to be functionally significant. Mechanical sensitivity is still a possible function—for some ampullae in some species, at any rate—and electroreception is certainly the function of other ampullae. The range of electrical stimuli, however, remains to be worked out, for it may include the compound muscle action potentials of prey, salinity changes, or other more improbable physical effects such as the interaction of the earth's magnetic field with water turbulence or the fish's own movements. But whatever they may be, the stimuli must be compatible with the smoothing and adaptation properties of the receptors.

REFERENCES

Barets, A., and T. Szabo (1962). Appareil synaptique des cellules sensorielles de l'ampoule de Lorenzini chez la torpille, *Torpedo marmorata. J. Microscop.* 1, 47-54.

Bennett, M. V. L. (1961). Quoted by H. Grundfest, in *Bioelectrogenesis* (C. Chagas and A. Paes de Carvalho, eds.), Elsevier, Amsterdam, p. 53.

Dijkgraaf, S., and A. J. Kalmijn (1963). Untersuchungen über die Funktion der Lorenzinischen Ampullen an Haifischen. *Z. Vergleich. Physiol.* 47, 438-456.

Doyle, J. (1963). The acid mucopolysaccharides in the glands of Lorenzini of elasmobranch fish. *Biochem. J.* 88.

Fuchs, S. (1895). Über die Funktion der unter der Haut liegenden Canalsysteme bei den Selachiern. *Pfluegers. Arch. Ges. Physiol.* 59, 454-478.

Hagiwara, S., and H. Morita (1963). Coding mechanisms of electroreceptor fibers in some electric fish. *J. Neurophysiol.* 26, 552-567.

———, K. Kusano, and K. Negishi (1962). Physiological properties of electroreceptors of some gymnotids. *J. Neurophysiol.* 25, 430-449.

———, T. Szabo, and P. S. Enger (1965). Electroreceptor mechanisms in a high-frequency weakly-electric fish, *Sternarchus albifrons. J. Neurophysiol.* 28, 784-799.

Hensel, H. (1955). Quantitative Beziehungen zwischen Temperaturreiz und Aktionspotentialen der Lorenzinischen Ampullen. *Z. Vergleich. Physiol.* 37, 509-526.

——— (1957). Die Wirkung verschiedener Kohlensäure- und Sauerstoffspannungen auf isolierte Lorenzinischen Ampullen von Selachiern. *Pfluergers. Arch. Ges. Physiol.* 264, 228-244.

Lissmann, H. W., and K. E. Machin (1958). The mechanism of object location in *Gymnarchus niloticus* and similar fish. *J. Exptl. Biol.* 35, 451-486.

Loewenstein, W. R. (1960). Mechanisms of nerve impulse initiation in a pressure receptor (Lorenzinian ampulla). *Nature (London),* 188, 1034-1035.

——— and N. Ishiko (1962). Sodium chloride sensitivity and electrochemical effects in a Lorenzinian ampulla. *Nature (London)* 194, 292-294.

Machin, K. E. (1962). Electric receptors. *Symp. Soc. Exptl. Biol.* 16, 227-244.

Murray, R. W. (1960). The response of the ampullae of Lorenzini of elasmo-branchs to mechanical stimulation. *J. Exptl. Biol.* 37, 417-424.

——— (1961). The initiation of cutaneous nerve impulses in elasmobranch fishes. *J. Physiol. (London)* 159, 546-570.

——— (1962). The response of the ampullae of Lorenzini of elasmobranchs to electrical stimulation. *J. Exptl. Biol.* 39, 119-128.

——— (1965a). Electroreceptor mechanisms: The relation of impulse frequency to stimulus strength and responses to pulsed stimuli in the ampullae of Loren-zini of elasmobranchs. *J. Physiol. (London)* 180, 592-606.

——— (1965b). Receptor mechanisms in the ampullae of Lorenzini of elasmo-branchs. *Cold Spring Harbor Symp. Quant. Biol.* 30, 233-243.

——— and W. T. W. Potts (1961). The composition of the endolymph, peri-lymph and other body fluids of elasmobranchs. *Comp. Biochem. Physiol.* 2, 65-75.

Sand, A. (1938). The function of the ampullae of Lorenzini, with some observa-tions on the effect of temperature on sensory rhythms. *Proc. Roy. Soc. (London)* B125, 524-553.

Smith, H. W. (1929). Body fluids of elasmobranchs. *J. Biol. Chem.* 81, 407-419.

Szabo, T. (1965). Sense organs of the lateral line system in some electric fish of the Gymnotidae, Mormyridae and Gymnarchidae. *J. Morphol.* 117, 229-250.

Thomas, B. D., T. G. Thompson, and C. L. Utterback (1934). The electrical conductivity of sea water. *J. Conseil Perm. intern. Exploration Mer* 9, 28-35.

Waltman, B. (1966). Electrical properties and fine structure of the ampullary canals of Lorenzini. *Acta Physiol. Scand. Suppl.* 264.

## COMMENTS

DIJKGRAAF: We, of course, expected that we would also get a mechanical response in ampullary nerves in the free-swimming dogfish, on the basis of your measurements, and we were very astonished that this was not the case. We got no mechanical response to moving objects, nor to water flow, nor even on touching the skin, all of which are stimuli for normal lateral line organs. But if the recording was from lateral line nerves, we found a wonder-ful response. A possible explanation for the difference in responsiveness be-tween our experiments and yours is that in our preparation the skin and tissues around the ampullae were undisturbed, whereas in yours there was considerable dissection. This opening-up could allow the mechanical stimu-lus to produce deformation at the sensory epithelium.

MURRAY: This is certainly possible, although the stimulated ampullae in my experiments were *in situ* and still enclosed in their capsule. I dissected up to the base of the capsule in order to cut the nerve branch to the adjacent lateral line canal under visual control, since I wished to be certain that the mechanical responses were not from lateral line organs (Murray, 1960).

DIJKGRAAF: Have you ever compared the mechanical sensitivity of the ampullae with that of the lateral line; and if so, is there a big difference?

MURRAY: Yes, indeed. This is the main reason why I do not put forward the mechanical sensitivity with too much enthusiasm.

DIJKGRAAF: We get the impression that these fish are not very sensitive to pressures, even surface pressures. They are rather insensitive as compared with many bony fish.

VAN BERGEIJK: About the electrical sensitivity and its possible function: there must be potentials associated with wounded animals, with their blood and body tissues exposed to the water, although they are difficult for us to detect. These would allow the prey to be detected by a passive electrical system, as opposed to the active electrical system of the weakly electric fish.

SUCKLING: Is it possible that the receptors themselves are putting out a very small electric field? Is there any time when you can pick up fluctuating, maybe generator, potentials?

MURRAY: Nothing has been reported except damped oscillations of about 1 mV recorded by a large wire inserted firmly into the opening of a tube, with the fish in air (Murray, 1965b).

SUCKLING: I gather that you thought that the external electric field continued through the fish. Now, if you have a fairly old fish, with skin resistance of 1000 ohms · sq cm or more, this will act as an insulator. It is not possible that the field detecting depends on having tubes opening on opposite sides of the fish, to provide the low-resistance pathway to and from the central receptor region?

MURRAY: Yes, this will certainly be part of the system, especially when the relevant ampullae are close together in one capsule. It will also be involved when bipolar electrodes are used to apply local fields to the surface of the fish at a point some distance from the ampullae, but above the tube openings, as Dijkgraaf and Kalmijn did.

HARRIS: About the salinity response—since salinity gradients involve electric fields in the same way as do temperature gradients, it would be nice to measure what the electric field is right above the sense organ when it is stimulated by salinity changes, and to see how it compares.

MURRAY: I have measured some of the junction potentials individually in isolation. The difficulty is to know what combination of them provides the actual stimulating circuit, for there are junctions between normal and dilute seawater, jelly and seawater, and seawater and body fluids across the skin, and any or all of these may be involved. Certainly the individual components are many times the threshold, but they are mostly opposed to each other. Moreover, the polarity of the potentials recorded with dilute seawater seems to be reversed compared with their effect on impulse frequency (Murray, 1965b).

BENNETT: I am happy to see this analysis of the part the accessory structures, i.e., tubes, play in determining the electrical sensitivity. Certainly, it is much more meaningful to talk about sensitivities of the single receptors in terms of the voltage differences across the sensory epithelia. Sensitivity to voltage gradients along the body tells us very little unless we know how accessory structures affect current flow. In mormyrids and gymnotids the skin rather than ampullary tube is the significant structure (Bennett, Chapter 20 of this volume).

As far as your diagram (Fig. 7) is concerned, the gymnotids have tonic as well as phasic receptors. Probably that in Fig. 7D is a phasic receptor. The tonic receptors are similar to the ampullae of Lorenzini, and may be used primarily for the detection of extrinsic fields. In the eels there are also receptors that respond to both mechanical and electrical stimuli (Hagiwara et al., *J. Neurophysiol.* 28, 775-783, 1965). Of course, the electrical stimulus in the eel is rather large, and although we are not really sure of the normal responses or their central significance it may not be uncommon that a receptor in the lateral line system can respond to two modalities. This after all is a system that is evolving. I noticed in your record of mechanical stimulation that the off response did not look the same as the off response for electrical stimuli. Is this a consistent finding?

MURRAY: Both adaptation and rebound times with mechanical stimulation are often faster than with electrical stimulation. I think that this is because of accommodative processes in the tissues and is a question of their viscous and elastic properties (Murray, 1960).

GRUNDFEST: I should like to comment on the very high value of the specific resistance of the tube wall, which is something like 2 to 3 orders higher than that of excitable membrane and much closer to the resistivity one finds in the lipid bilayers in artificial model membranes. The distinction between the two is remarkable, and it would bear looking into.

NELSON: I was not quite clear on whether your animal measures gradient from the floor of one ampulla to the floor of another, through the capsule, or is it from the floor of the ampulla to the general potential level in the fish in the region of the capsule?

MURRAY: Presumably the important thing is the potential difference across the sensory cells. This could be established when the external potential at the tube opening differs from that induced in the fish's tissues at the other end of the tube by an external voltage gradient. It will also occur locally in a capsule when any two tubes whose ampullae lie adjacent to each other are exposed to a localized potential difference.

# 19 ACTIVITY OF PERIPHERAL AND CENTRAL NEURONS INVOLVED IN ELECTRORECEPTION

THOMAS SZABO

Centre National de la Recherche Scientifique
Centre d'Etudes de Physiologie Nerveuse
Paris, France

The free neuromasts and canal organs are not the only sensory organs of the lateral line system of certain fish. Many selachians, as well as teleosts, possess specialized cutaneous receptors belonging to their lateral line system, i.e., cutaneous organs related through peripheral nerves to the lateral lobes of the rhombencephalon (medulla).[†]

The three families of weakly electric fish—Gymnotidae, Mormyridae, and Gymnarchidae—are provided with such specialized lateral line organs, and it was proposed by Lissmann and Machin (1958) that these might be involved in a particular object-locating mechanism. These authors demonstrated by means of training experiments that *Gymnarchus* and similar fish can distinguish between a conductive and a nonconductive object placed near them in the water. The following sensory mechanism was proposed by Lissmann (1958): specialized cutaneous organs are stimulated by the fish's own electric organ discharge; the sensory impulse pattern evoked in such a way will vary if an object placed near the receptor changes the stimulating current intensity flowing through the receptor. This variation provides the fish with information about the presence of the object. Hagiwara et al. (1962) and Szabo and Fessard (1965) have demonstrated by electrophysiological methods that the lateral line nerves are involved in the mechanism proposed by Lissmann.

The object of the present work was to analyze and localize, by physiological and anatomical methods, events occurring in the specific lateral line system at peripheral and at different central levels. This

---

[†] Affiliation of cutaneous sense organs to the lateral line system should be defined rather by their central connections than by the peripheral course of their innervating nerve trunks.

paper also reports some data already published (Hagiwara et al., 1965a, 1965b; Enger and Szabo, 1965).

## MATERIALS AND METHODS

*Gnathonemus stanleyanus* and *petersi*, *Eigenmannia virescens*, *Steatogenys elegans*, *Gymnotus carapo*, and *Sternarchus albifrons* were used for experiments and for histological investigations.

**Histology.** Whole fish and brains were fixed in Helly's solution or in 10% formalin and cut in serial sections. Bodian's silver impregnation was used for peripheral nerve and CNS staining, while special fixation was employed for Sholl's impregnation method. Degenerated axons were stained by Nauta's silver-impregnation technique.

**Experimental.** The general procedure was similar to that which has been described previously (Hagiwara et al., 1965a). The fish was anesthetized with tricaine methanesulfonate, 50 mg per liter (MS 222, Sandoz), or with urethane, 1.3 g per liter, in the circulating water.

Single units were recorded by dissection of single fibers at the cranial end of dorsal and posterior (recurrent) branches of the (anterior VII) lateral line nerve complex. Single-unit recordings were obtained from the brain at rhombencephalic and mesencephalic levels (specific regions are described in Figs. 5 and 8) with 3 $M$ KCl-filled micropipettes.

Movements of conductive and nonconductive objects ($2 \times 2$- and $2 \times 4$-cm Ag or plastic plates) were registered on the second beam of the oscilloscope by means of a device in which a potentiometer coupled with the mechanical system delivers a voltage signal linearly related to the displacement.

## RESULTS

**Analysis of Peripheral Activity.** It has been demonstrated in many kinds of gymnotids (Hagiwara et al., 1962, 1963; Bullock and Chichibu, 1965), mormyrids (Szabo and Fessard, 1965), and *Gymnarchus* (Hagiwara et al., 1964) that sensory impulses are evoked in many of the lateral line fibers by each electric organ discharge. The sensory impulse pattern is different in fish having low-frequency (1 to 60 cps) and high-frequency (100 to 1000 cps) electric organ discharge (Hagiwara and Morita, 1963). In the former, a single electric organ discharge produces 10 to 15 impulses (Fig. 1, 1), and the number of impulses depends on the intensity of current flowing through the re-

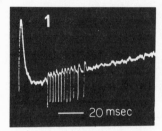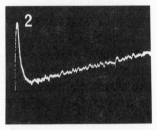

Fɪɢ. 1. In (1) a train of sensory impulses follows the electric organ discharge, while in (2) the sensory impulses are suppressed by the short-circuiting effect of two Ag plates placed at the head and the tail of the fish. Sweep triggered by the low-voltage electric organ discharge of *Electrophorus electricus.* [From Hagiwara et al., *J. Neurophysiol.,* 28, 775-783 (1965b), fig. 2, detail.]

ceptor (Fig. 1, 2). In other words, the stimulating-current intensity is coded by the number of sensory impulses.

However, in mormyrids (African freshwater fish) having low-frequency (1 to 2 cps) electric activity, each electric organ pulse evokes only 1 to 3 (maximum 5) sensory impulses. This clearly does not allow precise coding through the mechanism indicated above. Figure 2 shows an electroreceptor fiber in which only two impulses are evoked by each electric organ discharge. (The sweep of the oscilloscope is triggered by the electric discharge.) If a 2 × 2-cm (nonconductive) plastic plate is moved in the water parallel to the long axis of the fish, the two sensory impulses disappear successively at certain positions of the plate. Besides variations in the number of impulses, a marked variation of spike latency is also observed. Before the spikes disappear, their latency (with respect to the electric organ discharge) increases, sometimes up to 7 or 8 msec. However, for a given position of the plate, the latency remains constant. It has been shown, by varying the imposed electric field (Szabo and Hagiwara, 1966) or by changing the fish's own electric field with a short-circuiting system (Szabo and Fessard, 1965), that the spike latency is an indicator of the electric-field intensity at the level of the receptor.

Threshold stimulation studies, associated with histological control, have shown that two kinds of cutaneous sensory organs are connected to the sensory fibers examined: the tuberous organs in gymnotids (Hagiwara et al., 1965a), and the mormyromasts (Cordier's type II = Szabo's type B) in mormyrids (Szabo and Roth, 1966). The density of the two organs is somewhat similar in the two species and is many times higher than that of ordinary lateral line organs (Fig. 3). However, in gymnotids they are distributed all over the surface of the fish

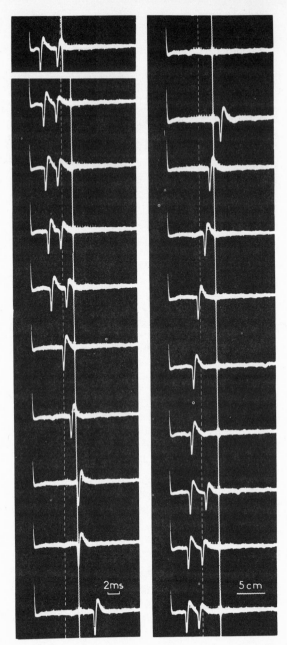

Fig. 2. Upper left trace: Two sensory impulses are elicited by the electric organ discharge of a mormyrid fish, *Gnathonemus petersi* (sweep triggered by electric organ discharge). Remaining traces in both columns (read from top to bottom): Phase-shift effect of the sensory impulses is obtained when a plastic plate is moved in the water parallel to the fish's long axis. Plate movement indicated by increasing separation of solid and interrupted vertical lines. The total movement of the plate in this recording was about 1.5 cm.

298

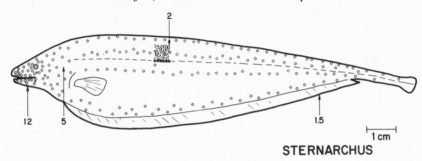

STERNARCHUS

FIG. 3. Distribution of different types of lateral line organs in a gymnotid fish, *Sternarchus albifrons*. Dashed lines and black squares indicate canal organs in the trunk, while dots show density of tuberous organs in a 5-sq-mm area. Figures with arrows indicate approximate number of tuberous organs per sq mm. Ampullary organs are represented by diamonds. Ordinary lateral line organs (canal organs and free neuromasts) are not indicated in the figures. [From Szabo, *J. Morphol.*, 117, 229-250 (1965), fig. 8, detail.]

(Fig. 3), whereas in mormyrids they are found only on the head, the dorsal and ventral edges of the body, and not on the tail.

**Activity Recorded in the Lateral Lobe.** In contrast to ordinary lateral line organs, which have directional sensitivity and provide dynamic information (Dijkgraaf, 1963), the electroreceptors were thought to indicate simply the presence of a stationary object placed in the electric field of the fish. Thus, sensory impulses evoked in electroreceptors may give no information about movement or direction of movement of an object.

It seemed reasonable to assume that detection of movement and direction of movement would be reflected in the firing pattern of central neurons of the lateral lobes, where the primary sensory fibers of the electroreceptor system converge. Single units were therefore recorded with micropipettes, and the location of the electrode tips was determined from the position of the micromanipulator. The electrosensitivity of a unit was tested by a short-circuiting system that modified the electric-field intensity around the fish without any mechanical stimulation.

Electrosensitive units of the lateral lobes displayed a "spontaneous" and "irregular" activity that was accelerated (or inhibited) when a silver or plastic (conductive or nonconductive, respectively) object was moved in the water, forward or backward, parallel to the fish. The units responded only to movements (Fig. 4A, curves with arrows) and adapted rapidly when the movement was stopped (Fig. 4A, curves with vertical bars). The variation in the activity of some of these units was dependent also on the direction of the movements; e.g., headward

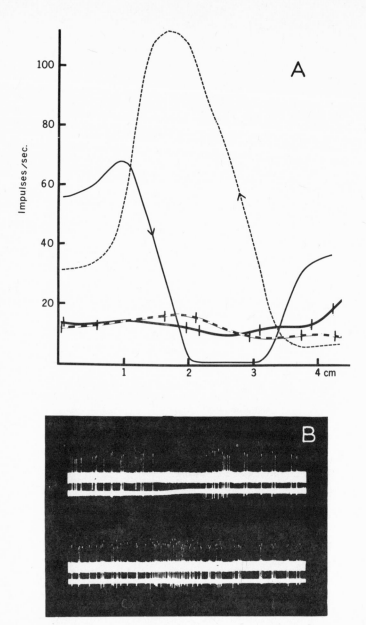

FIG. 4. (A) Curves with arrows obtained with a continuously moving plastic plate in headward direction (solid) and tailward direction (broken). Heavy curves show adapted responses obtained by stepwise movements. Impulse frequency was determined 3 sec after each stop (vertical bars). (B) Records of a lateral lobe unit responding with acceleration to headward movements and with inhibition to tailward movements of a plastic plate. Lower traces in each record show positions and movements of the plate. Note opposite effect for opposite direction of movement. [From Enger and Szabo, *J. Neurophysiol.*, 28, 800-818 (1965), fig. 9.]

movement caused acceleration, and tailward movement inhibition. (In Fig. 4A, compare heavy and dashed lines with arrows with traces in Fig. 4B.) Thus, some units of the lateral lobes are movement detectors and give no information about stationary objects; others signal the direction of movement by opposite effects in the neuronal activity for opposite movements (Enger and Szabo, 1965).

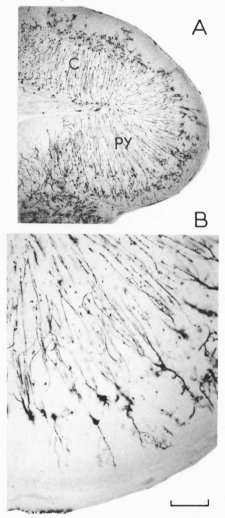

FIG. 5. Transverse sections of the brain of *Gymnotus carapo* at the level of the lateral lobe. (A) c, cerebellum; py, dendritic field of pyramidal cells. (B) Pyramidal cells of the lateral lobe. Note basal processes of pyramidal cells penetrating in the region of terminal network of primary neurons. Sholl's impregnation. [Scale: 500 $\mu$ for (A) and 200 $\mu$ for (B).]

Histological controls have shown that the recorded activity originates from pyramidal cells of the lateral lobes. These cells, similar to Purkinje cells of the cerebellum (Fig. 5A), possess a dorsally directed dendritic arborization but, in addition, send a ventral process through the granular layer into the terminal network of primary sensory neurons (Fig. 5B). Hence it is difficult to determine whether the pyramidal neurons of the lateral lobe represent second-order or higher-order neurons in the electroreceptive pathway. However, the integrative

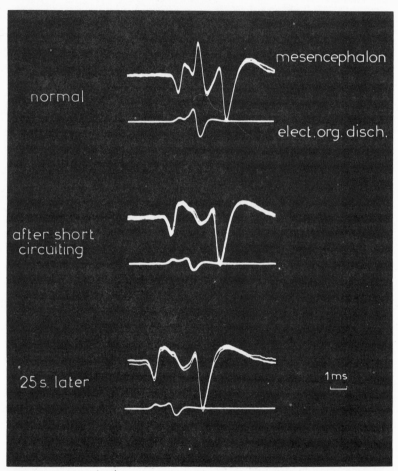

Fig. 6. Multiphasic responses obtained from mesencephalon (upper traces) and from electric organ (lower traces). Note maintained phase relation between electric organ discharge and mesencephalic activity after short-circuiting and increased frequency 25 sec later. In mesencephalic records negative deflections are downward.

process occurring at this level (differentiation of the rate of impulse discharge of single primary neurons; see Enger and Szabo, 1965) has a latency two to five times longer than the peripheral event (conduction time, sense-organ event included), suggesting a higher-order neuron character for the pyramidal cells.

**Some Mesencephalic Structures Involved in the Electroreceptive Mechanism.** It was stated that integrative processes occur at the level of the pyramidal cells of the lateral lobes. However, not the whole structure of the lateral lobe is involved in this mechanism. Wallenberg (1907) has shown by degeneration experiments that the lateral lobe in fish is connected through the lateral lemniscal pathway to the mesencephalon. Micropipette recordings from the anterior part of the mesencephalon (Fig. 6, upper traces) show a multiphasic potential in *Steatogenys*: a small negative deflection followed by an initially positive diphasic spike and a large negative deflection with positive afterpotential. After comparing these traces with those of the electric-organ discharge recorded by means of two silver plates dipped into the water

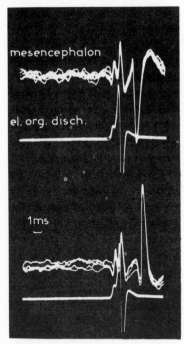

Fig. 7. Upper traces: Same as in Fig. 6. Lower traces: Positive potential obtained after partial penetration into the cells connected synaptically to the lateral lobe neurons. Note time interval between negative (upper) and positive (lower) spike of the mesencephalic records.

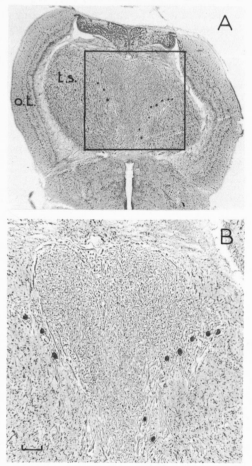

FIG. 8. Transverse section of the mesencephalon in *Sternarchus albifrons*. (A) o.t., optic tectum; t.s., torus semicircularis. (B) Higher magnification of the region indicated by square in (A). Note the impressive network and relatively big cells on its ventral border. Bodian's impregnation. [Scale: 40 $\mu$ for (A) and 100 $\mu$ for (B).]

(at the head and the tail of the fish), one can conclude that the initial negative deflection and the diphasic wave are artifacts of the electric-organ discharge. Indeed, a shunt of the electric-organ discharge reduces the diphasic wave but leaves the large negative deflection unchanged. (The first negative wave originates in the accessory submental electric organ and is little affected by the external shunt.) This experiment shows that the negative wave represents mesencephalic activity and that this activity is phase-related to the electric organ discharge. The very short latency (2.5 msec, measured from the rising phase of the first deflection of the discharge, i.e., from the earliest possible peripheral stimulation of electroreceptors) suggests a rapid pathway from the periphery to the mesencephalon.

Occasionally, during penetration through the mesencephalon, a sudden change in polarity of the negative wave occurred (Fig. 7, upper trace). This positive wave appeared 0.5 to 0.7 msec later than the negative wave and was associated with a negative d-c shift of the base line, indicating intracellular penetration. The positive potential was also tightly locked to the electric organ discharge, suggesting that it represents the postsynaptic event related to the negative wave.

Histological control revealed that the tip of the electrode was located in a peculiar network of the torus semicircularis, which is situated immediately beneath the optic tectum in *Steatogenys* (Fig. 8A and B), and was inserted between symmetric parts of the torus semicircularis. This network represents the terminal arborization of neurons having their pear-shaped soma in the most ventral layer of the lateral lobe (Fig. 9). In silver-stained serial sections, one can follow the large axons of these cells within the lateral lemniscal pathway into the torus semicircularis. Also, after destruction of one of the lateral lobes, de-

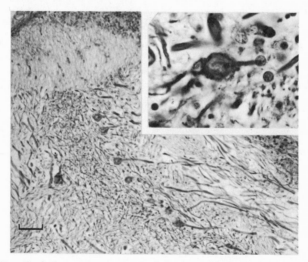

FIG. 9. Detail of a transverse section of the lateral lobe (*Sternarchus*) showing its most ventral cell layer. Note the large axons originating in the relatively small cells. Inset: Higher magnification of one cell in the ventral layer with cuplike ending on its perikaryon. Bodian's impregnation. [Scale: 100 $\mu$ (10 $\mu$ for inset).]

generating fibers (Fig. 10B) can be followed into this characteristic network (Fig. 10C), indicating a direct connection between the lateral lobes and the mesencephalon.

The pear-shaped neurons appear, from histological sections, to represent an "interneuron" between the periphery and the mesencephalon. Each soma receives a cuplike ending (Fig. 9, inset) from thick fibers of the lateral line nerves (Szabo, 1965); in turn, the axons of the pear-shaped neurons presumably end on the large cells located in

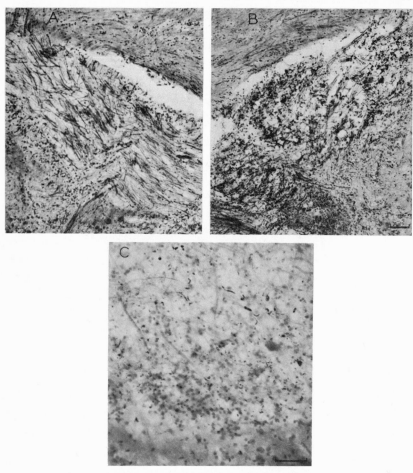

Fig. 10. (A,B) Transverse sections of the rhombencephalon of *Gymnotus carapo*, showing degeneration of the lateral lemniscus (B) after partial destruction of the contralateral lateral lobe (30 days survival). Ipsilateral lateral lemniscus (A) is almost intact. (C) Terminal degeneration in the mesencephalon. Same brain as in (A) and (B). Nauta's silver-impregnation method. [Scale: 50 μ.]

the ventral part of the mesencephalic network (Fig. 8B). The intracellular recording illustrated in Fig. 7 was probably obtained from these latter cells, and the negative wave represented the presynaptic events occurring in the terminal network. Thus, the mesencephalon receives impulses conveyed by a rapid pathway from some of the lateral line organs, over one synapse in the lateral lobes. This explains the very short time interval (2.5 msec for the negative and 3 msec for the positive potential) between mesencephalic potentials and electric organ pulse.

To support this notion, we demonstrated that the mesencephalic activity is evoked by the electric organ discharge. It was known that electric organ discharge activity in *Eigenmannia* can be stopped by repetitive direct stimulation of the pacemaker medullary nucleus (Szabo and Enger, 1964). A single shock applied to the pacemaker immediately stops or resets its activity (Fig. 11D, upper trace), which, in turn, leads to a drop-out of the third subsequent electric organ discharge (Fig. 11D, lower trace).

The traces of Fig. 11A show simultaneous recordings from the electric organ and the mesencephalon, both activities having identical frequency. A single shock applied to the pacemaker nucleus temporarily changes the rhythm of the electric-organ discharge, and an analogous modification occurs in the mesencephalic activities. The modified intervals (b and c) of the former are identical with those (b' and c') of the latter. This experiment shows clearly that the mesencephalic activity is dependent on the electric-organ discharge and that each electric-organ pulse is followed at short latency (3 msec) by a mesencephalic potential.

## DISCUSSION

The intensity of the electric field at different spots on the surface of the fish can be coded by two sensory mechanisms: in one, the local field intensity is reflected in the number of sensory impulses evoked by each electric-organ discharge (Hagiwara et al., 1962); in the other, it is signaled by the latency of sensory impulses with respect to the electric organ pulse. The first mechanism operates in low-frequency gymnotids, while both mechanisms exist in low-frequency mormyrids and also in one medium-frequency gymnotid, *Sternopygus* (Bullock and Chichibu, 1965). The second mechanism would seem to allow more-precise discrimination of different field intensities because of the smooth gradation of latency with changing intensity. The system dependent upon the number of impulses elicited by an electric organ

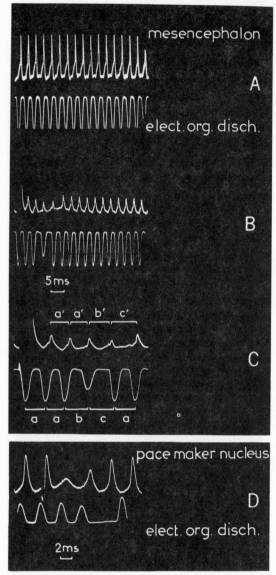

FIG. 11. Mesencephalon and electric organ activity of *Eigenmannia*. Upper traces recorded by micropipettes. Lower traces recorded by two silver plates placed in the water at the head and the tail of the fish. (Further explanation in the text.) The reduced amplitude of the mesencephalic potential in the second and third traces was due to the change in the recording condition, i.e., movements elicited by repetitive stimulation of the pacemaker nucleus.

pulse is limited in this respect, particularly when the spike rate is normally low. Hagiwara and Morita (1963) have shown that such a spike-counting system can discriminate, at best, field differences of 4%.

The sensory response conveyed by the peripheral system does not adapt and thus represents a stable source of information about the environment. This kind of information should be very important for integrative processes. For instance, a reflex mechanism can be more

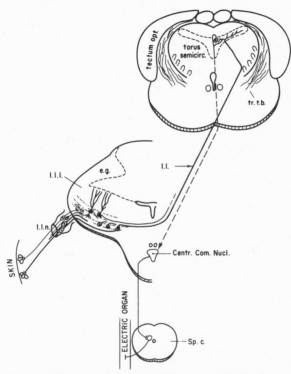

Fig. 12. Schematic diagram of the probable sensory feedback system. Primary neurons (thick) connect special tuberous organs directly with second-order neurons of the lateral lobe. The axons (thick) of the latter make synaptic contact with mesencephalic neurons, which presumably form the descending pathway to the pacemaker medullary nucleus of the electric-organ discharge. The electric discharge stimulates the special tuberous organs. Parts of the object-locating system are also indicated (thin fibers). tectum opt., optic tectum; torus semicirc., torus semicircularis; tr. t.b., tractus tectobulbaris; l.l., lateral lenniscal pathway; l.l.l., lateral lobe; l.l.n., lateral line nerve; e.g., eminentia granularis; centr. com. nucl., central command nucleus of the electric-organ discharge; sp. c., spinal cord.

easily controlled when a "reference" afferent input is known in advance.

Considering the large number of pyramidal cells, it is evident that the most important part of the lateral lobe is involved in an object-locating mechanism that also permits direction and movement detection; it is a center of complex integrative processes. Anatomical data indicates that information from the lateral lobe is transferred to the mesencephalon before reaching the descending efferent pathways that control the locomotory center of the animal (Lissmann and Machin, 1958).

It is known from earlier work (Szabo, 1964) that electrical stimulation of the specific region of the mesencephalon will modify pacemaker activity of the electric organ command nucleus. The present results have also demonstrated a rapid pathway from the lateral line system through the lateral lobe into the mesencephalon, which in turn projects caudally (Fig. 12). It is clear that such a pathway could serve in a feedback mechanism through which the sensory input to the skin organs could modify electric organ discharge frequency (Fig. 6). Watanabe and Takeda (1963) have demonstrated that *Eigenmannia* raises or lowers its discharge frequency if an imposed a-c field of neighboring frequency is applied to the fish. It would seem that the fish tries to keep the sensory information of its electric organ–electro-receptor system permanently identifiable and unambiguous, and it does this by shifting its own frequency away from contaminating frequencies. The sensory feedback described above may indeed be the nervous pathway for this "sensory" control of the electric organ frequency.

REFERENCES

Bullock, T. H., and S. Chichibu (1965). Further analysis of sensory coding in electroreceptors of electric fish. *Proc. Natl. Acad. Sci. U.S.* 54(2), 422-429.

Dijkgraaf, S. (1963). The functioning and significance of the lateral line organs. *Biol. Rev.* 38, 51-105.

Enger, P. S., and T. Szabo (1965). Activity of central neurons involved in electroreception in some weakly electric fish (Gymnotidae). *J. Neurophysiol.* 28, 800-818.

Hagiwara, S., and K. Morita (1963). Coding mechanisms of electroreceptor fibers in some electric fish. *J. Neurophysiol.* 26, 551-567.

———, K. Kusano, and K. Negishi (1962). Physiological properties of electro-receptors of some gymnotids. *J. Neurophysiol.* 25, 430-449.

———, T. Szabo, and P. S. Enger (1965a). Electroreceptor mechanisms in a high frequency weakly electric fish, *Sternarchus albifrons. J. Neurophysiol.* 28, 784-799.

———, T. Szabo, and P. S. Enger (1965b). Physiological properties of electroreceptors in electric eel, *Electrophorus electricus. J. Neurophysiol.* 28, 775-783.

———, T. Szabo, H. W. Lissmann, and T. H. Bullock (1964). Unpublished observations.

Lissmann, H. W. (1958). On the function and evolution of electric organs in fish. *J. Exptl. Biol.* 35, 156-191.

———, and K. E. Machin (1958). The mechanism of object location in *Gymnarchus niloticus* and similar fish. *J. Exptl. Biol.* 35, 451-486.

Szabo, T. (1964). Unpublished observations.

———, and P. S. Enger (1964). Pacemaker activity of the medullary nucleus controlling electric organs in high frequency gymnotid fish. *Z. Vergleich. Physiol.* 49, 285-300.

——— (1965). Sense organs of the lateral line system in some electric fish of the Gymnotidae, Mormyridae and Gymnarchidae. *J. Morphol.* 117, 229-250.

———, and A. E. Fessard (1965). Le fonctionnement des électro-récepteurs chez les Mormyridés. *J. Physiol. (Paris)* 57, 343-360.

———, and S. Hagiwara (1966). Effets de déphasage dans le mécanisme d' électroreception chez les Mormyridés. *J. Physiol.,* Paris 58, 267-268.

———, and A. Roth (1966). Unpublished observations.

Wallenberg, A. (1907). Beiträge zur Kenntnis des Gehirns der Teleostier und Selachier. *Anat. Anz.* 31, 369.

Watanabe, A., and K. Takeda (1963). The change of discharge frequency by a-c stimulus in a weak electric fish. *J. Exptl. Biol.* 40, 57-66.

# 20 MECHANISMS
# OF ELECTRORECEPTION †

Michael V. L. Bennett ‡

Department of Neurophysiology
College of Physicians and Surgeons
Columbia University
New York, New York

The recently described electrosensory systems provide new examples of what may be called an active sensory system, that is, where the energy detected by the receptors is supplied by the organism itself, especially by means of specialized generating organs. Obviously, receptors that are part of an active sensory system will also act passively when the suitable form of energy is present in the environment, and it might be better to speak of active and passive operation of receptors. The extent to which a given type of receptor is used actively or passively varies greatly in different sensory systems, and the extreme cases can be classified as active or passive with little difficulty. The best-known active sensory systems are those of the echo-locating bats, cave birds, and cetaceans (Griffin, 1958). An electrosensory system was first demonstrated convincingly by Lissmann (1958) in *Gymnarchus*, and evidence was also obtained for this system in *Gymnotus*. Subsequently it was shown that *Gymnotus* could detect resistance changes as signaled by acceleration of organ discharge (Bennett and Grundfest, 1959). Detection of a resistance change required that an organ discharge be emitted during the change. If the change was restricted to the time between pulses, no alteration of discharge rate occurred. It

† This investigation was supported in part by grants from the National Institute of Neurological Diseases and Blindness (Career Program Award K3-GM-5828 and Public Health Service Research Grants NB-3728, NB-3270, 5Tl-NB-5328, NB-03448, and NB-03313); from the National Science Foundation (GB-2940); from the United States Air Force (AFOSR-550-65); from the Muscular Dystrophy Associations of America; and from the United Cerebral Palsy Research and Educational Foundation, Inc. (R-190-65). I am indebted to Dr. G. D. Pappas, in whose laboratory the histological preparations were made.

‡ Present address: Albert Einstein College of Medicine, Yeshiva University, New York, New York.

was subsequently shown, in unpublished experiments, that mormyrids could be conditioned to accelerate their organ discharge rate in response to resistance changes (Mandriota et al., 1965). The acceleration did not begin until the first organ pulse following the resistance change, indicating the active nature of the detecting system. Unconditioned responses were obtained in similar experiments by Szabo and Fessard (1965).

A number of fish appear to use luminescent organs in examination of their environment, and certainly the visual system is operating actively under these circumstances. The work of Dr. Walters in this volume suggests that certain fish set up a pressure gradient around themselves by their forward movement and that distortion of this field is detected, presumably by lateral line receptors. This would be yet another kind of active sensory system. It is possible that many fish which "hover" by continual movement in fact detect objects by reflections of pressure waves generated by this movement. Particularly striking is the nearly continual motion of several gymnotids and mormyrids, which are, of course, also electric. Mechanoreceptors can also be used in an active way when the organism detects something of the physical properties of its environment by applying physical stresses to it.

For the most part, eyes and ears operate passively, and from these two examples it is obvious that thresholds in passive and active sensory systems may not be very different. Furthermore, as far as the eye is concerned, there is probably no difference in the sensory processing in the active and passive systems. The relative specialization of sensory centers in active and passive systems must depend on many factors, including the degree of dependence of the organism on the particular sensory modality. Certainly the auditory centers of echo-locating bats are greatly hypertrophied, as are the probable electrosensory centers in electric fish, and these systems involve large portions of the entire brains. Comparison with the owl, in which hearing appears to be exclusively passive, might well be instructive, for this bird is an expert at locating such small emitters of sound as mice and bats. In any case, the active emitter of energy, potentially at least, has important information unavailable to the passive receiver—that is, the time and strength of the signal emitted. It is not obvious whether this would require more or less data processing, particularly since the detected signal must be discriminated from the emitted one.

A little difficult to place in the scheme of active and passive operation of sensory systems is communication, both intra- and interspecific. The communicating organisms may possess both specialized generating and detecting organs, but primarily they receive from external energy sources. Nevertheless, the differentiation of active and passive operation appears to be one that is useful in analyzing the function of sensory systems.

It should be pointed out that the form of energy which electric fish detect is an electric field, not a wave disturbance. The frequencies are very low compared with those of electromagnetic waves of a length comparable with the size of the fish. The energy supplied to the environment is distributed essentially according to the diffusion equation, not according to the wave equations that describe the light and sonic energy emitted by other forms. The relationship is analogous to the distinction between near- and far-field effects in sound systems (see Van Bergeijk, Chap. 6 of this volume).

The work of Dijkgraaf (Chap. 7 of this volume) indicates that in the sharks the ampullae of Lorenzini are electroreceptors which operate, primarily at least, passively. The sensitivity to electric fields of certain catfish which are without electric organs but which possess "pit" organs in the skin also suggests that electrosensory systems can be passive as well as active (Lissmann, 1958; Mullinger, 1964). The measurement of demarcation potentials in cut muscle is an old electrophysiological technique, but perhaps one that was antedated by these fish. There remains some uncertainty whether these electrosensory systems operate exclusively passively, for fish may also detect distortions of the electric fields set up by their own muscle-action currents (Lissmann, 1958). While the similar sense organs in *Rajidae* and *Torpedinidae* are ideally suited to an electroreceptor function (see Murray, Chap. 18 of this volume; Waltman, 1966) and these forms possess electric organs, the extent to which the receptors operate actively or passively or even participate in communication with each other remains to be determined.

The present paper is concerned with operation of the electroreceptors in mormyrids and gymnotids. Most of the electrophysiological data for the mormyrids has been published previously (Bennett, 1965), and only a brief review of this material is given along with a few new observations and a correlation of electrophysiological and anatomical data. The primary concern is the origin of the potentials that can be recorded at the external openings of the receptors and the mode of transmission from receptor cells to innervating nerve fibers. The analysis is exclusively of the passive operation of the receptors, for in all experiments the electric-organ discharge was eliminated by curarization. Both morphological and physiological data indicate that electroreceptors are "secondary receptors" in the terminology of Davis (1961);

that is, they possess receptor cells which are the initial site of action of the stimulus energy. The receptor cells then excite the nerve fibers that innervate them. It is also clear that an important function can be ascribed to the supporting cells and skin surrounding the receptors: namely, to channel the electric current through the receptor cells.

The experimental results can be presented with greater simplicity if a summary of receptor function is given initially. Most electroreceptors can be divided into two groups with a number of distinct properties. These are termed tonic (or d-c) receptors and phasic (or a-c) receptors. Tonic receptors are slow-adapting and therefore are sensitive to d-c voltage changes. They are of a particular morphological type; that

## Tonic, Ampullary Receptor

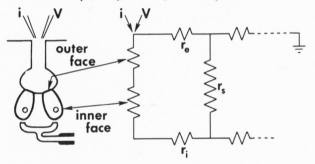

## Phasic, Tuberous Receptor

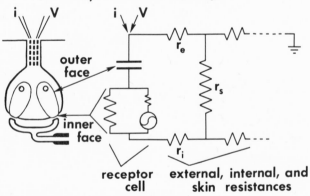

Fig. 1. Anatomical diagrams and equivalent circuits of electroreceptors. Diagrams are shown with the external medium to the top. The skin and wall of receptor cavities are shown in cross section as lines. The opening to the exterior of phasic receptor cavity is shown as occluded by a porous mass. The nerve fibers innervating receptor cells are indicated.

is, they are ampullary receptors (Szabo, 1965). They have a canal with a clear opening to the exterior. This canal usually enlarges at the base to form an ampulla. The receptor cells are embedded in the wall of the ampulla (Fig. 1). They have only a small, more or less flat surface in contact with the lumen and are, for the most part, surrounded by what are presumably supporting cells. The receptor cells in tonic receptors appear to behave as "linear elements" in an electrical sense when potentials are applied across them; that is, they are not electrically excitable. There are no "receptor potentials" according to the definition of Davis (1961). Electrical stimuli do, however, appear to cause secretion of a transmitter, presumably by acting directly on the inner surface of the receptor cell. The transmitter causes the initiation of impulses in the innervating nerve fiber, probably by a depolarization, the "generator potential" (Davis, 1961), arising in a specialized chemically sensitive postsynaptic membrane (Grundfest, 1958, 1961a).

One may draw an approximate equivalent circuit of the tonic receptors that consists entirely of resistors (Fig. 1). The inner and outer faces of the receptor cells can be represented as "lumped" resistances, and the external medium surrounding the skin and inside of the body as "distributed" resistances (Fig. 1). In this circuit, membrane capacities are ignored, as are the resistances of the canal and receptor cell cytoplasm. Current applied by an electrode at the receptor opening flows through the external medium and through the receptor. An anodal current passes inward through the external faces and outward through the internal faces of the receptor cells. The potential across the inner faces is thus made more positive on the intracellular side, which would be depolarizing if one assumes a normal inside negative resting potential. The resistivity of the body interior is small, and that of the exterior is also small when the skin is covered with a deep layer of water. The resistance of the skin immediately surrounding the receptor is large, but since there is a large area of skin far from the receptor, the resistance between inside and outside is small and the potential of the interior of the fish is only slightly altered by a stimulus applied at the receptor opening. Thus the potential between inside and outside faces of the receptor cells is close to that recorded between the external voltage electrode and ground.

When the overlying water in the region of the receptor is removed, the external resistance around the pore greatly increases ($r_e$ in Fig. 1). Provided that a large portion of the fish remains in contact with the water, the resistance from internal to external media remains small. In this condition a given voltage drop across the receptor can be produced by a much smaller current than when the water is present. Moreover, if the external resistance is sufficiently high, nerve impulses can be recorded external to the receptors. The mechanism appears to be that the action currents of the nerve produce a voltage drop across $r_i$ (Fig. 1), and the externally recorded fraction of this potential is larger when $r_e$ is larger. At a chemically transmitting junction, pre- and postsynaptic structures must be separated by an appreciable gap (Eccles and Jaeger, 1957), and the morphological data on ampullary receptors are in agreement with this (Barets and Szabo, 1962, 1964b; Mullinger 1964; Waltman, 1966). Nerve currents that produce a positivity external to the receptor must pass inward through the inner faces of the receptor cells (Fig. 2D). The effect would be to hyperpolarize them, which is opposite to the depolarization that occurs when an external positivity is generated by a superficial electrode.

The phasic, or a-c, receptors are "tuberous receptors" and are morphologically distinct from the tonic receptors. There is a cavity beneath the epidermal surface with no clear channel to the exterior, which may be considered the defining characteristic (Fig. 1; Szabo, 1965). Functionally, however, these receptors appear to be ampullary, in the sense of having a low-resistance, presumably intercellular path to the exterior. The receptor cells themselves protrude into the receptor cavity with most of their surfaces free. Only their bases are in contact with the wall of the cavity where they are innervated (Fig. 1).

Phasic receptors are insensitive to d-c potentials, although the frequencies to which they respond vary. A simple mechanism of achieving insensitivity to d-c potentials would be to have a "blocking" capacitor in series with the receptor. It is likely that such a capacitor is provided by the outer faces of the receptor cells. These faces have a large surface area and therefore appreciable capacity, and they also appear to be of high resistance and inexcitable. In contrast, the inner faces of the receptors in general change their electrical properties in response to electrical stimuli and may even generate spikes similar to those of nerve and muscle.

Electrically a phasic receptor is similar to a tonic receptor, as far as the resistances of skin and external and internal media are concerned (Fig. 1). In the proposed equivalent circuit, however, the external face of a phasic receptor cell behaves as a capacitor, while the internal face has a resting resistance in parallel with a voltage generator with an internal resistance. In this circuit the potential across the inner face of a receptor cell is not simply proportional to the externally applied voltage but is quite distorted. When a long-lasting positive (anodal) step is applied, the potential across the inner face is at first made more positive, i.e., presumably depolarized, by an amount equal to a large

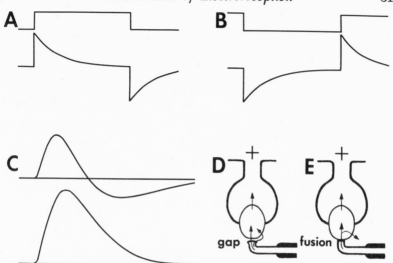

Fig. 2. External and internal potentials at model receptors. (A-C) At a phasic receptor. Upper line: form of potential recorded at external opening of receptor (positive upward). Lower line: form of potential that would be recorded across inner face of receptor cells (intracellular positivity upward). (A) If a rectangular anodal voltage pulse were applied at the external opening, the inner face would be depolarized at the onset of the stimulus and hyperpolarized at its termination. (B) If a rectangular cathodal voltage pulse were applied, the inner face would be hyperpolarized at the onset of the stimulus and depolarized at its termination. The potential transient across the inner face would, of course, be smaller than the applied potential, although the former is somewhat larger in the diagram (as if recorded at higher gain). (C) If the inner face generated the potential shown on the lower trace, the external potential would have the form indicated on the upper trace. [These data taken from model electrotonic junction given by Bennett (1966b), with the inner-face response identical to $V_1$ in Fig. 4 and the external voltage equal to $(V_1 - V_2)$, taking the constants $r_2 = 0$ and $\alpha = 0.8$ as there defined.] (D) Where the junction between receptor cell and nerve is chemically transmitting, there will be a gap, and nerve action currents flowing to make the exterior positive will tend to hyperpolarize the inner face (arrows). (E) Where there is an electrotonic junction between receptor cell and nerve fiber, action currents flowing to make the exterior positive will depolarize nonjunctional membrane of the inner face (arrows).

fraction of the external voltage (Fig. 2A). Most of the voltage drop occurs across the inner face because the other resistances in the current path are (presumably) small. Following the initial jump, the potential decays exponentially back to the resting value, assuming that the inner membrane is not excited. The time constant of decay depends on the resistance of the path from the outside to the inside of the cell through the $r_e$, $r_s$, $r_i$, and resistance of the inner face. At the end of the prolonged step, an equal and opposite change in potential occurs. When a long-lasting negative (cathodal) step is applied, the potential changes are like those produced by anodal stimuli, but reversed in sequence (Fig. 2B). The inner face is hyperpolarized at the onset of the stimulus and depolarized at its termination. Thus, equal anodal and cathodal stimuli, if they are long compared with the decay of the potentials evoked at their onset, produce equal effects except that the response at the onset of an anodal stimulus corresponds to that at the termination of a cathodal one, and vice versa. This property will be termed "equivalence of long-lasting stimuli." Since a prolonged stimulus produces only a transient change across the inner face, the excitability is unchanged during a maintained pulse. This property will be termed "d-c insensitivity," and in terms of receptor function it is a form of accommodation. A related characteristic is that the steady-state "input" resistance measured at the receptor opening will be linear (assuming linearity of skin, internal, and external resistances).

When a potential is generated by the inner face, the externally recorded response differs from what would be recorded intracellularly. Considering a positive-going spike, the capacity of the external-face charges during the rising phase of the response and positivity is recorded externally. As the spike decreases, the potential across the internal face becomes smaller than that across the outer face and the capacity begins to discharge, producing external negativity. Thus the external response is biphasic, positive-negative (Fig. 2C). Since the charge on the capacity of the external face is equal before and after the spike, no net current flows across the receptor cell. Since the voltage drops are recorded across a fixed resistance, a measure of total current flow is given by the integral of the external voltage with respect to time. Thus, the area under the positive phase of the externally recorded response must equal the area under the negative phase. This property of the response will be termed "absence of net current flow." In summary, three properties must be present if the external faces of the receptor cells behave as a capacity in series with the inner, sensitive membrane of the receptor: equivalence of long-lasting stimuli, d-c insensitivity, and absence of net current flow. It is primarily the presence of these properties which leads to the equivalent circuit of Fig. 1.

Transmission from the receptor cells to the innervating nerve appears to be chemically mediated at phasic receptors of gymnotids. In one kind in mormyrids, there is reason to believe that transmission is electrotonic. A large number of electrotonic junctions are now known in which the apposed membranes are fused and of low resistance and across which current passes between the interiors of the coupled cells

(Bennett, 1966b; Bennett et al., 1967a-d). The junctional membranes themselves are electrically inexcitable. As noted above in connection with tonic receptors, a nerve potential producing an external positivity at a chemically transmitting junction would tend to hyperpolarize the inner faces of the receptor cells (Fig. 2D). If the receptor-nerve junction were electrotonic, however, current generated by the nerve that produces an external positivity would pass across the low resistance of the junction. Some of the current would also flow outward through the surrounding, nonjunctional membrane, tending to depolarize it (Fig. 2E). An external potential of neural origin would have the same effect on the inner face as a potential of the same sign produced by an external electrode.

Stimulation and recording at the receptor openings was carried out in the same manner as previously, usually using one electrode for stimulation and one for recording (Bennett, 1965). Occasionally the stimulating electrode was recorded from at high gain, by using a bridge circuit. Single afferent fibers were recorded from in fine filaments of nerve by using a wire hook. The input amplifier was, like that for microelectrode recording, high-impedance and single-ended. In high-frequency volleys, the amplitude of the nerve impulses could decrease sharply after the first one. Apparently refractoriness caused propagation to fail at a node of Ranvier close to the recording site (Figs. 20, 21). To record simultaneously from nerve fiber and receptor, single fibers that responded to gross electrical stimuli were isolated from the afferent nerve. A needle insulated except at the tip was used to stimulate monopolarly, and the surface of the body was explored. By decreasing the stimulus strength, a maximum of sensitivity could be found that was inevitably over a single receptor or cluster of receptors.

GYMNOTID ELECTRORECEPTORS

**Morphology.** The electroreceptors of the gymnotids are readily visible on the skin as spots free of pigment cells (in sectioned material, pigment cells are seen to be absent around their bases, labeled M in Figs. 5, 6, and 8). The spots are distributed widely over the body surface and are somewhat more numerous rostrally and dorsally. There is some degree of regularity to the distribution of the different kinds of receptors (Szabo, 1965), but the precise pattern of distribution is yet to be determined. Primary attention was paid to receptors along the body, but there do not appear to be morphologically distinct receptors in the head region. In *Gymnotus* three distinct classes of receptor can be seen (Fig. 3). The most numerous and widely dis-

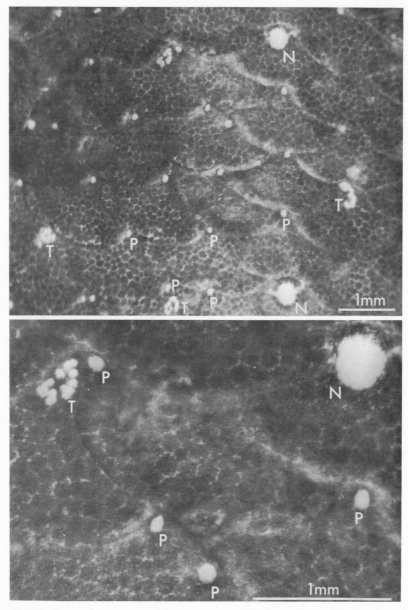

Fɪɢ. 3. External appearance of receptors in *Gymnotus*. From the dorsolateral quadrant near the middle of the body of a fish about 25 cm long. Rostral to the top, ventral to the right. A portion of the skin in the upper picture is shown with greater magnification in the lower picture. Pigment-free spots of three kinds can be seen: neuromasts (N), phasic receptors (P), and tonic receptors (T). These last occur in clusters. Scales and individual pigment cells are also visible.

tributed over the body are single spots about 100 $\mu$ in diameter (in a fish 25 cm long). These are the phasic receptors (P). Somewhat less numerous, but also widely distributed, are clusters of 5 to 10 smaller spots about 60 $\mu$ in diameter. These are the tonic receptors (T), and each cluster is innervated by a single fiber (see below). Larger spots, about 300 $\mu$ in diameter and protruding slightly, are free neuromasts (N). The last-named are found regularly spaced in several lines along the lateral and dorsal surfaces of the body. In addition to these receptors, the external openings of the lateral line canals can be seen in the usual position.

The external appearance of the receptors has been examined in several other gymnotids. In *Eigenmannia* three classes of receptors as found in *Gymnotus* are visible on the skin surface (Fig. 4A). The largest, about 50 $\mu$ in diameter in a fish 15 cm long, are the free neuromasts (N), which are more or less regularly distributed in rows along the body. The smallest, about 25 $\mu$ in diameter, occur in clusters of some 20 or more. These are the tonic receptors (T), and electrophysiological data indicate that all the receptors in a cluster are innervated by a single fiber. Intermediate in size (about 50 $\mu$ in diameter) are what are apparently phasic receptors (P). Unlike the phasic receptors in *Gymnotus*, these are mostly distributed in clusters of 5 to 10. Presumably all the receptors in a cluster are innervated by a single fiber, as has been shown physiologically in *Sternopygus*, which is closely related to *Eigenmannia* (Bennett, 1961). In the head region the spots are so numerous that the clustering of the phasic receptors is no longer distinct, although the tonic clusters are still recognizable. In *Sternopygus* the receptors are similar in appearance. The single phasic and tonic receptors are of more nearly the same size, but as in *Eigenmannia* the number of tonic receptors in a single cluster appears to be larger.

In *Sternarchus*, the larger species of *Steatogenys*, and in *Hypopomus*, single and clustered receptors are seen similar to those of *Gymnotus* (Szabo, 1965). In *Electrophorus*, clusters of phasic receptors are found in single pigment-free areas, but each receptor appears to be innervated by a single fiber (see below).

The tonic receptors of *Gymnotus* are of the ampullary type (Fig. 5). A canal that opens to the outside leads to a deep-lying ampulla, as shown by reconstruction from serial sections. The canal and ampulla are filled with a fairly dark-staining material that is presumably mucoid in nature. The section of Fig. 5A passes through three ampullae, one canal part of its way to the exterior, and two canals at their openings. The central portion is enlarged in Fig. 5B. At the outer end of

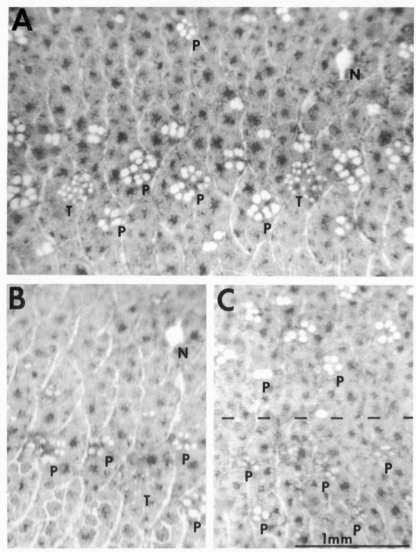

Fig. 4. External appearance of receptors in *Eigenmannia*, normal and following nerve degeneration. The facial branch of the left posterior lateral line nerve was sectioned at the level of the operculum two months prior to preservation. The fish was about 15 cm long. (A) On the normal side in the dorsolateral quadrant of the anterior of the body. Dorsal to the top, rostral to the right. Three classes of pigment-free spots can be seen, as in Fig. 3: neuromasts (N), phasic receptors (P), and tonic receptors (T). The latter two occur in clusters. (B) A corresponding point on the operated side; dorsal to the top, rostral to the left. The receptors are reduced in size and appear less differentiated from the surrounding skin. (C) A view of the dorsal midline (dashes); normal to the top, operated to the bottom, and rostral to the left. Most of the receptors on the operated side are greatly deteriorated, but one cluster of three to the lower left appears normal and perhaps is innervated from the unoperated side.

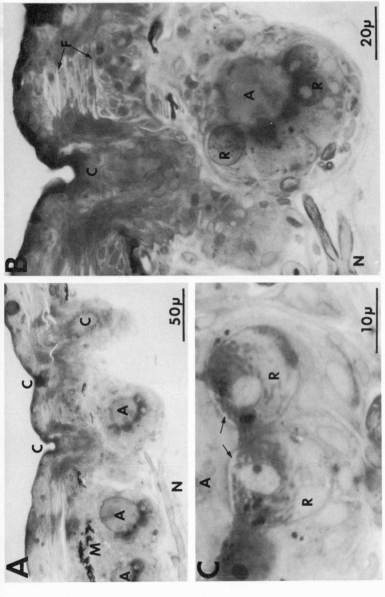

Fig. 5. Histology of tonic receptors (*Gymnotus*). For this and subsequent histological figures, material was fixed in osmic acid or in glutaraldehyde followed by osmic acid, embedded in Epon, sectioned at 2 μ, and stained with toluidine blue (Bennett et al., 1967a). (A) Low magnification of a section perpendicular to the skin surface through a cluster of tonic receptors, external surface upward. (B) Higher magnification of central portion of (A). (C) Section through ampullary wall of another receptor, showing two receptor cells (R). (A) Lumen of ampulla; (C) canal; (N) nerve; (F) layer of flattened epidermal cells; (M) melanophore.

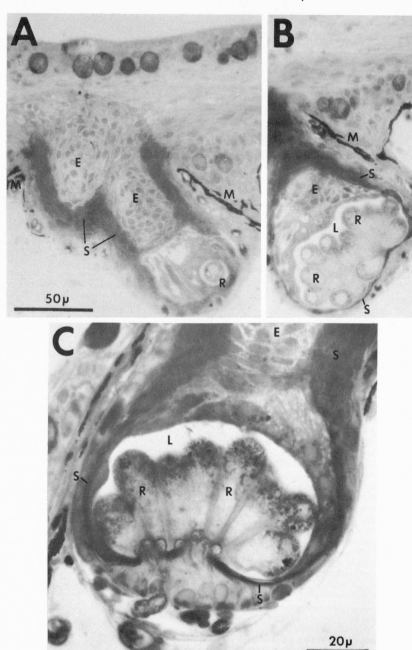

the canal, there is a characteristic space where the mucoid substance is absent. In the walls of the ampulla are relatively large, round cells (R) that are undoubtedly the receptor cells, although their innervation was not seen in toluidine-blue-stained, osmic-acid-fixed material (Szabo, 1965). The receptor cells are embedded in the wall of the ampulla, and only a small portion of the circumference is in contact with the lumen (Fig. 5C). At the luminal border of the cells, there is a pale band that suggests the presence of microvilli (arrows). The nuclei lie near the outer margins of the cells, where there are also peculiar dark bodies and other fairly densely staining material. Similar cytological details were observed by Szabo (1965) in the ampullary and, presumably, tonic receptors of several other gymnotids. The single nerve fiber that innervates the cluster of receptors is seen in Fig. 5A running beneath the ampullae and branching twice (N).

The histological appearance of the phasic receptors in *Gymnotus* (Figs. 6-8) is quite different from that of the tonic receptors. The receptor cells lie in one or two cavities (L) beneath the surface, but there is no well-delineated canal connecting these cavities to the exterior. The phasic receptors are thus of the tuberous type. A large mass of apparently very loosely packed epidermal cells extends from the receptor cavity upward to the outer layer of the skin (Fig. 8E). The receptor cells (R) are gourd-shaped and lie almost entirely free in their cavity (Figs. 6, 7). They are attached only at their bases to several hillocks in the cavity wall. As in the tonic receptor cells, the nuclei are peripheral, and there are similar perinuclear inclusions. Primarily along their lateral margins the cells appear to have an extracellular coat of fibrillar material (V in Fig. 7A). Presumably this appearance is due to microvilli.

The single fiber innervating the receptor (N in Fig. 7B) enters the wall of the cavity and loses most or all of its myelin sheath before branching. In toluidine-blue-stained, osmic-acid-fixed material, the

---

Fig. 6. Histology of phasic receptors (*Gymnotus*). (A) Section through phasic receptor perpendicular to skin surface. Mass of loosely packed epithelial cells (E) extends from outer layer of epidermis inward to receptor cavities. At this receptor there are two cavities, one lying to the left that is not visible in this section. Section passes through nucleus of one receptor cell (R) in cavity to the right. (B) Nearby section through right cavity, showing many more receptor cells. The cavity is surrounded by a dark-staining sheath (S). (C) Section through a different receptor, showing epithelial mass (E), dark-staining sheath (S), and attachments of receptor cells (R). (L) Lumen of receptor cavity; (M) melanophore. (A) and (B) are at the same magnification.

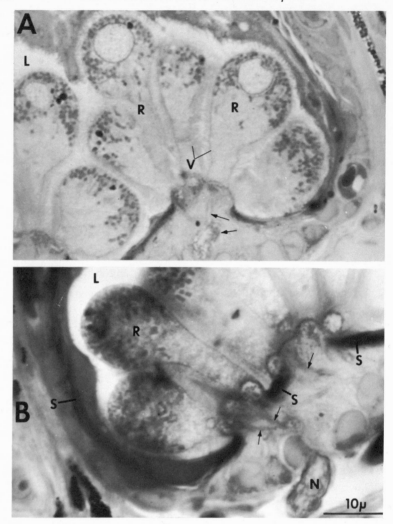

FIG. 7. Phasic receptor cells (*Gymnotus*). (A) Section through an attachment hillock of receptor cells (R). Apparent borders of microvilli (V) along the lateral margins of the cells are shown particularly clearly. Arrows indicate what are probably terminal portions of innervating nerve fiber. (B) Same section as Fig. 6C at a higher magnification. The dark-staining sheath (S) is interrupted at the two attachment hillocks of receptor cells. The nerve fiber (N) is seen entering cavity wall. Arrows indicate what may be terminal branches of the nerve. (L) Lumen of receptor cavity.

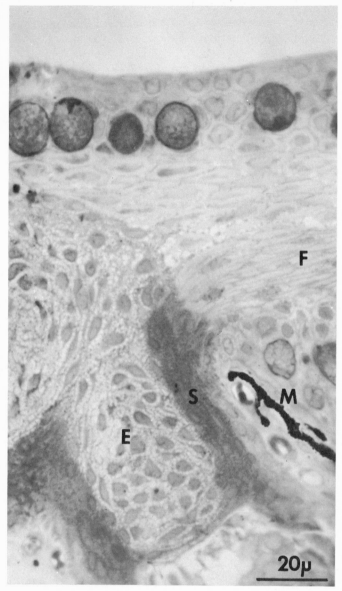

Fig. 8. Epidermal layers at a phasic receptor (*Gymnotus*). Same section as Fig. 6A at a higher magnification. Layer of flattened epidermal cells (F) is seen to merge with dark-staining sheath (S), also of flattened cells, extending inward around loose epithelial mass (E). Cells immediately above loose epithelial mass appear to have small spaces between them. Outer epidermal layer of rounded cells is uninterrupted over receptor; small spaces at top left of figure are an artifact of sectioning. (M) Melanophore.

terminal filaments running to the bases of the receptor cells are not clear, although indications of them are seen in Fig. 7 (arrows).

The efficient operation of an electroreceptor requires that the inside and outside surfaces of the receptor cells be electrically insulated from each other, and the physiological data indicate that this is in fact true. While the morphological basis of the insulation must be defined experimentally, several structures have the required geometrical relations. Near the middle of the epidermis, there is a layer of flattened, closely packed cells (F)—features that might be anticipated of an insulating layer (Figs. 5, 8). At the margins of the phasic receptors, this layer merges with a dark-staining layer (S) that extends ventrally to surround the receptor cavity (Figs. 6, 7). At the bases of the receptor cells, there are openings in this apparent insulating sheath (Fig. 7). In the tonic receptors the canals also have a thick wall that fuses with the layer of flattened epidermal cells, although there is less marked staining of the wall (Fig. 5B). The physiological data require that the phasic receptors have a blocking capacitor in series with the sensitive membrane. If the dark-staining sheath and flattened epidermal cells were insulating, this capacity would have to be located at the receptor cells themselves, most probably in their outer faces. The loose epidermal mass would presumably have a low resistance. The cells immediately over it also appear somewhat loosely packed (Fig. 8). The structure of the outer layer of epidermis does not suggest that it is of particularly low resistance, but it is unlikely to be of high resistance since it extends quite uniformly over the openings of the phasic receptors.

**Tonic Receptors in *Gymnotus*.** *Patterns of response.* Many single nerve fibers in the facial component of the posterior lateral line nerve carried spontaneous impulses that occurred at rather regular intervals (Fig. 9A). The average frequencies were from about 60 to 130 impulses per sec. When a positive pulse was applied through a monopolar stimulating electrode and the surface of the fish was explored, a region of maximum sensitivity for acceleration of discharge was always found over a single cluster of small receptors. Separate monopolar stimulating and recording pipettes were then placed over the clusters, which were termed tonic receptors, for reasons that will now become apparent.

The steady discharge of nerve impulses could be modified in the way shown in Fig. 9. Anodal stimuli caused acceleration of discharge with a threshold as low as a few tenths of a millivolt (B). Stronger stimuli caused a greater acceleration, and frequencies in excess of 500

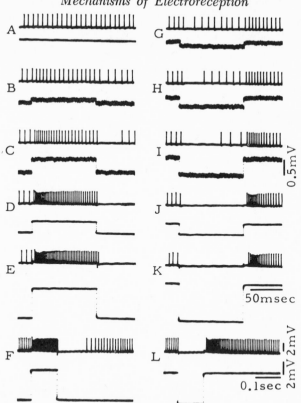

Fɪɢ. 9. Responses of a tonic receptor (*Gymnotus*). Upper trace: impulses in afferent nerve. Lower trace: potentials at receptor opening produced by rectangular current pulse. Receptor was covered with water, and "input resistance" (or ratio of voltage recorded to current applied) was about 18 kΩ. Potentials positive at recording electrode shown upward in this and all subsequent records; anodal currents also upward. (A) Spontaneous discharge at an average frequency of about 130 impulses per sec. (B-F) Responses to increasing anodal stimuli. (G-L) Responses to increasing cathodal stimuli. Slower sweep in (F) and (L) of same-strength stimuli as (E) and (K), respectively. Higher voltage gain in (B), (C), and (G-I).

impulses per sec could be evoked by stimuli of a few millivolts (C-F). When a long-lasting (rectangular) stimulus was given, the initial acceleration was followed by some reduction in frequency, but even with stimuli that were several seconds in duration the accommodation was incomplete. Termination of an anodal stimulus was followed by a reduction in frequency below the resting value. Recovery from this "depression" took place over a time course similar to that for accommodation to maintained stimuli. A brief anodal stimulus could evoke a prolonged acceleration, which was followed by a depression similar to that at the termination of a maintained stimulus (Fig. 11A, C).

Cathodal stimuli reduced the resting discharge (Fig. 9G-L). With weak, long-lasting pulses, considerable accommodation could be seen; that is, the deceleration was not maintained at its initial value, and some recovery toward the initial rate occurred (G-I). However, with stronger stimuli the discharge was blocked throughout the entire pulse (J-L). Termination of a cathodal pulse was followed by an acceleration in discharge rate, with subsequent restoration to the resting value. This "rebound" discharge was also observed following brief cathodal pulses (Fig. 11E). These patterns of response are similar to those observed at the ampullae of Lorenzini (see Murray, Chap. 18 of this volume) and at other receptors with both tonic and phasic response components.

*Externally recorded potentials.* When rectangular current pulses were applied with the receptor covered by a large amount of water, the voltage produced was also nearly rectangular (Fig. 9). When the water was drained away from the skin surface however, the evoked voltages became much more slowly rising and falling, and the currents required to produce them were much smaller since shunting through the water was greatly reduced (Fig. 10A, B). For instance, the input resistance in Fig. 10 was about ten times greater than that in Fig. 9. The rising and falling phases of the pulses had the same shape and were symmetrical around the base line for cathodal and anodal pulses. In addition, the steady-state voltages changed linearly with applied current of either sign. These results indicate that the receptor and adjacent skin are electrically passive and that the slowness of rise and fall of the potentials is due to the capacity of the tissues.

Under these conditions of reduced shunting, it became possible to record what were apparently nerve impulses in the fiber innervating the receptor. These responses were small positive potentials that preceded each impulse in the nerve by a constant interval. They are barely discernible in Fig. 10C and D. When the skin was quite dry, the nerve response at the receptor opening could be as large as 0.5 mV, although in these conditions the sensitivity of the receptor to applied stimuli was greatly reduced (Fig. 10E). Antidromic stimulation of the afferent fiber evoked a potential that was identical to the spontaneous discharge, with the exception that the rising phase was somewhat slowed. The difference in antidromic and orthodromic nerve impulses is ascribable to differences in the spatial pattern of activation in the two cases. An antidromic impulse delayed the onset of the next ortho-

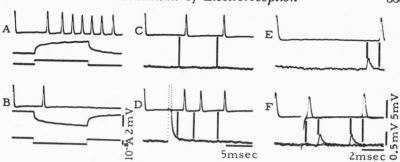

FIG. 10. External potentials at a tonic receptor (*Gymnotus*). Same receptor and display ,as in Fig. 9, but lower trace in (A) and (B) shows stimulating current. (A, B) Overlying water had been drained away; "upset" resistance was greater and time course of potentials was slowed compared with that in Fig. 9. (C) On increasing the gain, a small positive potential could be seen at the receptor opening preceding each spontaneous nerve impulse by a constant interval (vertical lines). (D) Evoked impulses could also be seen. (E) After some drying of the skin, externally recorded impulses at receptor became larger. (F) Antidromic stimulation of innervating nerve fiber evoked a nearly identical nerve impulse at receptor and delayed next spontaneous discharge. Stimulating electrodes were close to recording site in the nerve (two superimposed sweeps at threshold; the fiber was excited in one). Rising phase of the antidromic impulse was somewhat slower than that of the spontaneous response. Antidromic and orthodromic conduction times were equal (vertical lines); average conduction velocity 35 m per sec. Lower voltage gain for receptor recording in (A) and (B).

dromic discharge, although the delay was less than that observed at the ampulla of Lorenzini (Murray, 1965). The conduction velocity of the axons illustrated in Figs. 9 and 13B were 35 and 40 m per sec.

By means of averaging techniques, the nerve impulse could also be recorded when the receptor was covered with water. While the time of the discharge is not known before it occurs, the nerve impulse arrives at a fixed interval afterward. In Fig. 13C are shown a number of superimposed sweeps in which the oscilloscope was triggered by the nerve impulse (upper traces). The potential simultaneously recorded at the receptor opening is shown on the middle traces, but the nerve response, of course, does not appear on these traces. This signal was fed into a delay line and delayed by about 4 msec. The output of the delay line was further amplified and is shown on the lower traces. The calibration pulse (0.2 mV, 1 msec) on the middle traces is thus delayed and enlarged on the lower traces. In the superimposed and delayed traces, the nerve impulse is clearly discernible as a small positive potential that preceded the impulse in the fiber by the same interval as recorded when the receptor was in air [vertical lines in (B) and (C); the arrow in (C) indicates the amount by which

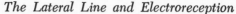
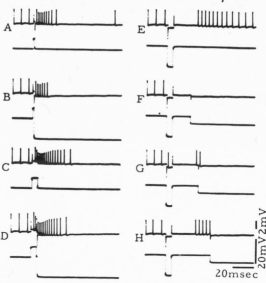

FIG. 11. Duration of excitation following brief stimuli (*Gymnotus*). Same receptor and display as in Fig. 9. (A) Brief anodal stimulus evoked a burst of impulses and subsequent silent period. (B) Strong cathodal stimulus given just afterward could reduce the length of the burst only slightly. (C) Somewhat longer anodal stimulus evoked longer burst. (D) This discharge was less affected by cathodal stimulus than was the response in (A) and (B). (E) Brief cathodal stimulus produced a cessation of firing, followed by burst of impulses. (F-H) This burst could be terminated at any point by a moderately strong cathodal stimulus.

the upper and middle traces are shifted with respect to the lower].

*Mode of transmission from receptor cells to innervating fiber.* A simple experiment provided evidence that transmission at the receptor-nerve junction is chemically mediated. A brief anodal stimulus evoked a burst of impulses that long outlasted the stimulus (Fig. 11A, C), and this discharge could not be blocked by a strong cathodal stimulus given shortly after the anodal stimulus (B, D). In Fig. 11 the cathodal stimulus was 17 mV in amplitude, about ten times that necessary to block the resting discharge of this receptor (cf. Fig. 9I, J). Only a slight reduction in the later part of the evoked discharge was obtained, nor were stronger stimuli more effective. This result indicates that there was some persistent excitatory influence that was independent of the potential across the receptor cell. No purely electrical mechanism seems to account for the data in a reasonable fashion, but an obvious possibility is that transmitter substance accumulated in the synaptic gap (Hagiwara et al., 1962). An additional mechanism is that the receptor cell was "activated" to secrete transmitter by the brief anodal pulse in a manner that could not be reversed by cathodal polarization. Reasons are given below for believing that the second mechanism did, in fact, contribute to the persistent excitation.

The evidence for chemical transmission at the receptor-nerve junction also confirms that the externally recorded impulse is generated by the nerve and not by the receptor cells, since the electrically evoked secretion of transmitter would be found in the latter. The synaptic delay at this junction may be defined as the time between onset of a strong stimulus and initiation of a postsynaptic potential (p.s.p.) in the innervating fiber. The p.s.p. itself was never recorded at the receptor opening, and in the presence of such strong stimuli as in Fig. 10 it would be difficult to record even the nerve impulse. Since the orthodromic conduction time is known (Fig. 10), however, the time of impulse initiation can be determined from the time of the impulse in the afferent fiber. The latency of the first impulse was about 1.25 msec in Fig. 12A and B and 1.9 msec in Fig. 13D. These values would exceed

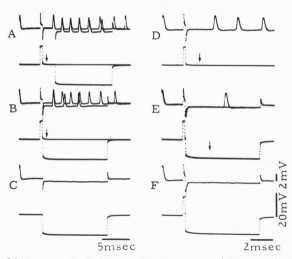

Fig. 12. Minimum activation time at tonic receptor (*Gymnotus*). Same receptor and display as in Fig. 9. Time of first impulse (arrows) calculated from orthodromic conduction time (Fig. 10). (A, B) Two superimposed sweeps where a brief anodal stimulus was and was not followed by strong cathodal stimulus. (A) Cathodal stimulus delayed and blocked the later impulses in the response. (B) When cathodal stimulus was given earlier, only the first impulse was unaffected, although it arose after the onset of the stimulus. (C) Cathodal stimulus alone blocked the resting discharge. (D) Response to a briefer anodal stimulus was of somewhat longer latency (faster sweep in D-F). (E) Cathodal stimulus just afterward delayed and occasionally blocked the evoked discharges (two superimposed sweeps). (F) When cathodal stimulus was slightly closer to anodal stimulus, response was entirely blocked.

the synaptic delay by the time required for the p.s.p. to reach threshold of the nerve fiber.

When the anodal pulses were made as brief as about 0.3 msec, an immediately following cathodal pulse could block the subsequent discharge completely (Fig. 12D-F). With somewhat longer stimuli, the early part of the subsequent response could be reduced but not blocked (B). With the strong anodal stimuli used, the minimum duration required for excitation could not be much reduced by further increasing the stimulus strength. The duration of the stimulus in Fig. 12B was shorter than the delay in impulse initiation at the receptor by 0.7 msec, and the difference is greater in Fig. 12D. At the nerve-muscle junction, the time required for the transmitter to diffuse across the synaptic gap and act on the postsynaptic membrane is apparently less than 0.1 msec, and only a small part of the synaptic delay can be accounted for by these factors (Katz and Miledi, 1965). At the electroreceptors the rise time of the p.s.p. is not known, but with strong stimuli it is unlikely to be more than a few tenths of a millisecond. Thus, if times for diffusion and postsynaptic action of transmitter are similar to those at the nerve-muscle junction, secretion of transmitter must occur after the stimulus producing it. Assuming similar diffusion and action times at the squid giant synapse (Takeuchi and Takeuchi, 1962) and at the hatchet fish giant synapse (Auerbach and Bennett, 1966, and unpublished data), where in each case the presynaptic impulse can be recorded intracellularly, transmitter secretion can occur after the presynaptic impulse. It may also do so at the nerve-muscle junction, where the presynaptic impulse can only be externally recorded (Katz and Miledi, 1965). Given that transmitter secretion can occur after the pulse evoking it, the failure of an oppositely directed pulse to block secretion in the electroreceptors is not surprising. To be sure, the length of an impulse train can be reduced, and the effect is greater with shorter stimuli (Fig. 11B, D; Fig. 12A, B). This result suggests that the later-occurring secretion of transmitter could, in fact, be reduced by the cathodal pulses. If it could be affected at all, it probably could be blocked—which suggests that the long-lasting excitations were due to persistent transmitter.

Activation of the secretory mechanism can be considered analogous to any of the ionic activation processes that outlast the evoking stimulus (Hodgkin and Huxley, 1952; Grundfest, 1961b). A particularly clear example is potassium activation, which may last for several hundred milliseconds after the end of a depolarizing stimulus. It should be noted that the linearity of the voltage current relations at the tonic receptors suggests that there is no ionic activation process in the receptor cells and that activation of the secretory mechanism does not involve a change in conductance. The short latency of the responses to anodal stimulation is the primary reason for assigning electrical sensitivity to the inner instead of the outer faces of the receptor cells. Transmitter secretion must take place from the inner faces, and there appears insufficient time for a nonelectrical message to be relayed from the outer faces.

A further indication of chemical transmission at the tonic receptors is provided by experiments using very strong stimuli. In Fig. 13A a brief stimulus of about 0.8 V evoked the initial nerve impulses at latencies of either 2.8 or 4.2 msec. The orthodromic conduction time was 2.3 msec in (B) and probably slightly greater in (A) because of refractoriness after the spontaneous response that triggered the sweep. Thus,

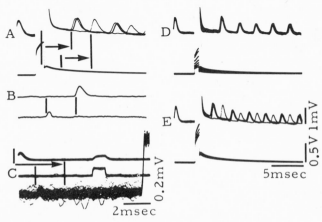

Fig. 13. Latencies of evoked and spontaneous impulses (*Gymnotus*). Display as in Fig. 9, except for lower trace of (C), but with a different receptor. (A) A strong stimulus evoked an impulse at either of two latencies (preparation in water, voltage calibration in E). Times of impulse initiation calculated from orthodromic conduction times shown in (B) are indicated by vertical lines. (B) Preparation in air, showing externally recorded impulse and orthodromic conduction time (2.3 msec). (C) Preparation in water. Lower traces (superimposed sweeps) show externally recorded potential at receptor (middle traces) delayed and amplified; calibration pulse near the middle of upper two traces is 0.2 mV and 1 msec. The nerve impulse at the receptor can be seen in superimposed traces as brief positive or positive-negative potential preceding the nerve impulse by a time identical with that in (B) (vertical lines, delay time indicated by arrow). (D) Stimuli weaker than in (A) evoked impulses at a minimum latency of 4.2 msec in the nerve (i.e., 1.9 msec at the receptor). (E) Stronger stimuli evoked impulses at a minimum latency of 2.3 msec in the nerve (i.e., at zero latency at the receptor). (A), (B), and (C) are at faster sweep speed. Voltage gains are the same in (A), (D), and (E) and in (B) and (C).

the impulses arose at latencies of about 0.5 and 1.9 msec, or slightly less. The somewhat stronger stimuli in (E) evoked responses at a latency very close to the orthodromic conduction time, and the weaker stimuli in (D) evoked responses at a latency of about 3.9 msec, indicating the longer conduction time in (A). The shorter latency responses were undoubtedly due to direct stimulation of the nerve fiber. The delay of the nerve impulse with weaker stimuli could have been due to the time required for chemical transmission. Direct stimulation of the nerve was not obtained by using cathodal stimuli. The threshold was certainly much higher, but it was not measured to avoid damage to the receptor. The strong stimuli used in Fig. 13 did not have a deleterious effect, for the thresholds were unchanged when tested subsequently. Direct stimulation of the innervating nerve was also obtained with anodal stimulation at the ampullae of Lorenzini (Murray, 1965). Presumably anodal stimuli excite the nerve fiber at some distance central to the terminal. The lower sensitivity of the nerve to cathodal stimuli may be a result of higher threshold of the terminal or of the spatial arrangement of the nerve and surrounding tissue. That the externally recorded impulse is positive and monophasic, or nearly so, suggests but does not prove that the terminal is not invaded by the impulse (Bennett, 1964).

The acceleration of discharge following a brief cathodal pulse is not due to a persistent excitatory influence that is independent of the potential in the receptor cells. If a cathodal pulse is given at any time during such a response, it is possible to prevent the initiation of further impulses (Fig. 11E-H); of course, an impulse requires some time to reach the site of recording in the afferent nerve and may arrive there after the onset of the cathodal pulse (cf. Fig. 11G; the precise latency of the block has not been determined). It is clear from this experiment that the "rebound" excitation following cathodal stimuli is not identical with the excitation following anodal stimuli. Several explanations could be suggested: for example, that the rebound is due to an increased probability of secretion of transmitter at the normal resting potential or to an increased amount of transmitter available to the secretory mechanism responsible for the resting discharge. The graded reduction of the resting discharge by weak cathodal stimuli does indicate that a continual release of transmitter occurs, and the variations in the intervals between impulses may result from the "quantal" secretion of transmitter.

It cannot now be said whether the depolarizations of the nerve fiber from all the receptors in a cluster summate, but the clusters are sufficiently large that it should be possible to determine if this is in fact the case. A central impulse initiation site would be indicated if weak stimuli to separate receptors could combine in their effect on the discharge frequency. In this event, it should also be possible to separate the components of accommodation that arise in the nerve fiber and in the receptor cells themselves.

*Sensitivity to voltage gradients and the role of the skin.* Up to this point it has been assumed that the receptors are sensitive to the voltage difference across the skin. Direct evidence for this is given in Fig. 14. A conventional micropipette electrode was pushed through the skin to record the potential in the interior of the body near the receptor, and a second recording electrode was placed at its opening. If a stimulating electrode was placed directly over the receptor, a given potential could be produced across it, leading to a particular response (Fig. 14D). When the stimulating electrode was moved a few millimeters away from the receptor, the current required to produce an equal response

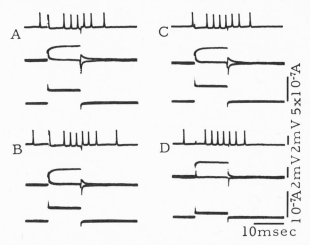

Fig. 14. Sensitivity to potentials across the skin and independence of tangential gradients: tonic receptor of *Gymnotus.* Same receptor as in Fig. 9. Upper trace: nerve recording. Middle traces starting from the same base line: potential at receptor opening and potential recorded by microelectrode pushed through outer layers of skin nearby; the former potential is the larger in each record. Lower trace: stimulating current through separate electrode. .Stimulating electrode was 2 mm anterior in (A), 2 mm dorsal in (B), and 2 mm in ventral (C). The same current pulse produced about the same potential change across the receptor and the same nerve response. External potential was somewhat slowed due to capacity of the skin, and internal potential was more or less differentiated as in Fig. 2. (D) Stimulation over the receptor. A much smaller current was required to produce the same potential across the skin, which evoked nearly the same nerve response. Potential across the skin was less slowed by the capacity because recording and stimulating electrodes were closer together.

became much larger, but the potential across the skin (the difference between external and internal electrodes) was virtually unchanged (Fig. 14A-C); the time course was somewhat slower due to skin capacity and the separation of the electrodes, compared with (D). To be sure, the potential at the inside surface of the skin was a little larger, and the potential recorded monopolarly by the external electrode was also correspondingly increased. This change indicates that the larger current produced a larger voltage drop across the resistance of the current path from inside the receptor to the indifferent electrode. The dependence of the response on the potential across the skin held whether the stimulating electrode was anterior (Fig. 14A), posterior (B), dorsal (C), or ventral to the receptor. When stimulating electrodes were at the head and the tail of the fish, the direction of response corresponded to the direction of the potential difference across the skin (Bennett, 1965), although quantitative comparison was not made with stimulation at the receptor opening. Thus, when the electrode at the head end was an anode, current entered rostrally and left caudally. Correspondingly, tonic receptors in the head region were excited, and those in the tail region inhibited. A similar result was obtained with currents running perpendicular to the body axis.

If the skin near a receptor was scratched and a stimulating electrode

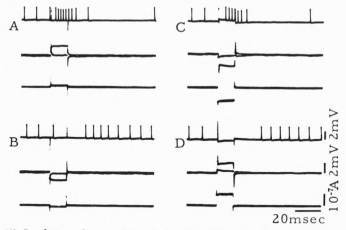

Fig. 15. Insulating characteristic of the skin (*Gymnotus*). Same receptor and display as in Fig. 14. (A, B) Anodal and cathodal stimulation at receptor opening; external potential was the larger. (C, D) Stimulating electrode pressed against superficial scratch in the skin, 2 mm caudal to receptor. Cathodal stimulus evoked acceleration, and anodal stimulus deceleration; internal potential was the larger. However, potentials across the skin associated with a given neural response were the same as in (A) and (B). Current required in (C) was much less than that in Fig. 14C.

pushed against the lesion, the potential across the receptor produced
by a given polarity of stimulation was reversed with respect to the
condition when the skin was intact or when the electrode was at the
receptor opening (Fig. 15). Again, the response corresponded to the
potential across the receptor. This observation indicates that the skin
is a barrier to current flow and emphasizes its role in determining the
potentials affecting the receptors. The scratch made in the experiment
of Fig. 15 was very superficial and did not involve the pigment cells;
presumably the layer of flattened epidermal cells was affected (cf.
Fig. 8). The current required to stimulate in Fig. 15C was less than
that in Fig. 14C, indicating that the spatial decrement of potential was
less internally than externally. This difference is probably also due to
the high resistance of the skin.

**Phasic Receptors in *Gymnotus*. *Patterns of response*.** Fibers that led
from the phasic receptors were also found in the facial component of
the posterior lateral line nerve. There was usually no spontaneous
activity in these fibers, but impulses were easily evoked when a strong
brief stimulus was applied through a wire electrode near the fish, and
a maximum of excitability was always found at a single phasic receptor.
The properties of the receptor were usually determined after draining
away the overlying water. Under these circumstances, the externally
recorded responses were larger since shunting by the water was
reduced.

The responses to anodal and cathodal stimuli threshold for a nerve
impulse are shown in Fig. 16A and B (several superimposed sweeps in
each record). The anodal stimulus occasionally evoked a single impulse

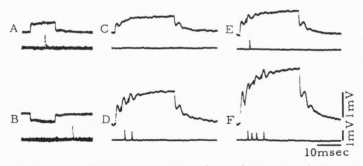

FIG. 16. Responses of phasic receptor to weak stimuli (*Gymnotus*). Upper trace:
potential at receptor opening. Rectangular current pulses were applied through a
second electrode. Lower trace: recording from afferent fiber. Several superimposed
sweeps in (A) and (B). (A) Anodal stimulation threshold for a nerve impulse.
(B) Cathodal stimulation threshold for a nerve impulse. (C-F) Responses to increasing strengths of stimuli—stronger in (E) than in (D)—when the skin was
somewhat dryer.

at its onset, and the cathodal stimulus evoked an impulse at its termination. A small oscillation was recorded outside the receptor opening at onset and termination of both stimuli, independent of whether
or not an impulse was initiated. The voltage thresholds for impulse
initiation were the same for the two polarities of stimulation.

The responses to 25-msec anodal pulses near threshold, obtained
when there was somewhat less water on the skin, are shown in Fig.
16C-F. In (C) no impulses were evoked, but there were small oscillations at the beginning and end of the pulse that were somewhat
larger than those in (A). Stronger stimuli evoked larger oscillations
and an increasing number of impulses at the onset of the stimuli (D-
F), and these impulses became of shorter latency and higher frequency. As described more fully below, the generation of impulses
was accompanied by a characteristic potential at the external receptor
opening. Weak cathodal stimuli evoked very similar responses, except
that the onset and termination phases were interchanged (cf. Fig.
21C). In different receptors, thresholds for impulse initiation varied
from a few tenths of a millivolt to slightly more than a millivolt.

When stronger anodal stimuli were applied to the receptor, the
externally recorded response at the onset could become rather spikelike, although its amplitude was usually smoothly graded up to a maximum of 10 to 15 mV (measured from initial peak to following trough;
Fig. 17A-D). Fifteen or more impulses could be initiated in the nerve
fiber. The oscillations at the termination of the pulse also increased in
amplitude, but to a lesser degree than those at the onset. Furthermore,
these oscillations became progressively delayed with stronger stimuli
until at some threshold value they disappeared entirely (D). With
intermediate-strength stimuli, both onset and termination of the stimulus were accompanied by impulse initiation (C). These pulses were
short-lasting in order to show the time courses of the externally recorded responses, and the nerve discharges at the termination of the
stimuli were reduced by refractoriness following those at the onset.
With longer-lasting stimuli a larger number of impulses were observed
at the termination (I, K).

The externally recorded responses evoked by cathodal stimuli of
intermediate strength were very similar to those evoked by equal-
amplitude anodal stimuli, except that the onset and termination phases
were interchanged (Fig. 17A, B, E, F). If the pulses were sufficiently
long, this correspondence also held for the nerve discharges (I-L).
Thus, over a wide range of stimulus strength, both nerve and externally recorded receptor response showed equivalence of long-lasting
stimuli. Also, the steady-state potentials varied linearly with applied

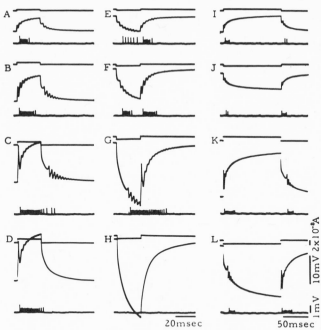

FIG. 17. Responses of phasic receptor to stimuli of intermediate strength. Same receptor as in Fig. 16. Same recording and display except that upper trace shows polarizing current. (A-D) Responses to increasing strengths of anodal stimulation. (E-H) Responses to cathodal stimuli. (I-L) Responses to longer-lasting stimuli showing "stimulus equivalence" with respect to impulse initiation (slower sweep speed; the skin was somewhat more moist at this time, as indicated by more rapid damping of evoked oscillations and lower input resistance; cf. Fig. 19).

current; that is, the input resistance was constant. With stronger cathodal stimulation, the oscillations at onset became progressively delayed (G). At some threshold they were blocked, and the response to termination of the stimulus simultaneously disappeared (H). No impulses were recorded in the nerve fiber during or immediately after the stimulus. In this case, the equivalence of long-lasting stimuli did not hold, but as shown in the following paragraphs, the failure was due to a long-lasting "unresponsive state" of the receptor.

*Delayed responses and the unresponsive state.* The termination of strong anodal stimuli was followed after several hundred milliseconds by a small and slow positive-negative potential (Fig. 18A) on which a spikelike response was occasionally superimposed (B). This delayed response was triggered by the termination of the anodal stimulus, because its latency from this point was approximately constant, independent of the duration of the stimulus (C). A similar delayed re-

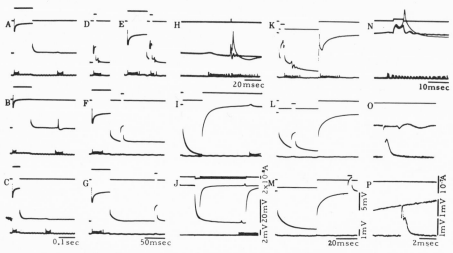

FIG. 18. Delayed responses and "unresponsive state." Phasic receptor in *Gymnotus*. Same receptor, recording, and display as in Fig. 17 except for (J). (A) Strong anodal stimulus evoked small and slow delayed response accompanied by a burst of discharges in the nerve fiber. (B) Occasionally a diphasic spikelike potential was superimposed on the delayed response. (C) Latency of delayed response was approximately constant as measured from termination of anodal stimulus. (D) Test stimulus well above threshold. (E) Excitability immediately after termination of anodal stimulus was reduced. (F, G) Somewhat later the receptor was unresponsive; the test stimulus evoked no oscillations or impulses in the nerve. (H) During the delayed response a brief stimulus could evoke an all-or-none spikelike response. This potential was diphasic, and areas under positive and negative phases were equal to within 15%, as measured by planimeter. (I) Strong cathodal stimulus evoked delayed response. (J) Latency of delayed response was independent of whether or not cathodal stimulus was maintained (two superimposed traces, a different receptor than in the rest of the figure). (K) Shortly after onset of stimulus of the same strength as in (I), receptor was still excitable for a stimulus like that in (D), and the unresponsive state could be blocked as indicated by response to termination of conditioning stimulus. (L, M). Somewhat later the receptor was unresponsive. (N) During delayed response following a cathodal stimulus, a brief stimulus could evoke a spikelike potential as in (H). Areas under positive and negative phases were approximately equal (measured on slower sweep recordings). (O) Antidromic stimulus applied close to nerve recording site evoked a small brief positive potential, a larger brief negative potential, and a slower oscillation (several superimposed sweeps). (P) Antidromic stimulus during the unresponsive state following strong cathodal stimulus evoked only a small positivity followed by a still smaller negativity. Voltage gain is the same in (A-I) and (K-N), higher in (O-P). Time calibrations are the same in (A-C), in (D-G) and (I-J), in (K-M), and in (O-P), respectively.

sponse could be evoked by strong cathodal stimuli of sufficient duration (I). The response was triggered by the onset of the stimuli and occurred at an approximately constant latency that was independent of whether or not the stimulus was maintained (J). The stimuli in Fig. 17D and H presumably evoked delayed responses that occurred after the end of the sweep.

Brief stimuli during a delayed response could evoke an additional diphasic potential that was spikelike and all-or-none (H, N). The delayed response was accompanied by a burst of impulses in the nerve fiber, and when the spikelike potential occurred spontaneously or was evoked, there were additional nerve impulses. Between a delayed response and the stimulus adequate to produce it, the receptor was inexcitable even to stimuli well above threshold (F, G, L, M). Neither external oscillations nor nerve impulses were evoked. The onset of this unresponsiveness was gradual (E), and a large testing stimulus could prevent its establishment (K) and also block the ensuing delayed response.

*"Ringing" of the receptors.* The amplitude of the externally recorded responses was larger when the skin was not covered by water, and the evoked oscillations became less rapidly damped if the skin was allowed to dry (cf. Figs. 16, 17). The decreased damping of the oscillations is simply a result of the increase in resistance at the receptor opening and is neither a "pharmacological" effect nor due to injury by drying. In the experiment of Fig. 19 a large (1-mm diameter) electrode filled with aquarium water was placed over the receptor, in addition to a much smaller Ringer-filled electrode. The surrounding skin was then allowed to dry. When the large electrode was connected to the indifferent electrode (ground) by way of a 10-M$\Omega$ resistance, a cathodal stimulus of about 5 mV (measured by the small electrode and applied by the large electrode in a bridge circuit; Bennett, 1965) evoked a slowly damped oscillation at a frequency of about 190 impulses per sec (Fig. 19A, C). When a 100-k$\Omega$ resistance connected the large electrode to ground, the same voltage stimulus, as measured by the small electrode, evoked a smaller and much more rapidly damped response (B, D). The effect of the shunting was fully and immediately reversible. The reduction in response amplitude by a shunting resistance indicates that the receptor had an appreciable internal resistance. That the oscillations are more rapidly damped indicates that this resistance is in the receptor cells themselves rather than in the pathway to the exterior. If the internal resistance were primarily in the latter, there would be only a change in the response amplitude and little change in its time course.

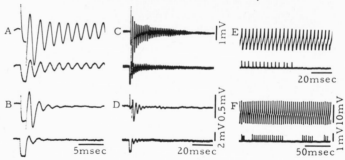

Fɪɢ. 19. "Ringing" of phasic receptors (*Gymnotus*). (A-D) A large electrode (upper trace) filled with aquarium water in agar and a smaller Ringer-agar electrode (lower trace) were placed over the receptor, water was drained away, and the skin was allowed to dry. Stimulating currents were applied through the large electrode using a bridge circuit. (A, C) The large electrode was connected to stimulator by means of a 10-MΩ resistance. Cathodal stimulus of approximately 4 mV, measured by the small electrode, evoked a slowly damped oscillation. Well after the stimulus, there appeared to be little net current flow during the oscillation, which was nearly symmetrical around the base line. (B, D) The large electrode was connected to the indifferent electrode by a resistance of 100 kΩ. Same voltage stimulus as measured by the small electrode evoked a smaller and more rapidly damped oscillation. The change from (A) and (C) was immediately reversed by disconnecting the shunt resistance. Same sweep speed in (A) and (B) and in (C) and (D). Lower trace gain is the same in (A-D). Upper trace gain is higher in (B) and (D) than in (A) and (C). (E-F) A different experiment, in which the receptor was oscillating continually. Periods in which the nerve impulses tended to follow the oscillation one-to-one alternated with periods in which impulses failed altogether.

Often when the skin was allowed to dry, maintained oscillations could be recorded at frequencies of from several hundred to over a thousand cycles per second (Fig. 19E, F). Usually the negative-going phase was more rapid than the positive-going phase, although the waveform could be nearly sinusoidal (A). The oscillations apparently were merely a result of damping decreased to the point where the receptor began to oscillate, with each cycle triggering the subsequent one without decrement. Flooding the skin with water stopped the oscillations immediately.

During sustained oscillations, the impulses in the nerve often failed intermittently (Fig. 19E, F). At lower frequencies, there tended to be one impulse per cycle during a number of cycles and then no impulses during an ensuing period. At higher frequencies, the nerve impulses never followed the receptor oscillation one-to-one.

The increase in oscillations associated with drying of the skin could be accompanied by an increase in the number of nerve impulses evoked by a given stimulus. However, the patterns of response seen in Figs. 16-18 were unaffected; that is, bursts of impulses could be evoked at both onset and termination of anodal and cathodal stimuli when the preparations were immersed, and the externally recorded oscillations were quite small and rapidly damped. The delayed responses and unresponsive state could also be evoked independent of the amount of shunting.

*D-C insensitivity.* Except when the unresponsive state was evoked, the phasic receptors were found to be rapidly adapting, and during maintained stimuli their excitability rapidly returned to normal. Thus they are insensitive to d-c potentials. This property is illustrated in Fig. 20 for anodal and cathodal stimuli well above threshold. The anodal testing pulse (A) evoked nearly identical damped oscillations when given alone or when it was superimposed on either long-lasting stimulus (B, C), and similar results were obtained with brief cathodal testing stimuli. The number of impulses evoked was smaller in (B), but this effect was due to the onset rather than continuation of the

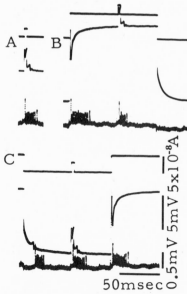

Fig. 20. "D-C insensitivity" of phasic receptor (*Gymnotus*). Same receptor, recording, and display as in Fig. 18. (A) Brief testing stimulus well above threshold. (B) When testing stimulus was superimposed on strong long-lasting anodal stimulus, externally recorded response was unchanged. The number of nerve impulses was reduced due to refractoriness following the response at onset of the stimulus, as shown by testing following a brief conditioning stimulus. (C) Responsiveness during a strong long-lasting cathodal stimulus was unchanged.

stimulus, for a brief conditioning stimulus that evoked about the same number of impulses as the long-lasting one had the same effect. In general, the refractoriness measured in terms of nerve impulses was longer-lasting than that for generation of the externally recorded oscillations (Fig. 17A-C, E, G, I, L). During even very strong anodal stimuli, the excitability rapidly returned to normal; but of course, strong cathodal stimuli triggered the long-lasting unresponsive state (Fig. 18L, M).

*External signs of impulse initiation.* The oscillations recorded at the receptor openings were presumably generated in the receptor cells, for there was little correlation between these potentials and the nerve responses, and quite large external potentials might not lead to any nerve impulses (Figs. 17B, 21C). Moreover, with near-threshold stimulation and when the skin was not very wet, the nerve impulse was detectable at the receptor opening. It was recorded as a small and brief positive component followed by a larger negative phase and was similar in responses to both anodal and cathodal stimuli (Fig. 21A, B, D). A similar sequence was evoked by antidromic stimulation of the innervating fiber (E, F), and the antidromic and orthodromic conduction times were very nearly equal (vertical lines in A, B, D, E). The brief diphasic potential could be followed by a slower damped oscillation of the same frequency as that evoked by direct stimuli. This oscillation, which was larger when the skin was not so wet, is seen particularly clearly following the last impulse in Fig. 21C and D and in the first impulse in Fig. 21G. Similar oscillations followed an antidromic response (Figs. 18O, 21J). However, an antidromic response was greatly reduced during the unresponsive state, and it became a brief positivity followed by a small negativity that was often obscured by noise (Fig. 18P). The larger brief negativity and subsequent oscillations were lost (O).

It is likely that the unresponsive state involves only the receptor cells, for no impulses are initiated at its onset, and the stimuli required to evoke it are much weaker than those required to directly stimulate the nerve (cf. Fig. 23). Probably the antidromic response during this state represents the contribution of the nerve to the externally recorded potential when an impulse is initiated. The remaining components would be generated by the receptor cells as a result of electrical stimulation by the nerve. These components summate with those evoked by direct stimulation and occasionally appear to initiate further impulses, such as in responses to antidromic stimulation (Fig. 21K).

When stronger stimuli that set up a train of impulses in the nerve were given, the externally recorded impulses could be greatly reduced

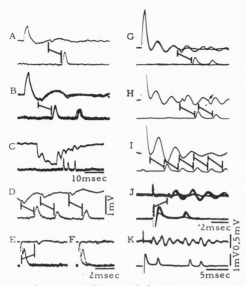

Fig. 21. Nerve impulses externally recorded at receptor opening (*Gymnotus*). Several superimposed sweeps in (B), (E-G), and (J). (A-F) Same receptor recording and display as in Fig. 16; voltage gains in (D). (A) Near-threshold anodal stimulus that evoked a single nerve impulse. External to the receptor a small primarily negative potential preceded the afferent impulse. The vertical lines indicate the conduction time obtained from (B), where a strong stimulus evoked two or three impulses. In (B) the initial positivity externally is clearly seen preceding the first impulse. In this response the negativity is obscured by potential ascribable to receptor cells, but can be seen in the second response. (C) Cathodal stimulus evoked three impulses at its termination (5 times slower sweep speed, taken at a different time during the experiment). (D) An expanded sweep as in (C), showing that each nerve impulse was preceded by a positive-negative potential at receptor opening at same latency as in (B) (vertical lines). The last external potential appeared to be followed by a slow positive-negative oscillation. (E) Antidromic stimulation (near the site of recording from afferent nerve) evoked a similar diphasic potential with a latency close to that of orthodromic response (vertical lines). A later slow positivity is apparent. (F) Threshold antidromic stimulation showing that external response occurred only when afferent fiber was stimulated. (G-K) A different receptor; calibrations in (K). (G) At threshold, two nerve impulses were evoked rather than a single one. The first was preceded by a brief positive-negative potential as in (H), but potential corresponding to second impulse (arrow) occurred too late for the impulse to have arisen at receptor. Vertical lines indicate same interval as in (H). (I) With stronger stimulation, a train of impulses was evoked. Small external potentials can be associated with the first few, but external sign of the later impulses was greatly reduced. (J) Threshold antidromic stimulation showing equality of antidromic and orthodromic conduction times. A pair of impulses was evoked in the nerve, and there were apparently two responses externally as well. Latency of the second indicates that it did not initiate the second impulse in the nerve. A prolonged oscillation was set up that could initiate further impulses, as in (K) (slower sweep speed).

in amplitude. In Fig. 21I, a small externally recorded component appeared to precede each of the first two impulses in the afferent nerve, but there was little detected preceding the last three. Probably the nerve terminal was sufficiently depolarized that the impulses were initiated more centrally and failed to propagate into the terminal.

Threshold stimulation of some receptors evoked impulses in pairs (Fig. 21G). In these cases, the second impulse was apparently initiated somewhere along the fiber, for the second externally recorded impulse at the receptor occurred at an interval preceding the second nerve response that was shorter than the orthodromic conduction time of the first impulse (Fig. 21H, K). The externally recorded response might even occur after the second impulse in the nerve. Antidromic stimulation also evoked pairs of impulses at these receptors and in their nerve fibers (J). These multiple responses perhaps resulted because of "reflections" at discontinuities in the fibers (Bennett, 1964) or because of a tendency of their membranes to oscillate in certain regions (Bennett et al., 1967b).

*Mode of transmission.* The general lack of correlation between the potentials at the receptor opening and the nerve volleys suggests that transmission from receptor to nerve cells is chemically rather than electrically mediated. Experiments in which an anodal stimulus was followed by a cathodal one (similar to those of Figs. 11 and 12) confirm this inference. A brief anodal stimulus was given that evoked a small oscillation at the receptor opening and a train of nine impulses in the innervating fiber (Fig. 22A). A strong longer-lasting cathodal stimulus, which itself evoked no responses at its onset (H), was given shortly afterward (B). This stimulus blocked the later external oscillations and would have evoked the unresponsive state if it had been longer-lasting (cf. Fig. 18). No change in the impulse train was obtained. The first two impulses had already arisen by the time of onset of the cathodal stimulus, but the third and later impulses arose during it. Thus there must have been some form of persisting excitation, such as accumulated transmitter. Large increases in the cathodal stimulus had no effect (Fig. 23D, E). When a very strong (about 0.1 V) but brief anodal stimulus was given and immediately followed by a cathodal stimulus, the early impulses were unaffected even when the anodal stimulus was as short as 0.1 msec. These stimuli were not so strong as to stimulate the nerve directly (see below). Shorter stimuli could not be used because of limitations of the pulse generators.

The responses to a short cathodal pulse were not identical with those following an anodal stimulus. When the strong cathodal pulse

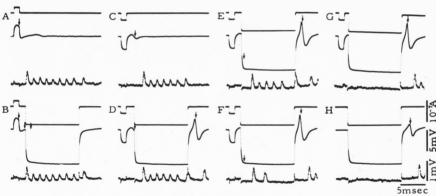

Fɪɢ. 22. Persistent excitation following a brief stimulus to phasic receptor (*Gymnotus*). Same receptor, recording, and display as in Fig. 17. Time of initiation of the first impulse(s) as determined from data in Fig. 21A-D indicated by an arrow. (A) Brief anodal stimulus evoked a small external oscillation and a train of nine impulses in the nerve fiber. (B) Strong cathodal stimulus given after second impulse had arisen had no effect on impulse train. (C) Brief cathodal stimulus evoked a small external oscillation and seven impulses. (D) Stronger cathodal stimulus given at time of initiation of first impulse as in (D) had virtually no effect on response train. (E-G) As the interval between stimuli was shortened, the number of responses was gradually reduced to zero. (H) Strong cathodal stimulus itself evoked no impulses at onset and probably would have initiated the unresponsive state if it had been sufficiently long-lasting. Because it was relatively short, an external oscillation and nerve impulses appear at its termination. Magnitude of the response varied, depending on timing and polarity of initial stimulus (B-G).

followed a brief one at shorter intervals, the number of nerve impulses could be gradually decreased to zero (Fig. 22C-G). This result indicates that the response to a brief cathodal stimulus required a relatively long time to develop. Presumably the response at the termination of a *long* cathodal pulse would have been identical with that at the onset of an anodal one.

As at the tonic receptors, the latency for impulse initiation could be measured by subtraction of orthodromic conduction time, determined as in Fig. 21, from the latency of the impulse in the afferent nerve. The calculated values were from about 0.5 to 0.7 msec (unless the nerves were directly stimulated, as discussed in the next paragraph).

As the strength of an anodal stimulus was increased beyond 10 or 20 mV, the calculated latency decreased to a plateau value of about 0.5 to 0.7 msec. At some threshold, of the order of a few tenths of a volt, the nerve impulse jumped to a shorter (calculated) latency of

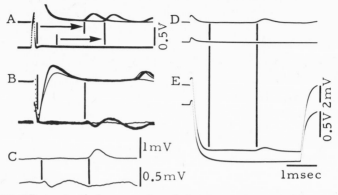

Fig. 23. Effects of stimulus strength and duration on latency of first nerve impulse at phasic receptor (*Gymnotus*). Upper trace: recording from afferent fiber. Lower trace: potential at receptor opening. Same receptor as in Fig. 21G-K. (A) When brief stimuli were very strong, latency of the first nerve impulse could jump to a new, shorter value. Apparently, the nerve fiber was then directly stimulated, because the new latency was only slightly longer than orthodromic conduction time (vertical lines). (B) Antidromic conduction time; a second impulse was initiated in the nerve. Vertical lines indicate orthodromic conduction time from (C). (C) Orthodromic conduction time in a response following a brief stimulus (vertical lines). (D, E) When a very strong and brief stimulus (about 0.1 msec) was followed by a stronger cathodal stimulus, no effect on the first impulse was observed. Vertical lines indicate latency and conduction time as in (C).

about 0.1 msec (Fig. 23A). Apparently the nerve fiber was directly stimulated in these cases. The threshold for direct stimulation by cathodal stimuli was much higher and was not determined.

The minimum synaptic delay at the receptors would be less than the minimum latency for impulse initiation by the time required for the postsynaptic potential to evoke an externally detectable response. This time would be a few tenths of a millisecond at most, and the synaptic delay at the phasic receptors is thus comparable with that at other chemically transmitting junctions in cold-blooded forms (Bennett et al., 1967c). Moreover, the synaptic delay at the phasic as well as the tonic receptors appears much longer than the minimum stimulus duration, and it is likely that at both types the secretion of transmitter can occur after the stimulus evoking it.

*Equivalent circuit of phasic receptors.* The phasic receptors exhibit the previously discussed properties of equivalence of long-lasting stimuli and d-c insensitivity, as seen in Figs. 16, 17, and 20. During an evoked response, it was usually difficult to determine if there was net current flow because of the stimulus, although some responses appeared to oscillate rather symmetrically around an average value presumably determined by the passive properties of the skin and receptors (Fig. 17C, G, K, L). When a short stimulus evoked a relatively prolonged oscillation, there was clearly little or no net current flow during the later part of the response (Fig. 19C). Also, the spikelike responses that occasionally were superimposed on delayed responses were biphasic (Fig. 18B), and the areas under the positive and negative phases of evoked spikelike responses were equal to within 15% (as in Fig. 18H, N). The discrepancy is probably due to error in determining the base line because of continuation of the delayed response.

From the foregoing remarks, it can be inferred that there is functionally at least a blocking capacitor in series with the receptor. Provisionally, this capacity can be ascribed to the outer faces of the receptor cells. These faces have a large surface area (Fig. 7), which would give them an appreciable capacity, whereas the area of the inner faces is much smaller. It is also necessary that the outer faces be inexcitable and have a high resistance compared with that of the inner faces— which is to say that they behave as capacitors.

In this formulation the responses externally recorded at the receptors would be generated by the internal faces of the receptor cells (and the nerve). The polarity of the responses to anodal stimulation is what would be expected if the inner faces responded to depolarization as do the more familiar excitable membranes and if the outer faces were inactive. Graded responses and more or less damped oscillations are well known in various arthropod muscles and in any bistable system where the amount of positive feedback is reduced (Fitzhugh, 1961; Grundfest, 1957). The external responses to weak stimuli of opposite polarity are approximately mirror images around the base line (Figs. 16A, B, D and 21C), as also occurs with small polarizations in squid axon (Hodgkin and Huxley, 1952). However, the responses at the onset of cathodal stimuli become progressively delayed as the stimulus strength is increased, in contrast to the responses at the onset of anodal stimuli. Cathodal stimuli hyperpolarize the inner faces, but as may be seen from Fig. 2B, the hyperpolarization would not be maintained. It is likely that the inner faces give anode break responses following this hyperpolarization. The larger and longer-lasting is the hyperpolarization, the longer the latency of these responses.

These aspects of the receptor responses can all be explained by essentially normal, electrically excitable membrane in the inner faces of the receptor cells. Indeed, this normality is one reason for assigning the responsiveness to the inner faces, for the electrical measurements— being made across the receptor—do not distinguish one face from the other.

The unresponsive state and subsequent responses are difficult to explain. In contrast to hyperpolarizing responses, the unresponsive state is maintained following termination of the evoking stimulus (Bennett and Grundfest, 1966). It is perhaps due to a prolonged hyperpolarizing action potential, but analogous cases are difficult to find in other cells under normal conditions.

Transmitter secretion probably occurs only in the positive-going phase of the receptor potential, since impulses of a minimum latency are evoked by strong anodal stimuli, whereas strong cathodal stimuli evoked only delayed impulses.

**Electroreceptors in Other Gymnotids.** The tonic receptors of *Sternopygus* and *Eigenmannia* were studied only by recording at the receptor openings, but they appeared to be nearly identical with those of *Gymnotus*. There were greater differences between the phasic receptors. The externally recorded oscillations in *Sternopygus* were simpler in form and smaller than in *Gymnotus*, and "ringing" of receptors was never observed. The oscillations were larger in *Eigenmannia* but similar in form to those of *Sternopygus;* "ringing" did take place.

The responses of a phasic receptor of *Sternopygus* to weak stimuli

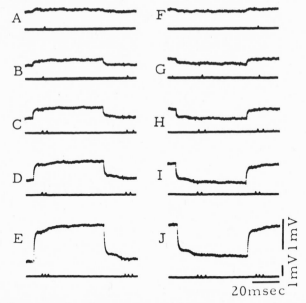

Fig. 24. Responses of a phasic receptor of *Sternopygus* to weak stimuli. Upper trace: potential at receptor opening. Lower trace: recording from afferent nerve fiber. (A-E) Responses to increasing anodal stimuli. (F-J) Responses to increasing cathodal stimuli of approximately equal amplitude. Impulse initiation was usually detectable external to receptor opening (cf. Fig. 27).

of fairly long duration are shown in Fig. 24. The externally recorded responses were quite small even when several impulses were initiated. The responses to sufficiently long anodal and cathodal stimuli of equal amplitude were nearly identical, except for inversion of onset and termination (Figs. 24 and 25A, D). Also, with these weak stimuli the external responses were approximately mirror images about the base line. In this example the threshold for impulse initiation was about 0.1 mV for onset of anodal and for termination of cathodal stimuli. In a number of receptors the thresholds for impulses at onset and termination of stimuli of both polarities were very nearly equal. As the strength of stimulus was increased over a moderate range, more impulses were evoked that were about equal in number at stimulus onset and termination (Figs. 24B-E, G-J and 25A, D). However, the latency of the responses at onset of an anodal and at termination of a cathodal stimulus decreased, while the latency of the other responses increased. The first impulses arose during the negative-going phases of the external response, suggesting that transmitter secretion was produced by the preceding positive phases, representing depolarizations of the inner faces of the receptor cells. When stronger anodal stimuli were given, their

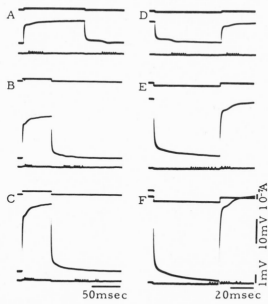

Fig. 25. Responses of phasic receptor of *Sternopygus* to strong stimuli. Upper trace: stimulating current; otherwise, as in Fig. 24. (A-C) Anodal stimuli of increasing strength. (D-F) Cathodal stimuli of increasing strength. Slower sweep in (B) and (C).

termination was followed by two groups of impulses at quite long latency (Fig. 25B, C). There were corresponding but small oscillations recorded externally. Similar responses were evoked at the onset of strong cathodal stimuli, but the pulses in Fig. 25E and F were too short to reveal them.

Brief anodal stimuli frequently evoked several cycles of oscillation externally and two or three corresponding groups of impulses (Fig. 26A-D). Oscillations were less frequently observed following brief cathodal stimuli (E, F). Similar damped oscillations were sometimes evoked by maintained pulses at the onset of anodal and the termination of cathodal stimuli. At least with weak stimuli, the later group of impulses was initiated by the later oscillations recorded externally, for both were blocked by a strong cathodal pulse. The very late responses evoked at the onset of anodal and the termination of cathodal stimuli appear to be related to the end of the unresponsive state in the phasic receptors of *Gymnotus,* and direct testing indicated reduced excitability preceding them. The externally recorded responses were more complicated in shape, however, and the excitability changes were less marked. These differences perhaps arose because the several receptors innervated by the same fiber were not acting entirely synchronously.

The period of oscillations is much longer in *Sternopygus* than in *Gymnotus.* This difference can be correlated with the form of discharge of the electric organ. In *Sternopygus* the discharge is roughly sinusoidal at a frequency of 50 to 100 pulses per sec, and there is little high-

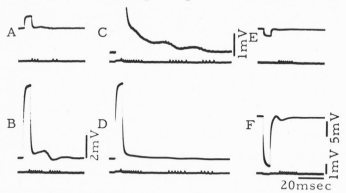

Fig. 26. Responses of phasic receptor of *Sternopygus* to brief stimuli. (A, B) Brief anodal stimuli evoked externally recorded oscillations and impulses that occurred in two groups (same gain). (C, D) Much stronger brief anodal stimulus evoked three groups of nerve impulses and corresponding externally recorded oscillations; higher gain in (C), same gain in (D), (E), and (F). (E, F) Brief cathodal stimuli evoked only a single group of impulses.

frequency energy in it (Bennett, 1961). In *Gymnotus,* however, the discharge is a triphasic pulse about 1 msec in duration (Bennett and Grundfest, 1959). Although the repetition rate is relatively low (40 to 100 impulses per sec), most of the energy is in the high-frequency range at which the receptors oscillate. In *Eigenmannia* (Bennett, 1961) and *Sternarchus* (Bennett, 1966a), where the organ discharges are of higher frequency, the oscillations at the phasic receptors are also of higher frequency.

In *Sternopygus,* as in *Gymnotus,* the nerve response could be recorded at the receptor opening (Fig. 27). The impulse was a brief initially positive biphasic potential. The negative phase was somewhat slower and smaller in amplitude. During high-frequency responses, the externally recorded impulse became greatly reduced, much more so than that recorded in the nerve (Fig. 27B, D). Little sign of the nerve impulse could be seen at the phasic receptors of *Eigenmannia.*

Experiments in *Sternopygus* like those of Fig. 22 gave similar results, indicating that transmission from nerve to receptor cell is chemically mediated. Impulse initiation required slightly less than a millisecond with moderately strong stimuli, but this value might have been less if stronger stimuli had been used.

In *Electrophorus,* receptors were studied in isolated lengths of the posterior of the body. Although deprived of circulation, the lateral line nerve fibers continued to conduct for an hour or more, and low threshold receptors (0.1 mV) could be found. Only phasic receptors were observed that responded at onset and termination of weak anodal and cathodal stimuli, respectively. Usually only the nerve impulse could be recorded externally, and there was no electrical response

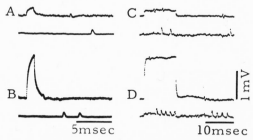

FIG. 27. Recording of nerve impulses at receptor opening (*Sternopygus*). Recording and display as in Fig. 24. Same receptor as in Fig. 24 in (A-B), a different receptor in (C-D). (A) Response to near-threshold stimulation. A single impulse in the nerve was preceded by brief positive-negative potential at receptor. (B) Two impulses were evoked by a stronger stimulus. Second impulse recorded at receptor was greatly reduced in amplitude. (C, D) When impulses were evoked at higher frequency, their amplitude was reduced later in the response train.

component ascribable to the receptor cells. Impulses were frequently initiated in twos or threes at threshold, and antidromic stimulation evoked similar multiple responses. Adjacent receptors in a cluster were innervated by separate fibers, since independent impulses could be recorded as little as 0.3 mm apart.

*Afferent pathways from the receptors.* The preceding experiments showed that fibers leading from the electroreceptors run in the facial component of the posterior lateral line nerve. In other experiments fibers running from the free neuromasts and ordinary lateral line receptors were found in the vagal component of this nerve. Experiments in which these nerves were sectioned confirmed the separate pathways of mechano- and electroreceptors. Gymnotids all tend to move away from a metal rod placed alongside the body, whereas glass rods of similar size are more or less ignored (Grundfest, 1957). The possibility of visual clues may be excluded by using blinded animals. This avoidance response can no longer be evoked by stimulating the posterior of the body when the facial component of the lateral line is sectioned bilaterally (at the level of the operculum). But, if the conductor is placed near the head, it still evokes the response. If the facial component is sectioned only on one side, the sensitivity to conductors approaching from that side is greatly reduced. Moreover, the fish generally moves toward the rod rather than away from it, suggesting that the object is being detected by the contralateral receptors. Sectioning of the vagal component of the posterior lateral line nerve has no ob-

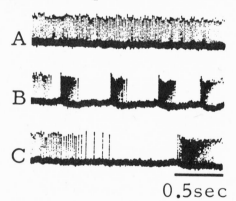

0.5sec

Fig. 28. Response of tonic receptor to a metallic rod (*Gymnotus*). Recording from afferent fiber in a curarized animal. (A) Resting discharge. (B) Responses to waving a screwdriver back and forth over the receptor. Discharge was alternately retarded and accelerated. (C) Response to slowly placing the tip over the receptor was gradual block of discharge. Upon removal, there was a long-lasting burst of impulses. The changes in base line in (B) and (C) are due to a-c coupling of amplifier.

vious effect on avoidance of conductors, but it has not been determined whether this operation affects mechanoreception (see Dijkgraaf, Chap. 7 of this volume).

While it appears that phasic receptors are stimulated by conductors in the normally discharging animal (Hagiwara et al., 1962, 1965), the tonic receptors are much more sensitive in curarized preparations. In Fig. 28 is shown the response in the afferent fiber of a tonic receptor to the passing of a screwdriver tip back and forth over the receptor opening. The response when the tip was directly over the receptor was an inhibition of discharge. When it was removed, there was a marked rebound. Apparently, there were eddy currents set up around the screwdriver because of inhomogeneities in the metal. Phasic receptors were much less sensitive to the same screwdriver. The electrical stimuli produced by movement must have been of too low a frequency to excite these receptors. The foregoing data illustrate that electroreceptors can operate passively and that sensitivity to metallic objects may result from detection of eddy currents rather than from resistance changes.

In several experiments on *Eigenmannia*, when the facial component of the lateral line nerve was allowed to degenerate following sectioning, the electroreceptors also began to degenerate, although these studies were not carried out over a period long enough to obtain complete disappearance. Figure 4B, derived from one such experiment, shows a superficial view of the operated side two months after sectioning. The electroreceptors are somewhat reduced in size, and their outlines are less distinct as compared with the normal side (A, C). No responses could be recorded at the tonic receptors, but smaller than normal oscillations were obtained at the phasic receptors. Responses on the unoperated side were normal. These results provide further confirmation that the externally recorded potentials arise in nerve and receptor cell in the two classes of receptor.

In normal animals, nerve impulses could be recorded external to the free neuromasts when the skin was allowed to dry, although under these conditions mechanical sensitivity was greatly reduced. Sectioning of the facial component of the lateral line nerve had no effect on these responses, which further confirmed the separate afferent pathways of electro- and mechanoreceptors.

## MORMYRID ELECTRORECEPTORS

**Morphology.** The external appearance and distribution of the electroreceptors in the mormyrids have been described in a previous publication (Bennett, 1965). As in the gymnotids, the receptors are visible on the surface as spots that are free of pigment (Fig. 29), and these often have a slightly pinkish cast. Along the body the receptors are found in two regions on the dorsal and ventral surface that extend posteriorly almost to the caudal margins of the dorsal and anal fins. On

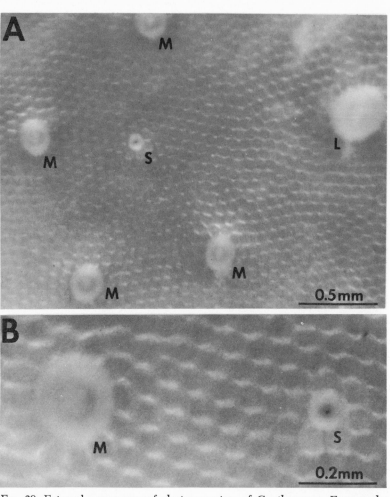

Fig. 29. External appearance of electroreceptors of *Gnathonemus*. From underside of the head of a 15-cm fish, following formalin fixation; higher magnification in (B). Three sizes of receptor are visible: large (L), medium (M), and small (S). Large and medium receptors have a lighter area at their centers, but no obvious opening is present. External opening of small receptor appears as a small black spot at its center. Hexagonal plate structure of the skin is interrupted by receptors.

the head the receptors are distributed on the lateral surfaces as well. Three types of receptor can be identified physiologically, termed according to their average sizes as large, medium, and small. In a fish about 15 cm in length the apparent diameters are about 300, 150, and 75 $\mu$. There is some overlap, however, in the size ranges of the different types.

In the previous study (Bennett, 1965), all three receptor types were called pores, because in the living material there appears to be an opening in the center of many of the receptors of each type. However, in sectioned material it can be seen that in only one class, the small receptors, is there a clear external opening. When the fish is fixed in formalin, the external layers of skin become less transparent, and the external openings of the small receptors can be seen as small dark spots. No opening is visible in the large and medium receptors, although there is a lighter central region (Fig. 29). In the fixed material a hexagonal plate structure in the skin is particularly clear. As seen below, there is a layer of flattened cells in the middle of the epidermis that is responsible for this appearance. As noted by Szabo (1965), this specialized layer is absent in the regions where there are no receptors.

The microscopic anatomy of the three types of receptors in mormyrids has been studied by a number of workers. The descriptions by Szabo (1965) and by Barets and Szabo (1964a,b) are fairly complete, although only receptors that correspond to the large type were considered to be electroreceptive. For this paper, a number of single large and medium receptors were sectioned for histological study after they had been identified physiologically. Single small receptors were identified by their size in external view.

The small receptors correspond to the type I mormyromasts of Cordier (1937); and the type A receptors of Szabo (1965). They are tonic in function and of the ampullary type. A narrow canal (about 10 $\mu$ in diameter; labeled C in Fig. 30) can be traced from a small basilar enlargement or ampulla (A) to the external surface, where the opening is also visible in superficial view (Fig. 29). Several receptor cells are embedded in the wall of the ampulla. There is a dark-staining extracellular mass in the lumen at the surface of the receptor cells (arrows in Fig. 30A, B). Many cells, some of them quite darkly staining, surround the receptor cells, and there are what appear to be small glomeruli of glandular cells (labeled G in Fig. 30C, D) that discharge their contents into the receptor cavity. A single nerve fiber runs to each small receptor (Fig. 33D), but details of innervation have not been seen.

The large receptors correspond to the *Knollenorgane* of Franz (1921), the *organes bulbeaux* of Gérard (1940), and the type C receptors of

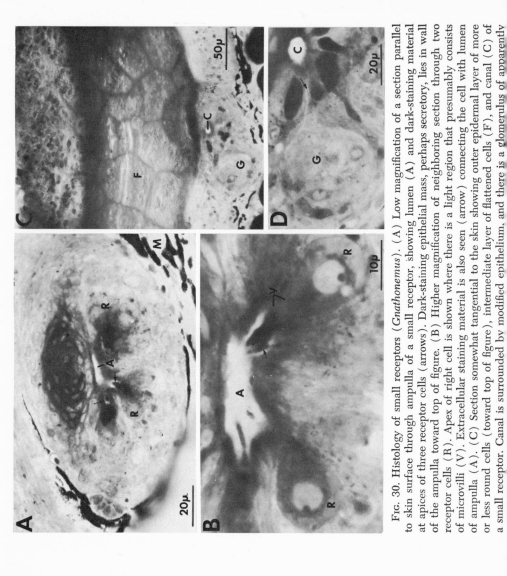

Fig. 30. Histology of small receptors (*Gnathonemus*). (A) Low magnification of a section parallel to skin surface through ampulla of a small receptor, showing lumen (A) and dark-staining material at apices of three receptor cells (arrows). Dark-staining epithelial mass, perhaps secretory, lies in wall of the ampulla toward top of figure. (B) Higher magnification of neighboring section through two receptor cells (R). Apex of right cell is shown where there is a light region that presumably consists of microvilli (V). Extracellular staining material is also seen (arrow) connecting the cell with lumen of ampulla (A). (C) Section somewhat tangential to the skin showing outer epidermal layer of more or less round cells (toward top of figure), intermediate layer of flattened cells (F), and canal (C) of a small receptor. Canal is surrounded by modified epithelium, and there is a glomerulus of apparently

362

Szabo (1965). These are phasic receptors which are very sensitive to high frequencies. Correspondingly, their morphology is of the tuberous type. Three or four large receptor cells (R) are found in neighboring but separate cavities beneath the surface of the skin (Fig. 31A). These cells are extraordinarily large compared with other electroreceptor cells; the larger in Fig. 31 is about 50 $\mu$ in diameter and 70 $\mu$ long. Szabo (1965) describes some large receptors with one or two receptor cells; these might appear as medium receptors to superficial view.

The cytoplasm of the receptor cells is relatively lightly staining, and somewhat less so at the external pole where the nucleus is located (as seen in sections neighboring those of Fig. 31). Most of the cell is surrounded by a clear layer of uniform appearance that presumably consists of microvilli (labeled V in Fig. 31B, C). This layer is absent only at the base of the cell, where it is attached to the cavity wall and where it synapses with the innervating fiber. The contents of the receptor cavity stain metachromatically, and a relatively thin layer of this material can usually be detected over the upper surface of the cell. The receptor cell is usually constricted near its base (giving it a pear shape), and the lumen of the cavity (L) is larger in this region.

A single nerve fiber (N) runs to each large receptor (labeled L in Fig. 33D) and sends a single branch to each receptor cell. At its terminal this branch is about 2 $\mu$ in diameter (arrow in Fig. 31C), and it abuts the base of the receptor cell in a manner similar to the club endings on the Mauthner cell (Bodian, 1952; Robertson et al., 1963). A thick (about 3 $\mu$), darkly staining sheath, probably consisting of loosely packed myelin, extends right up to the base of the receptor cell. The physiological data indicate that transmission at this junction is electrical, which is consistent with its distinctive morphology.

The medium receptors correspond to the type II mormyromasts of Cordier (1937) and the type B receptors of Szabo (1965). These are also tuberous receptors without a clear channel to the exterior. There is an outer cavity (O), as well as one to three inner cavities (I), each of which is connected to the outer one by a small canal (labeled C in Fig. 32). The contents of the cavities are usually metachromatically staining, but the various cavities usually stain differently. There are fairly large receptor cells (20 $\mu$) embedded in the wall of the outer cavity (labeled R in Fig. 32C). These cells are innervated on their inner surfaces, as shown by Barets and Szabo (1964a). Their outer surfaces have a small area in direct contact with the lumen of the cavity (L) by way of a small channel (C). There is a light band at the contact region suggesting the presence of microvilli (V). The cells

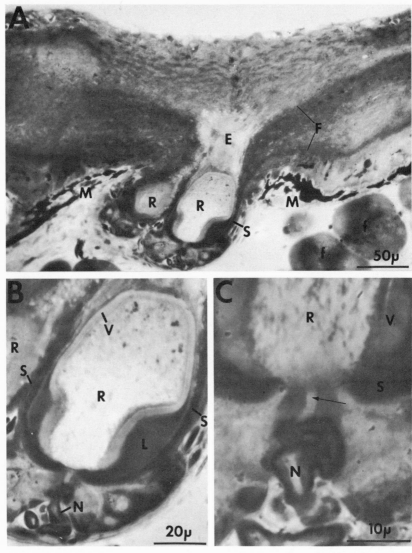

Fig. 31. Histology of large receptors (*Gnathonemus*). (A) Low-power micrograph of section through a large receptor perpendicular to skin surface (external side upward). There is an extensive depression over the receptor. The section shows major part of one receptor cell (R) and part of another. Layer of flattened epidermal cells (F) thins to a dark-staining sheath (S) that passes down around the bases of receptor cavities. A loosely packed epithelial mass (E) extends from receptor cell cavity to outer layer of the skin. (B) Higher magnification of central portion of (A). Receptor cell is surrounded except at its base by clear layer of what are presumably microvilli (V). There is an accumulation of staining material

are generally vacuolated, and the nucleus tends to lie somewhat below the center of the cell.

Other receptor cells (R), cuboid in shape, protrude into the lumen of the inner cavity (Fig. 32B, E). All but the base of the cells is covered by a clear layer that consists of microvilli (Barets and Szabo, 1964a). The nuclei are peripheral.

Each medium receptor is innervated by three fibers (Fig. 32D), one of which is often somewhat smaller. In one case, the small fiber was observed to innervate the receptor cells embedded in the wall of the outer cavity, but usually the details of innervation could not be seen. Whether or not each fiber innervates only a single kind of receptor cell remains to be determined. Only phasic responses were recorded in fibers from the medium receptors, but these were of two types, perhaps arising from the two types of receptor cells.

The relations of the receptors to the surrounding skin is similar to that in gymnotids. The central layer of the skin consists of many flattened cells that are hexagonal and stacked one above the other, giving the skin its characteristic appearance (labeled F in Fig. 33A). Around the large receptors the flattened layer connects with a narrow dark-staining layer (S) which surrounds most of the receptor cavities and which is open only at the bases of the receptor cells (Fig. 31A-C). At the apices of the receptor cells, this layer is seen to be more or less round in sections tangential to the surface (Fig. 33A, B). Over the receptor cells there is a lightly staining region that extends up to the outer layer of skin (Fig. 31A). This region is perforated by many small holes (about $\frac{1}{2}$ to 2 $\mu$; arrows in Fig. 33B), but these holes become reduced in number farther out and do not extend all the way to the exterior (Fig. 33C, arrows).

At the medium receptors the outer cavity extends above the layer of flattened cells to the superficial part of the epidermis. As at the large receptors, the flattened cells merge into a dark-staining sheath (S) that extends around the base of the outer cavity and is interrupted by the outer edges of the embedded receptor cells (Fig. 32C, D). This layer also extends along the canals from outer to inner cavities and probably surrounds the inner cavities in the regions where there are

---

in the apical cytoplasm; nucleus also lies in this region, as seen in another section. Lumen of receptor cavity (L) is metachromatically staining, and a thin layer extends around apical margin of cell. Branch of myelinated fiber (N) approaches receptor cell. (C) Details of junction between receptor and nerve cell from adjacent section. Terminal portion of the nerve (arrow) is about 2 $\mu$ in diameter and abuts onto receptor cell. Dark-staining sheath (S) of receptor cavity is interrupted in this region. (F) Fat cell; (M) melanophore.

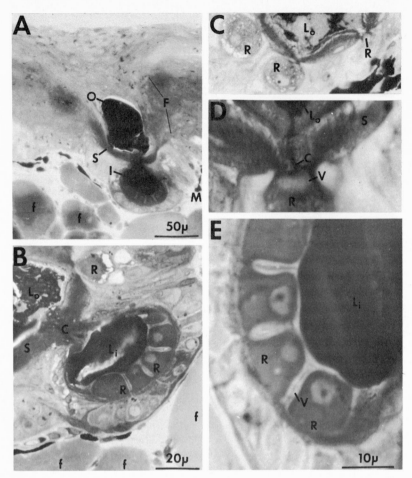

FIG. 32. Histology of medium receptors (*Gnathonemus*). (A) Low-magnification micrograph through medium receptor. There are outer (O) and inner (I) receptor cavities. Layer of flattened epidermal cells thins down to form dark-staining sheath (S) around outer cavity. (B) Higher magnification from neighboring section, rotated somewhat compared with (A). Lumen of outer cavity ($L_o$) is connected to lumen of inner cavity ($L_i$) by canal (C). Section passes through one receptor cell (R) in wall of outer cavity and five receptor cells protruding into inner cavity. (C) From a different receptor, showing receptor cells (R) embedded in wall of outer cavity. Section passes more or less through the centers of two cells to the left, but only the contact of the right cell with lumen ($L_o$) of outer cavity is seen. (D) Details of apical margin of embedded receptor cell; same receptor as in (A) and (B). Narrow canal (C) runs from lumen of outer cavity ($L_o$) to receptor cell. Clear area seen at cell's apex presumably consists of microvilli (V). (E) Details of protruding receptor cells (R) in inner cavity ($L_i$). Cells are cuboidal, and a clear layer presumably consisting of microvilli (V) covers them except at their bases. (F) Fat cell; (M) melanophore. Magnifications are the same in (B) and (C) and in (D) and (E).

no receptor cells. Where the canal of a small receptor passes through the hexagonal cells, it is surrounded by a differentiated layer of dark-staining cells (Fig. 33A). This layer thins considerably below the hexagonal layer, but some dark-staining material persists down to the outer surfaces of the receptor cells (Fig. 30).

In summary, the small receptors appear directly connected to the exterior. The cavities of the medium receptors extend above the flattened layer of cells, and the small holes above the large receptors probably connect their cavities to the superficial layer of the epidermis. If the dark-staining layers and the flattened cells are of relatively high resistance, they tend to channel current flow through the receptor cells. The physiological data suggest that the outer layers of the epidermis are of relatively low resistance and that most of a potential applied at the receptor opening appears across the receptor cells.

**Responses of the Small Receptors.** The small receptors are tonic in function. A small (about 1 mV) spike that appeared to be the nerve impulse was recorded externally, and there was maintained spontaneous activity at fairly regular frequencies from about 50 to 100 impulses per sec. The potentials were initially positive, followed by a smaller and longer-lasting negativity. Prolonged anodal stimuli increased the frequency of firing, and prolonged cathodal stimuli decreased it (Fig. 34). A readily detectable change occurred with stimuli a few mV in amplitude. The evoked impulse frequency could exceed 300 per sec, but the maximum was not reached until several impulses into the response train. When the receptor was covered by water, a rectangular current pulse produced a rectangular voltage change (Fig. 35D-F), but when it was in air a slowly changing potential was produced as a result of capacities in the skin (Fig. 34B-H). A stimulus evoked little or no change in the electrical properties of the receptor. The steady-state potentials indicated an extreme of 10% change in chord resistance over the entire range of polarization, as in Fig. 34—a difference ascribable to changes in the nerve rather than in the receptor cells. During stimuli that were of the order of a second in duration, an appreciable decrease in frequency occurred, but accommodation was much less marked than in the tonic receptors of *Gymnotus*. A large evoked increase in frequency could be followed by a decrease below the resting level (Fig. 35D). The fibers innervating the small receptors presumably were relatively small, since they conducted at about 20 m per sec, which was more slowly than the fibers running to the large receptors. Only once was a fiber connected to a small receptor isolated in the afferent nerve, and in this case a propagated impulse followed each externally recorded spike (Figs. 34, 35). In this experiment the

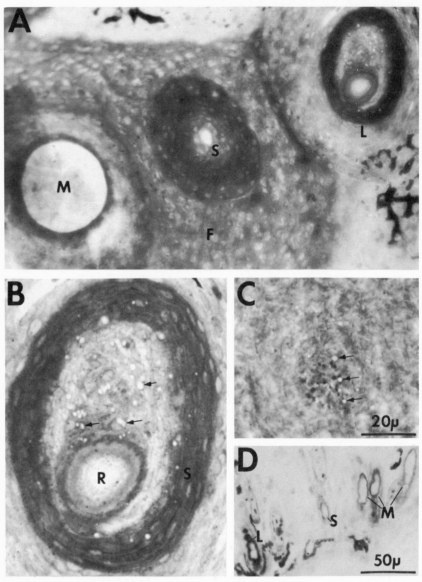

FIG. 33. Epidermal structure over the receptors and innervation (*Gnathonemus*). (A) Tangential section through outer cavity of medium receptor (M) and canal (C) of small receptor at level of the layer of flattened epidermal cells (F), and through large receptor (L) just beneath the flattened cells. (B) Higher magnification of region of large receptor. Apex of one receptor cell (R) is shown, and there is an oval dark-staining sheath (S). There are many small holes (arrows) in the light-staining epithelial cells over adjacent receptor cells. (C) Closer to the ex-

spontaneous discharge occurred in the nerve before localization of the receptor, thus proving that the discharge was not an artifact of electrode potentials.

The increase in frequency produced by an anodal stimulus persisted after the end of the stimulus. If a cathodal stimulus was given at this time (one that was more than adequate to block normal spontaneous activity), the response to the anodal stimulus could be reduced but never blocked entirely (Fig. 35D-F). This result indicates that some excitatory influence outlasted the stimulus which produced it. Since the time involved was quite long (50 msec or more), it is reasonable to ascribe this maintained activity to persistence of secreted transmitter, although continued postsynaptic action or continued secretion are also possible. With stimuli of moderate strength, the minimum delay for excitation was several milliseconds, but the minimum duration of stimulus required was not studied. In the experiment of Figs. 35 and 36, in which the nerve impulse was recorded centrally, very strong anodal stimuli caused a sudden decrease in latency of about 1 msec, probably owing to direct stimulation of the nerve fiber (cf. Figs. 13 and 23). These observations are also consistent with there being chemical transmission at the junction between receptor cell and nerve fiber. Since the transmitter would be secreted by the receptor cells, the externally recorded response would presumably arise in the innervating nerve fiber.

In agreement with a neural origin of the externally recorded response, a nearly identical potential was evoked by antidromic stimulation of the nerve (Fig. 35C). The similarity of antidromic and orthodromic response suggests that impulses normally arise central to the nerve terminal. The negative phase in the responses could represent propagation into the terminal or capacitive currents through nerve or receptor cell membranes. The antidromically evoked spike was always slightly larger than the spontaneous response (about 10 to 20%). This difference was found at all times during the cycle of spontaneous activity when the antidromic response could be evoked. Because of conduction time and refractoriness, the antidromic response could not immediately follow the orthodromic one, when its amplitude would presumably have been reduced by refractoriness. The difference in amplitude is likely to have been a result of greater "loading" of the

---

terior, the number of holes over large receptors is reduced. (D) Section running deep to receptors in (A), also inverted, showing nerve fibers running to receptors. Single fiber runs to large (L) and small (S) receptors, but three fibers run to medium receptor (M). Magnifications are equal in (A) and (D) and in (B) and (C).

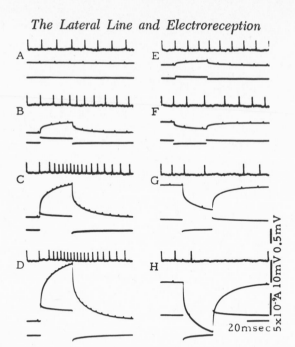

FIG. 34. Responses of small receptor (*Gnathonemus*). Upper trace: recording from innervating fiber. Middle trace: recording from receptor opening with over-lying water removed. Lower trace: current applied through a second external electrode. (A) Spontaneous discharge; each impulse at receptor was followed by one in the nerve. (B-E) Responses to increasing strength of anodal stimulation; discharge frequency was increased up to about 325 per sec. (F-H) Cathodal stimulation slowed and blocked the resting discharge. Voltage changes produced by the stimuli were relatively slowly rising and falling, owing to capacities of the skin and receptors. Steady-state potentials under these conditions indicated a change in chord resistance of less than 10% over the range of stimulation illus-trated.

spike-generating membrane when the impulse was proceeding ortho-dromically. In the orthodromic direction the resistance at the impulse initiation site would have been the input resistance "looking down" the fiber. The resistance for the antidromic impulse would probably have been greater because it was arriving at the closed end of the fiber. These externally recorded impulses had a characteristic inflection dur-ing the falling phase, the origin of which is not known. During high-frequency orthodromic volleys, the externally recorded response was reduced in amplitude. This reduction was probably due to refractori-ness, since a similar change in amplitude occurred in the responses recorded in the innervating fiber. It is to be expected that the post-synaptic membrane of the nerve would have had a lower resistance during these responses because of the stronger activation. This factor

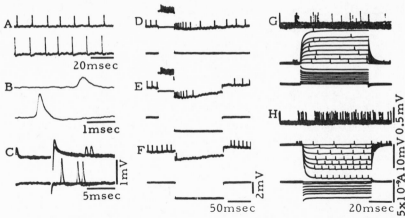

Fig. 35. Properties of small receptor (*Gnathonemus*). Same receptors and display as in Fig. 34, but current omitted except in (G) and (H). (A, B) Spontaneous discharge; faster sweep in (B), where response is also larger because of less moisture on the skin. Orthodromic conduction time was 1.5 msec, and calculated conduction velocity was 18 m per sec. (C) Threshold antidromic stimulation (three superimposed sweeps at about 2 per sec triggered by spontaneous discharge). In one sweep the nerve fiber was excited, and 1.5 msec later a spike was recorded at receptor opening. The following spontaneous discharge occurred after the sweep. Antidromic response was somewhat larger than the orthodromic. (D-F) Receptor was covered with water, and rectangular current pulses produced rectangular voltage changes. (Small fraction of applied voltage appeared on the nerve recording and was distorted because of a-c coupling.) (D) Response to a strong anodal stimulus outlasted the pulse and was followed by period of reduced activity. (E) Strong cathodal stimulus following anodal stimulus (with a slight overlap) did not block the evoked discharge, but spontaneous discharge did not resume during the pulse. (F) Cathodal stimulus blocked the resting discharge. (G, H) After considerable experimental manipulation and drying, receptor responded in an inverse manner: it was accelerated by cathodal and decelerated by anodal stimuli (several superimposed sweeps in each record). Normal response pattern returned following removal of electrodes and reimmersion in water.

would also have tended to reduce the amplitude of the orthodromic spike.

A peculiar phenomenon was observed frequently at the small receptors, that is, an inversion of their normal sensitivity (Fig. 35G, H). A cathodal stimulus became excitatory, and an anodal stimulus became inhibitory. This change seemed to be a result of mechanical deformation. In general, it was not accompanied by much loss in excitability, and it was often reversible.

From the preceding data, one concludes that the small receptors have the same functional characteristics as the tonic receptors of *Gymnotus*, although there is somewhat less adaptation to maintained stimuli. These receptors appear to provide the fish with information about d-c voltages, and accordingly they were strongly activated by metal objects that generated eddy currents (see Fig. 28).

**Responses of the Large Receptors.** *Patterns of response.* The responses recorded at a large receptor and in its innervating nerve fiber are shown in Fig. 36. The externally recorded response was a brief, initially positive diphasic potential—the initial phase being larger and shorter-lasting. When the skin was covered with water, the amplitude was about 1 mV; but when the shunting was reduced, it could exceed

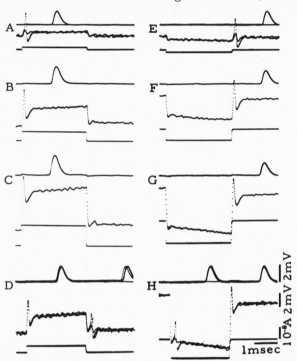

FIG. 36. Responses of large receptor (*Gnathonemus*). Upper trace: recording from afferent nerve fiber. Middle trace: recording from receptor opening by means of small, Ringer-filled electrode. Lower trace: polarizing current applied by means of large, water-filled electrode at receptor. The skin was somewhat dry, but spontaneous activity was reduced by connecting the large electrode to ground with a relatively low-resistance shunt (cf. Fig. 41). Several superimposed sweeps in (A), (D), (E), and (H). (A) Threshold anodal stimuli. (B, C) Increasing anodal stimuli. (D) Response to anodal stimuli of intermediate strength under conditions of increased spontaneous activity. Delayed spike sometimes occurred following termination of stimulus. (E) Threshold cathodal stimuli. (F, G) Increasing anodal stimuli. (H) Recorded under the same conditions as in (D), delayed response sometimes followed onset of cathodal stimuli.

10 mV (see below). At threshold, the response behaved similarly to that of the usual spike-generating membranes; that is, there was a subthreshold response and a large all-or-none component. Further increase in the stimulus produced little change in the response amplitude measured between peaks of the two phases. It is therefore reasonable to consider this response a spike.

Responses of short latency were evoked at the onset of an anodal stimulus and the termination of a cathodal one (Fig. 36A-C, E-G). Usually only a single spike was evoked. In different receptors, threshold measured as the strength of stimulus required to evoke a response about half the time ranged from 0.2 to 0.5 mV. Since there was generally considerable spontaneous activity in these preparations (see below), an arbitrarily low value for threshold presumably could have been obtained if a lower probability of response had been taken as the criterion. As the stimulus strength was increased, the probability of response rapidly approached unity.

The responses to anodal and cathodal stimuli of equal amplitude were very nearly identical, except that the onset and termination phases were interchanged (A-C, E-G). A small inflection occurred after the onset of a cathodal stimulus and the termination of an anodal one. When the rate of spontaneous activity was high, impulses arose from these inflections, impulses that were thus somewhat delayed from the preceding change in the stimulus (Fig. 36D, I). When these responses were observed, they usually occurred irregularly, even when the stimulus was quite strong. These delayed responses may be understood in terms of differentiation of the stimulus, as seen in Fig. 2. A brief hyperpolarization of the inner receptor cell membrane would occur at the onset of a cathodal and the termination of an anodal stimulus, and this potential change would tend to evoke an anode break response.

The responses at the large receptors are very rapidly adapting ones, as indicated by the fact that, in general, only a single spike was given to a prolonged stimulus. Also, the excitability during a long stimulus was unchanged even though the stimulus was many times the threshold amplitude. The receptors are thus d-c insensitive. This property is shown in Fig. 37 for anodal (B) and cathodal (C) conditioning stimuli. The responses in the nerve were also unaffected by these maintained stimuli. In addition, there was no resistance change during a prolonged stimulus.

There was little or no net current flow during an externally recorded response of a large receptor. This property could be seen particularly clearly in spontaneous spikes, because of the absence of interference

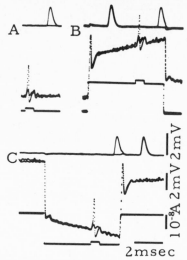

FIG. 37. D-C insensitivity of large receptor (*Gnathonemus*). Same receptor, recording, and display as in Fig. 36; several superimposed sweeps in each record. (A) Threshold stimulation using short pulse. (B) Superposition of same threshold stimulus on maintained anodal stimulus about ten times stronger had no effect on externally recorded response or nerve impulse. (C) Similar result was obtained when test stimulus was superimposed on large cathodal stimulus. Slow potential changes during prolonged pulses were probably due to capacity of the skin and neighboring receptors.

by a stimulus and the fairly clear base line. In the spike of Fig. 38A the areas under the initial, positive phase and the second, negative phase were equal to within 10%. This difference could easily have arisen as a result of a small error in the base line. When the receptor was oscillating, a phenomenon that is more fully described below, the areas under the positive and negative phases of the response were approximately equal, for instance, to within 10% in the case of Fig. 38B. In this experiment the base-line voltage was determined by moving the recording electrode to adjacent points on the skin where there was no oscillatory response. There appeared to be no net current flow in the threshold responses of Fig. 36 and 37, although it would be difficult to make accurate measurements because of alteration of the base line by the stimulus.

*Origin of the external potentials.* As at gymnotid phasic receptors, the external potentials of the large receptors appear to be generated primarily by the receptor cells rather than by the innervating nerve fiber. The evidence is less compelling, however, because of the closer correlation between external response and nerve impulse. The strongest

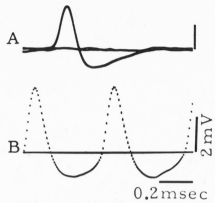

Fig. 38. Absence of net current flow during externally recorded response at large receptor (*Gnathonemus*). (A) Spontaneous spike (several superimposed sweeps to show base line). Areas under first and second phases were equal to within 10% as measured by planimeter. (B) When receptor was oscillating, areas under positive and negative phases were also equal to within 10%. Horizontal line shows zero level of potential obtained by moving the electrode to several places on surrounding skin. Voltage calibration: 2 mV in (A).

indication of receptor cell activity is that receptor responses were recorded 1 to 2 months after sectioning of the afferent nerve (just posterior and dorsal to the operculum, where it lies immediately beneath the skin). Histological examination revealed that the nerve was not completely degenerated after 1 month, although it was probably not excitable, and no responses could be recorded at the small receptors where the external potentials *are* generated by the nerve. Further careful histological study is required of receptors that are proved to retain their excitability for longer periods. A complication of this approach is that many of the receptors themselves degenerate when deprived of their nerve supply.

A further, but weak, argument for the origin of the spike in the receptor cells is the large size of the external potentials. When the skin is dry, these may exceed 15 mV. It is difficult to see how this response could be generated in the small innervating nerve terminal. Also, examination of serial sections shows that the area of the receptor cell base which is covered by nerve is much smaller than that free of nerve.

Finally, there is a point of low safety factor for conduction in the orthodromic direction, presumably at the junction between receptor cell and nerve. The externally recorded response or receptor spike can be generated at a much higher frequency than the innervating nerve fires. When a pair of stimuli was given to the receptor, a response to

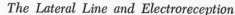
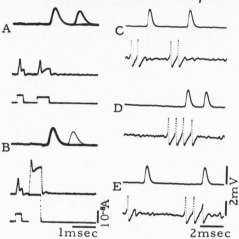

FIG. 39. Refractoriness in orthodromic pathway near a large receptor, presumably at receptor-nerve junction (*Gnathonemus*). Same receptor, display, and recording as in Fig. 36; several superimposed sweeps in (A) and (B). Current trace omitted in (C-E). (A) Paired stimulation; second stimulus was not far above threshold. Nerve impulse failed occasionally when interval between externally recorded spikes was 0.85 msec. (B) Second stimulus was considerably stronger. Nerve impulse occasionally failed when interval between externally recorded spikes was 0.6 msec. Intervals between nerve-impulse potentials were slightly greater than those between external spikes, ascribable to refractoriness in the nerve. Interval between nerve impulses was smaller in (B) than in (A). (C-E) As the skin dried the rate of spontaneous activity increased. The nerve impulses could fail to follow the external spikes during high-frequency bursts.

the second could fail to appear in the nerve although the receptor spike was full-sized (Fig. 39A). This "refractory period" could be shortened slightly by using stronger stimuli, indicating that the failure of the nerve response occurred close to the receptor (Fig. 39B). When the rate of spontaneous activity became high, the nerve responses could also fail. In Fig. 39E a single spontaneous spike at the receptor·was followed by a spike in the innervating nerve. When two, three, or four receptor spikes were generated at a high frequency (about 1200 impulses per śec in C-E), a nerve impulse failed to follow the receptor spike one-to-one. When a receptor oscillated at high frequency, the nerve responses could fail completely.

The data in the previous section indicate that there is a blocking capacitor in series with the receptor which is ascribable to the outer faces of the receptor cells. In this case, the excitability and the polarity of the external response could be explained by excitable membrane in the inner faces similar to that of nerve and muscle. The form of the external response is what would be recorded if an ordinary spike were generated in the inner faces (Fig. 2C), and the short latency spikes at the onset of anodal stimuli and the termination of cathodal stimuli would result from depolarization of these faces (Fig. 2A, B). Furthermore, the inner faces would be hyperpolarized at the termination of anodal stimuli and the onset of cathodal stimuli, and the delayed spikes that are evoked under these conditions could be anode break responses.

Arguments similar to those made with respect to the gymnotids suggest that the capacity does not lie in the overlying skin, although this possibility cannot be rigorously excluded.

*Mode of transmission at the junction between receptor and nerve cell.* Several lines of evidence suggest that there is electrical transmission at this junction. When the innervating nerve was antidromically stimulated, a small response was recorded externally at the receptor. This response consisted of a brief positive potential (Fig. 40B, D) that probably was followed by a negativity (F), as was the receptor spike; but this latter phase was usually difficult to observe because of noise. A receptor spike occasionally arose from the peak of the antidromic positivity (B, D). The antidromic response was indeed generated by the innervating fiber, for it was blocked by orthodromic stimulation of the receptor in the time relations that would be predicted (F-H) (Bennett et al., 1967b). The interval between the receptor spike and the orthodromic nerve impulse was always slightly longer than the interval between the antidromic stimulus and the externally recorded antidromic response at the receptor. In Fig. 40 the difference is 0.2 to 0.3 msec. Assuming that antidromic and orthodromic conduction times are equal, the difference in orthodromic and antidromic delays approximates the time required for the receptor spike to initiate an impulse in the innervating nerve fiber. This interval is short enough to make chemically mediated transmission from the receptor cell to the innervating fiber unlikely (Bennett et al., 1967c). However, the actual delay in impulse initiation is longer than that calculated by the (unknown) time required for the antidromic stimulus to initiate an impulse at the antidromic stimulation site. Because of this uncertainty, some doubt remains of whether chemical transmission is really excluded. However, an additional observation indicates that the receptor cells and innervating fiber are electrotonically coupled: that is, occasionally impulses arise from the peak of the positivity. As discussed in the introductory paragraphs (cf. Fig. 2D, E), this is the expected

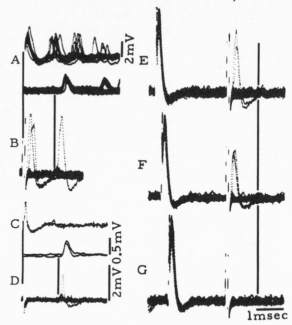

Fig. 40. Antidromic responses at large receptors (*Gnathonemus*). Recording external to receptor in all records and from the innervating nerve fiber in (A) and (C) (lower traces). Preparation in air. (C) and (D) were taken following rewetting of the skin, and there was less spontaneous activity at the receptor. Several sumperimposed sweeps in all records. (A) Sweep triggered by spontaneous discharges showing orthodromic conduction time. (B) Stimulus to the nerve evoked antidromic response that appeared as a small positivity, about 0.2 mV in amplitude, at a latency of about 1.2 msec. Antidromic conduction time (vertical lines) was about 0.3 msec shorter than orthodromic conduction time. In one sweep, a receptor spike arose from the peak of antidromic positivity. In two sweeps, antidromic stimulus directly excited the receptor, and ensuing orthodromic impulse must have collided with antidromic impulse; similarly in (E) and (F). (C, D) Similar to (A) and (B) but under conditions of reduced spontaneous activity. Orthodromic conduction time was about 0.2 msec longer than antidromic. (E) At this interval between stimuli, orthodromic response had no effect on subsequent antidromic response, which in this record appears diphasic. (F) At this interval, antidromic response was reduced. (G) At this interval, antidromic response was blocked because of refractoriness at the site of nerve stimulation. Recording at the receptor is at higher gain in (B-6).

result where the receptor cells and nerve fiber are coupled electrotonically. If the junction were chemically transmitting, the receptor spike would arise from the antidromic negativity.

In a few cases, there occurred in the innervating fiber spontaneous impulses that were preceded at the receptor by a small response no larger than an antidromic potential. The time between externally recorded responses and the nerve impulses indicates that these responses arose at or near the receptor, but the mechanism of initiation is unknown.

*Oscillations at the large receptors.* The rate of spontaneous activity of the large receptors was ordinarily not so great as to obscure their responses to pulses or prevent the measurement of threshold. However, when the water was removed from the preparation, the receptors often began to oscillate at a high frequency, which was usually about 1000 impulses per sec but occasionally in excess of 2000 per sec. These oscillations were immediately blocked by rewetting the preparation, suggesting that they were a result of the increase in resistance, similar to the "ringing" of gymnotid receptors. This explanation was confirmed by experiments like those of Fig. 19. A large electrode filled with aquarium water was placed over the receptor, and a much smaller Ringer-filled electrode was used to record voltage. The large electrode was then shunted to ground by various resistances, and the effect on the rate of spontaneous activity was determined. It was necessary to fill the large electrode with aquarium water because the oscillations were not maintained when a large Ringer-filled electrode was used. Apparently the Ringer solution caused a reduction in the skin resistance so great that the oscillations would no longer occur.

In Fig. 41A the oscillation of the receptor is shown with no shunting resistance present. When the large electrode was shorted directly to ground, oscillation ceased and the rate of spontaneous activity was reduced to about 100 per sec. As the shunting resistance was gradually increased, the rate of spontaneous activity increased. When the shunting resistance was 0.8 MΩ, the receptor was very nearly oscillating again; and when the shunt was disconnected, oscillations recurred at the same frequency as initially. As the shunting resistance was decreased, there was always an increase in frequency of oscillation before the oscillations failed. This observation suggests that, at some point as the resistance was decreased, the frequency of oscillation became too high for the receptor to maintain.

The change in rate of discharge produced by a change in shunting resistance occurred very rapidly. This is shown in Fig. 42A-D, in which a relay was used to connect the shunting resistor. The receptor was generating short trains of spikes, interrupted by brief quiet periods when only a high resistance connected the large electrode to the stimulator. When a 100-KΩ shunt to ground was connected, the frequency of discharge decreased almost immediately—so fast that a large number of trials would have been required to determine the latency. Probably

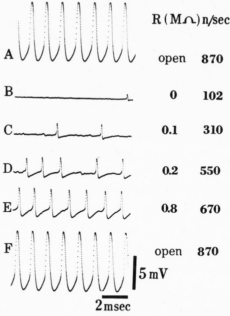

Fig. 41. Effect of shunting on spontaneous activity of large receptor (*Gnathonemus*). Recording from small, Ringer-filled electrode. Large (about 1 mm diameter) electrode filled with aquarium water, with a resistance of about 50 kΩ, was also placed over the receptor. This electrode was shunted to ground by various resistances. (A-F) From left to right: sample records from the small electrode, value of shunting resistance, and rate of spontaneous activity.

the time required was of the order of the spike duration. The frequency of discharge increased again immediately upon removal of the shunting resistance. The threshold during shunting remained quite low (Fig. 42B, D), and when the receptor was not oscillating at a frequency too high to allow measurement of threshold, it could be seen that the value of the shunting resistance had little effect on the voltage threshold (E-G). However, an increase in the shunting resistance increased the amplitude of noise recorded at the receptor as well as the amplitude of the spike. This noise was generated by the receptor itself, for moving the electrodes to adjacent areas of skin where input resistance was the same greatly reduced the noise amplitude.

Increase of the shunting resistance probably acts in a number of ways to increase the rate of discharge. Most obviously, the thermal or Johnson noise would be increased. However, the rate of spontaneous activity is higher than can be accounted for if noise in the shunting resistance were to trigger spikes in the receptor at the observed firing

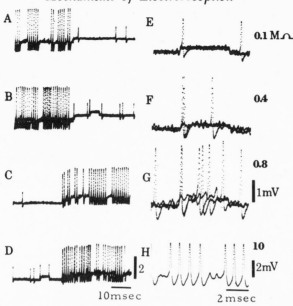

FIG. 42. Effect of shunting on threshold and noise at a large receptor (*Gnatho-nemus*). Recording as in Fig. 41. Stimulating through a 10-MΩ resistance attached to large electrode. (A-D) Shunting resistance of 100 kΩ was connected by means of a relay (small change in potential level was an artifact). Effect on spontaneous activity was virtually immediate. Threshold during shunting remained low, as shown by superimposed sweeps with a threshold stimulus in (B) and (D). (E-G) As shunting resistance was increased, as indicated on the left, noise recorded at the receptor increased, as did rate of spontaneous activity. However, threshold voltage did not decrease (several superimposed sweeps of threshold stimulation in each record). (H) With only the 10-MΩ resistance as shunt, receptor was too active to allow determination of threshold. Faster sweep speed in (E-H). Same voltage gain in (A-D) and (E-G).

level (Bennett, 1965). Moreover, most of the noise recorded at the receptors was generated there and must have represented subthreshold activity of the receptors. Probably this activity was triggered, at least to some extent, by the thermal noise; that is, subthreshold responses could be evoked by much smaller stimuli than those required to elicit spikes. Electrical noise due to activity essentially independent of potential is also possible (Derksen and Verween, 1966). The subthreshold activity was likely to involve little change in membrane resistance, and decreased shunting would have markedly increased its amplitude.

The foregoing factors are probably adequate to explain the changes in rate of more or less random spontaneous activity. Two other factors could contribute to the regular oscillations. As shown earlier (Bennett,

1965), a receptor spike is often followed after about 1 msec by a small external positivity and a corresponding increase in excitability. The positivity may be seen following the spontaneous discharges of Fig. 40C, and when the rate of spontaneous activity was high, a second spike often arose from this point (A). This potential and increased excitability reflect a tendency of the membrane to oscillate, and similar effects can be seen in squid axon (Hodgkin and Huxley, 1962). During this potential, the (active) membrane resistance probably is fairly high, so that decreased shunting would tend to increase the potential amplitude and might thereby lead to oscillations. Another effect of decreased shunting might also be important. The capacity of the outer face would discharge more slowly through the external resistance, and the charge remaining on the outer face might reexcite the inner face. Trains of discharges maintained in this way have been observed in the electroplaques of *Sternarchus* (unpublished data).

While it is probable that loading reduces the amplitude of subthreshold potentials that are (presumably) generated in the internal faces of the receptor cells, the effects on the spike are less certain. The impedance of the inner face is probably lower during the spike than at rest, and it would therefore be less affected than the subthreshold responses. The decrease in externally recorded spike amplitude as a result of shunting indicates that the receptor as a whole has an internal resistance, but this may be in the pathway to the surface rather than in the generating membrane. To achieve effective electroreception, the path to the exterior should be of low resistance compared with that of the internal face at rest, but during the spike the resistance of the internal face might become low enough so that most of the effective internal resistance is in this path. The reduction in duration of the externally recorded spike does not necessarily mean change in the spike generated in the inner face, for the observed changes could all be due to the more rapid time constant of discharge of the capacity of the outer face (Bennett, 1966b). It remains possible that decreased loading does increase the spike amplitude, and this factor may also contribute to the oscillations.

The presence of a series capacity at the receptor leads to differentiation of an applied stimulus. Since the derivative of a ramp voltage is a step function, a more or less constant current should be produced across the inner faces of the receptor cells by a ramp voltage applied externally. An anodal ramp voltage would depolarize the inner faces, and a cathodal ramp would hyperpolarize them. When anodal ramps were applied, the receptors ordinarily did not fire repetitively, although such firing was occasionally observed. When a receptor was

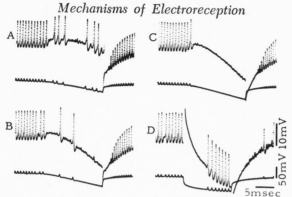

FIG. 43. Block of oscillation by "ramp" voltages (*Gnathonemus*). Upper trace: recording at receptor through bridge circuit. Lower trace: recording of potential level by means of separate electrode. Receptor was oscillating at high frequency (1240 per sec). When a gradually rising cathodal stimulus was given, oscillations could be blocked (A), and amount of spontaneous activity could be reduced in a graded fashion (B, C). A rectangular current pulse that produced a negative voltage in excess of that produced by any of the ramp currents blocked oscillations only at stimulus onset; oscillations resumed shortly afterward (D).

oscillating, a cathodal ramp could block the oscillations, as seen in Fig. 43. As the rate of change of the ramp was increased, the regular oscillations were first blocked, leaving more or less random spontaneous activity (A), and then this activity was decreased (B) and blocked (C). The effect required a gradually changing stimulus, and a rectangular current pulse that produced a larger final voltage than any of the ramps blocked the oscillation only at the onset of the stimulus. The termination of the stimuli must have produced a large depolarization of the inner faces, and a temporary cessation of the oscillations was evoked in each case. This cessation was of shorter duration in (C) than in (D), perhaps because the receptor had been oscillating at the end of the latter stimulus. Apparently the inner face could not oscillate when large enough depolarizing currents were passing through it. Receptor oscillations could also be blocked by anodal ramp voltages that were rapidly rising. Similar effects are observed in other spike-generating membranes (e.g., Bennett and Grundfest, 1966; Fitzhugh, 1961).

**Responses of the Medium Receptors.** The responses externally recorded at a medium receptor and in one of its innervating fibers are shown in Fig. 44. The thresholds of the medium receptors were in the millivolt range, and in order to see details of the response form a bridge circuit was often used. In Fig. 44 the upper traces are higher-gain recordings from the stimulating bridge, and the middle traces

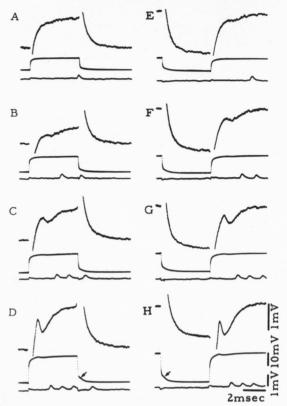

Fɪɢ. 44. Responses of medium receptor (*Gnathonemus*). Upper trace: high-gain recording at receptor using bridge circuit; rectangular current pulses were given (input resistance, 1.4 MΩ). Middle trace: low-gain recording from another electrode at receptor. Lower trace: recording from afferent nerve fiber from receptor. (A-D) Responses to increasing strength of anodal stimuli. (E-H) Responses to increasing cathodal stimuli. In (H) four nerve impulses were evoked in the nerve, but the last occurred after end of sweep.

are lower-gain recordings obtained with a separate electrode to show the potential during the stimulating pulse. The externally recorded response was positive-negative at the onset of an anodal stimulus and similar in shape at the termination of a sufficiently long cathodal stimulus. It was graded in amplitude and larger and shorter latency with stronger stimuli. There were corresponding impulses in the innervating nerve fiber that increased in number and decreased in latency as the stimulus strength was increased. In Fig. 44, up to four impulses were evoked in the nerve fiber. There was also a small external response at the termination of an anodal stimulus and the onset of a cathodal one (arrows in Fig. 44D, H). This was brief and positive, and if there was a following negative phase, it was slower than that of the other responses. As shown earlier (Bennett, 1965), at some medium receptors impulses were initiated at onset and termination of both anodal and cathodal stimuli, although the responses to negative-going stimuli were of a somewhat higher threshold. The impulses in these higher-threshold responses also decreased in latency and increased in number as the stimulus strength was increased.

As in other phasic receptors, the medium receptors show the property of equivalence of long-lasting stimuli. In addition, there is little change in excitability and no change in resistance during maintained stimuli; that is, the receptors are d-c insensitive. These results suggest the presence of a blocking capacitor ascribable to the external faces of the receptor cells. Whether there is net current flow during the responses is difficult to determine because of their high threshold. The response at onset of an anodal stimulus could be a graded response to depolarization at the inner faces of receptor cells. It is possible that the responses involve only delayed rectification and that there is no regenerative component. The responses at termination of anodal stimuli probably have a different site of origin. Their initial phase is more rapid and unlike the responses of other phasic pores to corresponding stimuli; they are not delayed as the stimulus strength is increased. If they are followed by a negativity, it is slower than that of the other responses, and they could not be recorded through the same series capacity although they also show equivalence of long-lasting stimuli. Perhaps the onset and termination responses are generated by the two classes of receptor cells in these receptors.

That the nerve volley can outlast the external response suggests that transmission from receptor cell to innervating nerve is chemically mediated. At receptors where no impulses occurred at the onset of a cathodal stimulus, the volley evoked by a brief anodal pulse could not be blocked by a subsequent cathodal pulse. This result also suggests the presence of maintained excitation following a brief stimulus, ascribable to secreted transmitter. But, since a receptor response occurs at the onset of a cathodal stimulus even though impulses do not appear in the innervating fiber, the results are somewhat ambiguous.

It is a morphological finding that there are three nerve fibers innervating the medium receptors. The technique of isolating a fiber and then finding its receptor is not suitable for determining the number of innervating fibers. Also, no component of externally recorded potential was found to be associated with the nerve impulses, although averaging techniques should reveal them. The only fibers found running from medium pores carried phasic responses which could, as already noted, be of two kinds: those at the onset of anodal and the termination of cathodal stimuli and those at both onset and termination of anodal and cathodal stimuli. Possibly one type of fiber innervates one kind of receptor cell, and the other innervates both kinds. A third type of fiber may also occur if the differences in innervation are responsible for the different fiber responses.

An unsatisfactory aspect of the foregoing picture is that embedded receptor cells in other instances are tonic rather than phasic in function and, in general, do not generate externally recordable potentials. Because the medium receptors are of quite high threshold, the anatomical modifications that occur at other, lower-threshold phasic receptors may not be necessary. There is also some evidence that the outer receptor cells may be innervated by smaller fibers, and these may not have been recorded from as yet.

COMMENTS

The similarities of tonic and phasic electroreceptors in gymnotids and mormyrids constitute an instance of convergent evolution as remarkable as that of the electric organs themselves. The tonic receptors have a canal opening to the exterior; i.e., they are ampullary. The receptor cells are embedded in the wall of the receptor cavity and appear to behave as linear elements in respect to their electrical properties. (Thus, in one sense they are electrically inexcitable.) Transmission from receptor cell to nerve fiber is chemically mediated.

The phasic receptors have no obvious opening to the exterior; i.e., they are tuberous. The receptor cells protrude into the receptor cavity and change their electrical properties in response to electrical stimuli; i.e., these cells are electrically excitable. Transmission from receptor cell to nerve fiber may be chemically or electrically mediated.

Several demonstrated or possible exceptions to this classification should be noted. Some phasic receptors in *Electrophorus* appear to behave as linear elements. The ampullae of Lorenzini in the skate are tonic receptors (see Murray, Chap. 18 of this volume), but there may be electrically excitable responses of the receptor cells (cf. Fig. 9; Waltman, 1966). The medium receptors of the mormyrids are tuberous and have no patent opening to the exterior, although they also have receptor cells embedded in the wall of the outer cavity. It is not yet certain that these cells operate phasically. There are cutaneous organs in *Gymnarchus*, some with and some without an obvious canal to the exterior (Szabo, 1965), which could be considered ampullary and tuberous types. But in each kind the receptor cavity invaginates into the receptor cells, and neither has protruding receptor cells.

The differences between tonic and phasic receptors can to some extent be understood in terms of function. The outer faces of the protruding receptor cells are increased in area to a greater or lesser extent. The microvilli further increase this area, which in turn leads to increased capacity. Several reasons have been advanced for believing that the capacity lies in these faces—the principal ones being the arrangement of the presumably insulating layer around the bases of the cells and the improbability of a many-layered structure having a large capacity. Two difficulties should also be mentioned: the skin does appear to have a fairly long time constant, and a function must be found for the layers of epithelia overlying the phasic receptors, if they are not acting as a series capacity. The first question may be resolved by careful measurements of time constants of skin with and without receptors, for much of the measured capacity may be in the receptors rather than in the skin. The answer to the second problem may be that the overlying epithelia serves some protective function. The protruding receptor cells have large surfaces exposed to the contents of the receptor cavity; yet the skin may be exposed to distilled water without loss of receptor function. Possibly the contents of the receptor cavity are maintained close to some physiological optimum by the overlying tissue. In spite of the overlying skin, the receptor cells are unlikely to be separated from the exterior by a large series resistance other than that in parallel with the blocking capacity, for this would lead to reduced sensitivity, and the sensitivity may be very great.

For the large receptors of *Gnathonemus*, the value of the series capacity may be approximated by taking the time constant of decay of the negative phase of a spike as 1 msec and the series resistance as 1 M$\Omega$. This gives a value of 1 nF, which could lie in $10^{-3}$ sq cm of membrane with a specific capacity of 1 $\mu$F per sq cm. The inner face of a single receptor cell has an area of about $10^{-4}$ sq cm uncorrected for microvilli, which would increase the area five- to tenfold. There are also several cells at each receptor, so that the specific membrane capacity of the outer faces of the receptor cells could be normal for biological membranes, that is, about 1 $\mu$F per sq cm. The time constants measured externally at the phasic receptors of *Gymnotus* are somewhat longer (about 10 msec), and the measured input resistances are lower (about 100 k$\Omega$). Thus a capacity of 0.1 $\mu$F is required at the receptor. The area of the outer face of a single receptor cell is about $2 \times 10^{-5}$ sq cm, or perhaps $2 \times 10^{-4}$ sq cm, considering microvilli. Assuming there were fifty receptor cells, a specific capacity of 10 $\mu F$ per sq cm would be required. While this would be a high value, the calculation could easily be in error by a factor sufficient to bring the value into the ordinary range.

For the outer faces of the phasic receptor cells to act as blocking capacitors, the resistance of these faces must be much higher than that of the inner faces despite the difference in area. Since specific membrane resistance can vary from a few $\Omega$ per sq cm to a few $M\Omega$ per sq cm (Waltman, 1966), the existence of a sufficient difference is not unreasonable. For the same reason, the outer faces of tonic receptor cells could be of low resistance compared with the inner faces without their being of greatly increased area. However, the outer faces do appear to have microvillous borders.

The series capacity at phasic receptors no doubt acts to make the receptors insensitive to low-frequency stimuli. The function of the electrical activity of the receptor cells, or receptor potentials, may be to modify the gain of the system. It is interesting that this feature can lead to oscillations—and to loss of afferent impulses—under certain conditions amounting to too much gain or feedback. The ionic processes involved and their equilibrium potentials, of course, cannot be determined from existing data. The receptor spikes that are externally recorded when the skin is dry represent a lower limit for the spike amplitude. It is quite possible that these responses are nearly the full potential generated internally. Very small changes in potential clearly produce large changes in permeability, and a spike of the usual amplitude might well not be required to elicit the full cycle of ionic activation processes—depolarizing and repolarizing, in the terminology of Grundfest (1961b). The specializations of the receptor spike generators have been discussed in a previous publication (Bennett, 1965); the most important of these is to remain poised very close to threshold, a property that must be aided by the blocking capacity. The large receptors are also extremely sensitive in terms of the energy required to stimulate.

Receptor potentials appear to be absent at least in most tonic receptors, although the accommodation during maintained stimuli could, from a design point of view, be mediated by electrical changes in the receptor cells. Presumably the lower frequencies to which tonic receptors are sensitive do not require rapid electrically excitable responses like those in the phasic receptors. The nerve impulses may to some extent modify the responses of tonic receptors, for these would tend to hyperpolarize the inner faces of the receptor cells (cf. Fig. 2D). Whether or not this factor is quantitatively important could probably be studied by antidromic stimulation of the innervating nerve.

Where transmission from receptor to nerve cell is chemically mediated, a brief stimulus may be transformed into a train of pulses. At the large receptors where transmission appears to be electrical, a brief stimulus can evoke only a single impulse, but the receptor cell response is also all-or-none, and there is no loss of information. Machin (1962) suggested that chemical transmission at this junction would allow isolation of the receptor cells from the nerve impulses. This isolation is imperfect when the skin is more or less dry but is probably adequate under normal conditions. As noted above, there may also be physiologically significant electrical feedback from the nerve to the receptor cells.

The skin is clearly of importance in electroreception in the gymnotids (Figs. 14, 15) and mormyrids (Bennett, 1965). For maximum sensitivity in passive operation, the skin should be of high resistance except at one end, and the receptors should be located in the skin opposite the low-resistance end. Obviously some compromise of this arrangement is necessary for spatial resolution, and perhaps also for active operation of the receptors. The resistivity of the skin in *Gymnotus* is about 1 to 3 k$\Omega$ per sq cm. This value is higher than in many fish but is considerably smaller than that in the mormyrids. It would be of interest to study the ultrastructure of the various layers of skin (Waltman, 1966). In the skates the skin is not much of a barrier to current flow, the potential gradients along the fish being about the same internally and externally (see Murray, Chap. 18 of this volume). The walls of the ampullary canals, however, are of very high resistance, and each receptor clearly detects the potential between two points, namely, the external opening of the ampullary canal and the internal side of the receptor cells in the ampullary wall. The presence of these modifying structures means that it is misleading to express the absolute sensitivity of the receptors in terms of voltage gradients at their openings. In behavioral experiments the total potential difference across the animal is likely to be a better measure of the sensitivity of the receptor itself.

Much further work is required to correlate the passive operation of the receptors as described in this paper with their role in the active operation of the electrosensory system. The work of Hagiwara and his colleagues (1962, 1965) constitutes a valuable start in this direction, but a combination of their methods and those of the present study will be required before a satisfactory description of the system is possible.

The significance of the findings to sensory physiology in general has already been considered elsewhere (Bennett, 1965). Electrically excitable activity of receptor cells may well occur at any secondary receptor and function to modify the sensitivity even though the specific stimulus energy is not electrical. Where transmission from receptor cell to nerve fiber is chemically mediated, the action of electrical stimuli or of receptor potentials on the secretory faces is likely to be the same. The relatively greater sensitivity of the electroreceptors to electrical stimuli may result primarily from more of an externally applied voltage appearing across these faces. In this case, the specialization would lie in the outer faces of the receptor cells as well as in the surrounding skin and other supporting structures. While the relation between presynaptic potential and transmitter release is likely to be quite different at receptor-nerve and nerve-nerve synapses, any general theory of synaptic transmission must account for both.

SUMMARY

Characteristics are presented of two types of electroreceptors: tonic and phasic receptors. The tonic receptors are ampullary, and a canal leads from the receptor cavity to the exterior. The receptor cells are embedded in the ampulla wall and behave linearly with respect to applied current. They are sensitive to low-frequency or d-c stimuli. The phasic receptors are tuberous, and there is no obvious channel leading from the receptor cavities to the exterior, although there are modifications suggesting that the high-resistance layer of the skin is absent over the receptors. The receptor cells protrude into the receptor cavity and are attached only at their bases. The outer membrane of the receptor cells appears to behave as a blocking capacitor, and these receptors are sensitive only to higher frequency stimuli. Several properties are derived that arise from the presence of a blocking capacity: (1) equality of responses at the onset of anodal stimuli and the termination of cathodal stimuli that are of equal amplitude and long-lasting, and similar equality at the termination of anodal stimuli and the onset of cathodal stimuli; (2) insensitivity to maintained stimuli; and (3) absence of net current flow during a response.

The electroreceptors of *Gymnotus* correspond morphologically to the two types. Tonic receptors show maintained spontaneous activity that is accelerated by anodal stimuli and retarded by cathodal stimuli. The nerve impulse can be recorded externally, but there is no other electrical response. Several properties indicate that transmission from receptor cell to nerve fiber is chemically mediated. The phasic receptors exhibit the properties that indicate the presence of a blocking capacitor in series with the receptive element, which is presumably the inner faces of the receptor cells. Externally recorded graded responses can be evoked at the onset and termination of both anodal and cathodal stimuli with concomitant nerve impulse activity. A prolonged unresponsive state can be triggered by appropriate stimuli, and under conditions of decreased loading the receptors can oscillate continually. The externally recorded responses arise primarily in the receptor cells, but a small nerve component can also be recorded. Transmission from receptor cells to nerve fiber is probably chemically mediated. Minor differences are observed in the electroreceptors of other gymnotids.

The morphology of the small and large receptors of mormyrids corresponds to the two types, but the medium receptors are tuberous and yet possess both embedded and protruding receptor cells. The small receptors are tonic and have similar properties to the tonic receptors of *Gymnotus*. The large receptors are phasic and generate all-or-none spikes externally that probably arise in the receptor cells. The responses have properties indicating the presence of a blocking capacitor in series with the receptive element. Transmission from receptor cell to nerve fiber is likely to be electrically mediated. Increase in external resistance causes oscillations. Two kinds of phasic responses can be recorded at the medium receptors and may arise in the two kinds of receptor cells. Transmission from receptor cells to nerve fibers is probably chemically mediated.

The functional significance of the differences between tonic and phasic receptors is discussed. The calculated value of specific membrane capacity of the outer faces of the phasic receptor cells is not inconsistent with membrane capacities of other cells.

REFERENCES

Auerbach, A., and M. V. L. Bennett (1967). Chemically and electrically transmitting junctions in the central nervous system of the hatchet fish, *Gasteropelecus*. *J. Gen. Physiol.* 50, 1090-1091.

Barets, A., and T. Szabo (1962). Appareil synaptique des cellules sensorielles de l'ampoulle de Lorenzini chez la Torpille, *Torpedo marmorata*. *J. Microscop.* 1, 47-54.

———, and T. Szabo (1964a). Ultrastructure des cellules sensorielles de mormyromastes de *Gnathonemus* et de leur appareil synaptique. *J. Microscop.* 3, 85-90.

———, and T. Szabo (1964b). Ultrastructure des cellules sensorielles de certains récepteurs du système latéral chez *Gnathonemus*. *Proceedings of the 3rd European Regional Conference on Electron Microscopy*, pp. 327-328.

Bennett, M. V. L. (1961). Modes of operation of electric organs. *Ann. N.Y. Acad. Sci.* 94, 458-509.

——— (1964). Nervous function at the cellular level. *Ann. Rev. Physiol.* 26, 289-340.

———— (1965). Electroreceptors in Mormyrids. *Cold Spring Harbor Symp. Quant. Biol.* 30, 245-262.

———— (1966a). An electric organ of neural origin. *Federation Proc.* 25, 569.

———— (1966b). Physiology of electrotonic junctions. *Ann. N.Y. Acad. Sci.* 137, 509-539.

————, and H. Grundfest (1959). Electrophysiology of electric organ in *Gymnotus carapo. J. Gen. Physiol.* 42, 1067-1104.

————, and H. Grundfest (1966). Analysis of depolarizing and hyperpolarizing responses in Gymnotid electroplaques. *J. Gen. Physiol.* 51, 141-169.

————, Y. Nakajima, and G. D. Pappas (1967a). Physiology and ultrastructure of electrotonic junctions. I. Supramedullary neurons. *J. Neurophysiol.* 30, 161-179.

————, G. D. Pappas, E. Aljure, and Y. Nakajima (1967b). Physiology and ultrastructure of electrotonic junctions. II. Spinal and medullary electromotor nuclei in Mormyrid fish. *J. Neurophysiol.* 30, 180-208.

————, Y. Nakajima, and G. D. Pappas (1967c). Physiology and ultrastructure of electrotonic junctions. III. Giant electromotor neurons of *Malapterurus electricus. J. Neurophysiol.* 30, 209-235.

————, G. D. Pappas, M. Giménez, and Y. Nakajima (1967d). Physiology and ultrastructure of electronic junctions. IV. Medullary electromotor nuclei in Gymnotid fish. *J. Neurophysiol.* 30, 236-300.

Bodian, D. (1952). Introductory survey of neurons. *Cold Spring Harbor Symp. Quant. Biol.* 17, 1-13.

Cordier, R. (1937). Sur les organes cutanés du Mormyridé *Gnathonemus monteiri. Ann. Soc. Roy. Zool. Belg.* 68, 77-90.

Davis, H. (1961). Some principles of sensory receptor action. *Physiol. Rev.* 41, 391-416.

Derksen, H. E., and A. A. Verweeen (1966). Fluctuations of resting neural membrane potential. *Science* 151, 1388-1389.

Eccles, J. C., and H. C. Jaeger (1957). The relationship between the mode of operation and the dimensions of the junctional regions at synapses and motor end-organs. *Proc. Roy. Soc. (London)* B148, 38-56.

Fitzhugh, R. (1961). Impulses and physiological states in theoretical models of nerve membrane. *Biophys. J.* 1, 445-466.

Franz, V. (1921). Zur mikroskopischen Anatomie de Mormyriden. *Zool. Jahrb. Abt. Allgem. Zool. Physiol. Tiere* 42, 91-148.

Gérard, P. (1940). Sur les appareils sensorielles de la peau de *Mormyrus caballus. Bull. Inst. Colon. Belg.* 11, 212-226.

Griffin, D. R. (1958). *Listening in the Dark.* Yale University Press, New Haven.

Grundfest, H. (1957). The mechanisms of discharge of the electric organs in relation to general and comparative electrophysiology. *Progr. Biophys.* 7, 1-85.

———— (1958). An electrophysiological basis for cone vision. *Arch. Ital. Biol.* 96, 135-144.

———— (1961a). General physiology and pharmacology of junctional transmission, in A. M. Shanes, (ed.), *Biophysics of Physiological and Pharmacological Actions.* AAAS, Washington.

———— (1961b). Ionic mechanisms in electrogenesis. *Ann. N.Y. Acad. Sci.* 94, 405-457.

Hagiwara, S., K. Kusano, and K. Negishi (1962). Physiological properties of electroreceptors of some Gymnotids. *J. Neurophysiol.* 25, 430-449.

————, T. Szabo, and P. S. Enger (1965). Electroreceptor mechanisms in a high-frequency weakly electric fish. *J. Neurophysiol.* 28, 784-799.

Hodgkin, A. L., and A. F. Huxley (1962). A quantitative description of membrane current and its application to conduction and excitation in nerve. *J. Physiol.* (*London*) 117, 500-544.

Katz, B., and R. Miledi (1965). The measurement of synaptic delay, and the time course of acetylcholine release at the neuro-muscular junction. *Proc. Roy. Soc.* (*London*) B161, 483-495.

Lissmann, H. (1958). On the function and evolution of electric organs in fish. *J. Exptl. Biol.* 35, 156-191.

Machin, K. E. (1962). Electric receptors. *Symp. Soc. Exptl. Biol.* 16, 227-244.

Mandriota, F. M., R. L. Thompson, and M. V. L. Bennett (1965). Classical conditioning of electric organ discharge rate in Mormyrids. *Science* 150, 1740-1742.

Mullinger, A. M. (1964). The fine structure of ampullary electric receptors in *Amiurus*. *Proc. Roy. Soc.* (*London*) B160, 345-359.

Murray, R. W. (1965). Receptor mechanisms in the ampullae of Lorenzini in elasmobranch fishes. *Cold Spring Harbor Symp. Quant. Biol.* 30, 233-243.

Robertson, J. D., T. S. Bodenheimer, and D. E. Stage (1963). The ultrastructure of Mauthner cell synapses and nodes in goldfish brains. *J. Cell Biol.* 19, 157-200.

Szabo, T. (1965). Sense organs of the lateral line system in some electric fish of the Gymnotidae, Mormyridae and Gymnarchidae. *J. Morphol.* 117, 229-250.

————, and A. Fessard (1965). Le fonctionnement des électro-récepteurs étudié chez les Mormyres. *J. Physiol.* (*Paris*) 57, 343-360.

Takeuchi, A., and N. Takeuchi (1962). Electrical changes in pre- and postsynaptic axons of the giant synapse of *Loligo*. *J. Gen. Physiol.* 45, 1181-1193.

Waltman, B. (1966). Electrical properties and fine structure of the ampullary canals of Lorenzini. *Acta Physiol. Scand. Suppl.* 264, 1-60.

# 21 ELECTROSENSITIVITY OF SPECIALIZED AND ORDINARY LATERAL LINE ORGANS OF THE ELECTRIC FISH, *GYMNOTUS CARAPO* †

Nobuo Suga

Department of Neurosciences, School of Medicine
University of California
San Diego, California

Some species of fish (Gymnotidae, Mormyridae, and Gymnarchidae) use short electric pulses discharged by an electric organ for orientation and probably for communication (Lissmann, 1958; Lissmann and Machin, 1958; Machin and Lissmann, 1960). When objects are brought into a fish trough so as to change the electric potential field resulting from the electric-organ discharge, the "electroreceptor" belonging to the lateral line system detects that change and sends the information about the object to the brain (Hagiwara et al., 1962; Hagiwara and Morita, 1963; Hagiwara et al., 1965a; Bullock and Chichibu, 1965).

These electric fishes have both the ordinary and specialized lateral line organs (Dijkgraaf, 1963; Szabo, 1965). The free neuromast and canal organs belong to the ordinary lateral line system; the tuberous and ampullary organs, to the specialized one. By both electrophysiological and histological methods, it has been revealed that the tuberous organ is the most likely electroreceptor (Hagiwara et al., 1965b; Szabo, 1965). Mormyrids have three sizes of pores, under which the sensory cells of the specialized lateral line organ are located: large, medium, and small pores. From the large and medium pores, phasic responses to artificial electric stimuli are recorded, while tonic responses are obtained from the small pores (Bennett, 1965). In the present experiment, phasic and tonic responses to artificial stimuli were

† The author wishes to acknowledge the discussions of Drs. T. H. Bullock and S. Hagiwara during these experiments, as well as the support of the U.S. Air Force Office of Scientific Research.

found in the lateral line nerve of *Gymnotus carapo*. The phasic fiber innervated the tuberous organ, and the tonic fiber innervated the ampullary organ. Electro- and mechanosensitivities and basic properties of these fibers were studied in order to explore the coding mechanism.

The ordinary lateral line organ has been known as a mechanoreceptor (Dijkgraaf, 1963). The sensory cell of this organ has many stereocilia and one kinocilium. Depolarization (excitation) of the sensory cell is caused by deformation of the sensory hairs (Flock, 1965). Conducted impulses in nerve fibers are caused directly or indirectly by this depolarization. Artificial depolarizing current applied to the sensory organ can also evoke impulses (Katsuki and Yoshino, 1952; Murray, 1962). If the sensory organ has a low threshold to such an artificial current, the organ may possibly assume the role of an electroreceptor in the electric fish. In this experiment, electrosensitivity of the ordinary lateral line organ was also studied.

MATERIALS AND METHODS

*G. carapo* (12 to 16 cm long) was immobilized with curare (30 mg. per kg body weight) or anesthetized with tricaine methanesulphonate (MS222; 0.05 to 0.07 g per liter) in the circulating water. The fish was placed in a lucite box (33 x 20 x 9 cm) filled with water. Artificial respiration was provided by means of a flow of water through the mouth and to and out of the opercula. The water temperature was 22 to 23°C. On the trunk of *G. carapo* four types of "pores," which are the receptor sites of the lateral line system, are easily discriminated (Szabo, 1965). The round pores lying along the lateral side of the trunk are the canal organs. At the rostral end of each scale is located a single round pore of medium size, which is the receptor site of the tuberous organ. Some scales have an irregular pore or a group of small pores; that is the ampullary organ. The receptor site of the free neuromast is the large round pore. The canal organ is innervated by the posterior lateral line nerve (10th cranial nerve); the tuberous and ampullary organs, by the posterior branch of the anterior lateral line nerve (7th cranial nerve). The innervation to the free neuromast is uncertain (Szabo, 1965). The posterior branch of the anterior lateral line nerve or the posterior lateral line nerve was exposed near the head and was covered with a drop of paraffin oil. Glass micropipette electrodes filled with 3 *M* KCl were inserted into the nerve in order to record single-unit activity.

To stimulate the lateral line organs, a pair of silver plates was immersed in the water, one in front of the head and the other behind the tail, along the long axis of the animal. Electric square pulses were applied through this pair of electrodes. The electric pulses were monitored with another pair of electrodes applied to the fish, and their intensity was expressed in millivolts per centimeter.

A receptor site of a single nerve fiber was localized by stimulating each pore separately with a weak electric current applied through a concentric electrode of 1.0 mm outside diameter and/or by weak mechanical stimuli applied by the tip of a glass or steel needle.

RESULTS

**Specialized Lateral Line Organs.** When a microelectrode was inserted into the posterior branch of the anterior lateral line nerve while a 50-msec electric pulse was being applied through a pair of stimulating electrodes, two types of responses of single nerve fibers were found to the stimulus—phasic and tonic. Out of 179 fibers studied in 13 fish, 82% of the units showed phasic responses. When weak head-negative electric pulses were applied, most phasic fibers showed "on" responses. After increasing the intensity, the fibers usually showed "on-off" responses (labeled A2 in Fig. 1). The "off" response seemed to be caused as a rebound from a hyperpolarizing current that might flow at the cessation of the pulse. Some fibers showed almost the same responses

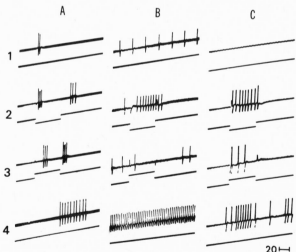

Fig. 1. Response pattern of three single fibers innervating to the tuberous (A), ampullary (B), and canal organs (C). (1) Spontaneous discharges; (2) responses to head-negative electric pulses; (3) responses to head-positive electric pulses; (4) responses to mechanical stimuli. The time scale is 20 msec. Intensity of electric pulses used is 1.7 mV per cm for (A), 3.0 for (B), and 80 for (C).

at the onset and the termination of the electric pulse. Only a small percentage of the fibers studied responded only to the break of the head-negative electric pulse. When a head-positive pulse was used, fibers showed the mirror image of the response to the head-negative pulse (A3 in Fig. 1). The receptor sites of these phasic fibers were always the tuberous organs. Hereafter, these will be called the "tuberous fibers." The tuberous fibers had irregular spontaneous discharges or none at all (A1). Out of 51 tuberous fibers studied with mechanical stimuli, 80% of the units were mechanically excitable. When the pore was pressed by the tip of a glass or steel needle, the fibers showed phasic responses to it (A4). However, the tuberous organ did not seem to be a mechanoreceptor in the usual sense, because it showed no response to strong water currents in various directions.

Out of the 179 nerve fibers, 18% of the units showed tonic responses to the electric pulses (Fig. 1, row B). These fibers always had regular spontaneous discharges, ranging between 30 and 70 per second (B1). When a head-negative pulse was applied, the spontaneous discharges of the fibers were augmented during the stimulus. After the termination of the stimulus, the rate of spontaneous discharges decreased (B2). The spontaneous discharges were suppressed by a head-positive electric pulse but were augmented after the termination (B3). The receptor sites of these tonic fibers were always the ampullary organs. Hereafter, these will be called the "ampullary fibers." All ampullary fibers were mechanically excitable. Tonic discharges were caused by pressing the receptor site with the tip of a needle (B4). However, the ampullary organ did not appear to be a mechanoreceptor, because it was scarcely stimulated by water currents.

The number of impulses per stimulus usually increased monotonically with intensity of a stimulus. Interspike interval and latency of a response also changed with stimulus intensity. In the tuberous fiber, it was seen that the response increased stepwise in the following manner. The last impulse in a train of impulses caused by an electrical stimulus appeared at first with an interspike interval longer than the others in the train. By increasing the stimulus intensity, the last interspike interval became shorter. The rate of shortening of the interval gradually became slow, but there was no change in the number of impulses in a certain intensity range. By further increase of the intensity, an additional impulse began to appear with a long interspike interval. The probability of the appearance increased with intensity, and the interspike interval shortened. Thus, both the number of impulse discharges and the last interspike interval in a train changed at this intensity range. The maximum number of impulses discharged for a

50-msec electric pulse was remarkably different from fiber to fiber in the tuberous organs (ranging from 1 to more than 13), but not in the ampullary organs (usually more than 12).

Electrosensitivity of the tuberous and ampullary fibers was measured with a 50-msec electric pulse. The threshold was defined as the minimum voltage which evoked 0.1 to 0.2 nerve impulse per stimulus on a given fiber or which modified a rate of spontaneous discharges when the fiber had regular spontaneous discharges. In Fig. 2 the abscissas represent the threshold voltage, in millivolts per centimeter and decibels, and the ordinates represent the number of fibers. Class interval was 2.5 dB. (A) and (B) show the distribution of thresholds of tuberous fibers without and with spontaneous discharges, respectively. There was no significant difference between (A) and (B). (C) shows the threshold distribution of the ampullary fibers. The lowest value of threshold obtained was 110 $\mu$V per cm for the tuberous fiber

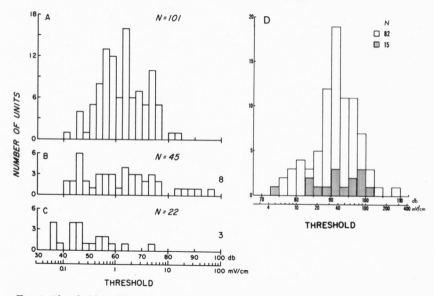

Fig. 2. Thresholds of the specialized (A-C) and ordinary (D) lateral line organs for 50-msec electric pulses. (A) and (B) show the distribution of thresholds of single tuberous fibers without and with spontaneous discharges, respectively. (C) shows that of single ampullary fibers. In (D), the open and shaded columns show the threshold distribution of single canal organ and free neuromast fibers, respectively. The abscissas represent thresholds in millivolts per centimeter and decibels, and the ordinates indicate the number of single fibers. The reference level of decibels is 1 $\mu$V/cm. The class interval in each histogram is 2.5 dB. The mean and standard deviation are 65.4 ± 9.1 dB for (A), 62.1 ± 13.2 dB for (B), 48.2 ± 9.4 dB for (C), and 91.4 ± 6.4 dB for (D).

and 58 $\mu$V per cm for the ampullary fiber. The mean value and standard deviation of thresholds were 63.1 (1.5 mV per cm) ±10.6 dB for the tuberous fiber and 48.2 (0.26 mV per cm) ±9.4 dB for the ampullary one. A 15-dB difference in threshold was significant.

Since the voltage of the electric-organ discharges of a 12-cm-long fish was about 10 mV per cm peak-to-peak at the head and about 70 mV per cm peak-to-peak at the tail, both the tuberous and ampullary organs seemed to be obviously excited or affected by the electric-organ discharges. However, the electric-organ discharge had a duration of 1.5 to 2.0 msec and was multiphasic. When the organ discharges were recorded by a pair of electrodes put at the head and the tail, a prominent head-positive phase was followed by a head-negative one. Each phase lasted about 0.5 msec. The repetition rate of discharges was 30 to 60 cps at 23 to 25°C (Hagiwara and Morita, 1963). To estimate the amount of excitation produced by the electric-organ discharges, the effect of stimulus duration on the tuberous and ampullary fibers was studied.

In the phasic fibers, an electric pulse of 0.5 to 1.0 msec evoked maximum responses when the intensity was 10 to 20 dB above the threshold of a given fiber. Even if the intensity was weak, a 4-msec electric pulse was long enough to cause the maximum response. Two examples are shown in Fig. 3. In (A), the fiber increased the probability of a response to a 6.8-mV-per-cm electric pulse when the duration of the stimulus was lengthened to 0.3 msec. Since the maximum number of impulses discharged by this fiber was one per stimulus, there was no further increase with duration. When the stimulus intensity was 2.3 mV per cm, the maximum discharge was evoked by a 1-msec electric pulse. There was no difference between the responses to the 1.0- and 50-msec electric pulses. The threshold of this fiber was 1.2 mV per cm for a 50-msec electric pulse. In (B), a 1-msec duration of the pulse was long enough to excite this fiber maximally when the intensity of the pulse was stronger than 6.6 mV per cm. Even if a 50-msec electric pulse was applied to the organ, the fiber did not discharge any additional impulses. By weakening the intensity of stimulus, the duration required to evoke the maximum response at a given intensity became longer. However, a 3-msec duration was still long enough even if an electric pulse of 1.4 mV per cm was used. The threshold for a 50-msec electric pulse was 0.9 mV per cm.

On the other hand, responses of the tonic ampullary fibers were more dependent on duration. In Fig. 3C, the abscissas represent time in milliseconds before and after the onset of the electric pulse, and the ordinates indicate the average number of impulses discharged

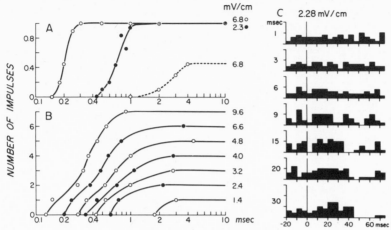

Fig. 3. Effect of stimulus duration on responses of two tuberous fibers (A and B) and an ampullary fiber (C). In (A) and (B), the ordinates represent the number of impulses per stimulus, and the abscissas indicate the duration of an electric pulse in milliseconds. The intensity of the stimulus is given to the right of each curve in millivolts per centimeter. In (C), the ordinates represent an average number of impulses discharged within a 5-msec class interval, and the abscissas show the time, in milliseconds, before and after the onset of an electric pulse, the duration of which is given to the left of each graph. The intensity of the electric pulse is 2.28 mV/cm.

within each 5-msec class interval. The threshold of this single fiber was 0.3 mV per cm for a 50-msec electric pulse. To a head-negative electric pulse of 2.28 mV per cm, the fiber showed a clear response when the pulse was longer than 15 msec—i.e., augmentation of spontaneous discharges during the pulse and suppression after it. When the pulse was shorter than 9 msec, the response was not clear (Fig. 3C). At 11.8 mV per cm, the response was clear when the duration of the stimulus was longer than 3 msec. The threshold of the ampullary fiber became higher than that of the tuberous fiber when shorter electric pulses were used for the measurement.

In order to examine the basic coding mechanisms of the tuberous and ampullary fibers, 0.5-msec electric pulses were repeatedly applied to the fish. The tuberous fiber responded to each electric pulse by discharging a train of impulses. The response did not adapt and die down to repetitive stimuli even if the repetition rate was higher than 100 cps. The number of impulse discharges per stimulus, the interval between nerve impulses (especially the interval between the last two impulses in a train), and the latency of the response (especially when the intensity of a stimulus was so weak that it caused only one or two impulses) were changed with the stimulus intensity. Change in the inter-spike interval and latency was not more than a few milliseconds.

On the other hand, the ampullary fiber responded to electric pulses within a certain range of repetition rate and intensity. Figure 4A shows responses of a single ampullary fiber to repetitive stimuli. The threshold of this fiber for a 50-msec electric pulse was 60 $\mu$V per cm. The rate of spontaneous discharges was 46 to 47 per sec (A1). When an electric pulse of 6.7 mV per cm was used, the spontaneous discharges were "locked," or in phase with the stimulus only at the repetition rate of about 46 per sec (A3). There was no "locking" phenomenon at rates lower or higher than 46 cps (A2, A4). With increasing stimulus intensity, the range in which the spontaneous discharges of the same fiber were locked became wide, for example, from 42 to

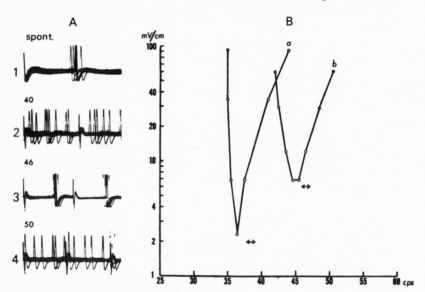

FIG. 4. Responses of ampullary fibers to repetitive stimuli of 0.5-msec electric pulses. In (A), the threshold of the fiber was 60 $\mu$V per cm for a 50-msec electric pulse, and the rate of spontaneous discharges was 46 to 47 per sec (A1). The sweep of an oscilloscope is triggered by spontaneous discharges of an ampullary fiber in (A1), but by 0.5-msec electric pulses in (A2), (A3), and (A4). The traces are superimposed several times in each photograph. When the repetition rate of electric pulses of 6.7 mV/cm is 40 and 50 per sec (A2, A3), spontaneous discharges are not locked by the pulses. However, these are locked by the pulses of 46 per sec. In (B) are shown two response areas (areas above curves a and b) in which spontaneous discharges of a given ampullary fiber are locked by the electric pulses. The abscissa represents the repetition rate of 0.5-msec electric pulses, and the ordinate indicates the intensity of the pulse. The arrows in the graph indicate rates of spontaneous discharges of fibers a and b.

50 cps at 60 mV per cm. The interval between the stimulus and impulse (latency) changed with the intensity of the stimulus, but the number of impulses per stimulus did not. By changing the repetition rate and intensity of electric pulses, the response area was plotted in which spontaneous discharges of a given fiber were locked (Fig. 4B). The response areas differed from fiber to fiber at minimum-threshold and best-repetitive frequency, because the threshold and rate of spontaneous discharges differed from each other (Fig. 4B, a and b). Therefore, spontaneous discharges of some fibers may be locked by electric-organ discharges of a certain frequency, but those of others may not be locked. If some objects are brought near to the fish, so as to change the electric field caused by electric-organ discharges, impulse discharges of some fibers may change from a locked to an unlocked state, or vice versa. When the fish changes its rate of electric-organ discharges, the same thing may occur in the ampullary fibers. This seems to be a possible coding mechanism of the ampullary fibers.

Such experiments with artificial electric pulses suggested that, for coding an object imposed near the fish, the tuberous fiber could use three parameters: the number of impulse discharges per electric-organ discharge, the latency of a response (i.e., phase), and the interspike interval. The ampullary fiber, on the other hand, could take two parameters: the "locking" phenomenon and the latency of a response. Neither the number of impulse discharges per electric-organ discharge nor the interspike interval may be included in the coding mechanism of the ampullary fiber.

This suggestion was examined by studying responses of the tuberous and ampullary fibers to the fish's own electric-organ discharges. Responses of the tuberous fiber to electric-organ discharges were most easily recorded. The three parameters enumerated above were modified by interposing a plastic or silver plate into the fish trough. On the contrary, responses to electric-organ discharges by the ampullary fiber were not found except for one fiber, the spontaneous discharges of which were locked by electric-organ discharges. It was not yet confirmed, however, that spontaneous discharges of the ampullary fiber were clearly influenced by electric-organ discharges. An example in which both a tuberous and an ampullary fiber were simultaneously recorded is shown in Fig. 5. The tuberous fiber discharged three impulses for each electric-organ discharge (smaller impulses in A3), while the ampullary one showed regular spontaneous discharges of about 65 per sec regardless of the presence or absence of organ discharges (larger impulses in A1-3 and B1). In A1 and A2, impulses of the ampullary fiber seemed to respond to electric-organ discharges, but

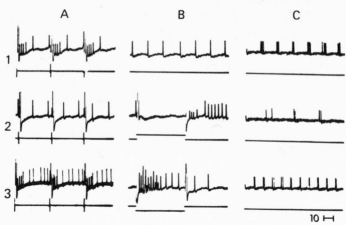

Fɪɢ. 5. Simultaneous recording of impulses of a tuberous fiber (small impulses) and of ampullary fibers (large impulses). (A) Responses of the tuberous fiber (upper trace) to the fish's own electric-organ discharges (lower trace) were influenced by interposition of a plastic plate near the fish, but the ampullary fiber did not respond to electric-organ discharges; i.e., its spontaneous discharges were not appreciably affected by the plate (1, 2). In (A3), several traces were superimposed to show explicitly spontaneous discharges of the ampullary fiber. (B) Regular spontaneous discharges of the ampullary fiber (1) and phasic and tonic responses of the tuberous and ampullary fibers to artificial electric pulses (2, 3) are clearly shown without electric-organ discharges. (C) In the absence of electric-organ discharges, the ampullary fiber responded to interposition of a silver plate by changing the rate of spontaneous discharges (2, 3). A rate of spontaneous discharges is 65 impulses per sec without a silver plate (C1). The sweep of an oscilloscope is triggered by spontaneous discharges of the ampullary fiber. Several traces are superimposed in each photograph.

it was not true. Spontaneous discharges were changing the position relative to organ discharges. This was explicitly shown by superimposing oscilloscope traces several times (A3). When a plastic plate was imposed near to the fish, the tuberous fiber changed the number of impulse discharges per organ discharge, latency of a response, and interspike interval, depending on the position of the plate (4 impulses in A1, no impulses in A2); but the ampullary one was not influenced by it (Fig. 5A). Evidence that the smaller and larger impulses were those of the tuberous and ampullary fibers, respectively, was easily obtained by studying responses of these fibers to artificial electric pulses. In Fig. 5B, the fish temporarily stopped electric-organ discharges, so that regular spontaneous discharges of the ampullary fiber were clearly observed (B1). The activity of the ampullary fiber was suppressed during a head-positive pulse and augmented after it, whereas the tuberous fiber showed a phasic off-response to it (B2). When a head-negative pulse was used, responses of these fibers reversed (B3).

Both the tuberous and ampullary fibers responded to the imposition of a silver plate by changing the number of impulse discharges. There was, however, no phase relation between nerve impulses of the ampullary fiber and electric-organ discharges. The same experiment was repeated when the fish temporarily stopped electric-organ discharges. In Fig. 5C, the sweep of the oscilloscope was triggered by spontaneous discharges of the ampullary fiber, and several traces were superimposed in each photograph. When the silver plate was imposed, the rate of spontaneous discharges (C1) decreased (C2) or increased (C3) depending on its position. The regularity of impulse discharges was maintained even in the modified situation. Responses by the tuberous fiber to the silver plate were not found in such a situation. The presence of electric-organ discharges was necessary for the tuberous fiber to code such an imposed object.

**Ordinary Lateral Line Organs.** The response pattern of fibers innervating the canal organ and free neuromast was tonic as long as 50-msec electric pulses were used (Fig. 1C). Such phasic responses as those of the tuberous fibers were not found in the posterior lateral line nerve. Different from the tuberous and ampullary fibers, most fibers of the posterior lateral line nerve discharged impulses during a 50-msec electric pulse irrespective of the polarity of the pulse, but the threshold was different depending on the polarity. A head-positive electric pulse was more effective on most fibers than a head-negative one. An example is shown in Fig. 1C. This fiber innervating the canal organ discharged more impulses to a head-negative electric pulse than to a head-positive one (Fig. 1, C2 and C3). The threshold of this fiber was lower for the head-negative pulse than for the head-positive one. There were some fibers which discharged impulses during head-negative pulses but which showed off-responses to head-positive ones. In those fibers, the threshold for the head-positive pulse was always higher than that for the head-negative one.

When a drop of water was applied to the fish trough, 82 out of 97 fibers studied (in 5 fish) with mechanical stimuli discharged clustered impulses synchronously with ripples (Fig. 1, C4). Receptor sites of these fibers were studied by stimulating each pore of the free neuromast and of the canal, tuberous, and ampullary organs with the tip of a glass needle. The fibers sensitive to slight water displacement were always stimulated strongly when the tip of the needle lightly touched one of the pores belonging to the canal organ. Hereafter, these fibers were called "canal organ fibers." The number of pores for which mechanical stimuli caused strong activation of a given fiber differed from fiber to fiber, ranging from 1 to 7. That is, some canal organ fibers seemed to innervate to many receptor sites, different from the tuberous and ampullary fibers. The canal organ fibers had no, or had irregular, spontaneous discharges. Regular spontaneous discharges were rarely found.

Of the 97 fibers, 15 responded neither to water ripples caused by water droplets nor to water currents applied to the fish trunk with a pipette. However, responses of these fibers were found when the tip of the needle was on the free neuromast. Hereafter, these were called "free neuromast fibers." Contrary to the author's expectation, the free neuromast was not sensitive to mechanical stimuli. Histological studies of the free neuromast showed that the cupula was not well-developed and was covered by mucus (Szabo, personal communication). The response pattern of the free neuromast fiber to electric pulses did not seem to differ from that of a canal organ fiber. Spontaneous discharges were irregular in some fibers, and were not present at all in others.

Thresholds of the canal organ and free neuromast fibers were measured with a 50-msec electric pulse. When the threshold was different, depending on the polarity of the electric pulse, the lower value was used for plotting (Fig. 2D). The histograms were drawn for two groups: one group sensitive to and another insensitive to water displacement. There was no significant difference in threshold between the two groups, so that these were added to each other and a mean value and the standard deviation of thresholds were calculated and found to be 91.4 (37 mV per cm) $\pm 6.4$ dB. Compared with those of the tuberous and ampullary fibers, the canal organ and free neuromast fibers were 28.3 and 43.2 dB less sensitive to a 50-msec electric pulse. Some fibers with low thresholds, however, seemed to be excited by electric-organ discharges. Responses to electric pulses of 0.5 to 1.0 msec similar to a fish's electric-organ discharges were studied. No fibers were excited by such a short electric pulse even if it was stronger than 400 mV per cm. A 0.5-msec electric pulse was repeatedly applied to the fish at rates from 10 per sec up to 100, but responses of these fibers did not occur. Spontaneous discharges, which were usually irregular in the canal organ fibers, were not locked by the repetitive stimuli.

In the posterior lateral line nerve, responses to the fish's own electric-organ discharges were not found. The canal organ was the mechanoreceptor. The function of the free neuromast was not explicit.

DISCUSSION

**Coding Mechanism of the Specialized Lateral Line Organ.** Both the tuberous and ampullary organs are assigned roles as electroreceptors, although their coding mechanisms seemed quite different from each other. The tuberous fiber responded well to the fish's own electric-organ discharges, as had already been reported by Hagiwara and co-workers. The tuberous fiber was informed of an object introduced near the fish by the use of three parameters: (1) number of impulse discharges per electric-organ discharge, (2) latency of a response, and (3) interspike interval. Although almost all tuberous fibers used three of these parameters, each parameter seems to have been used by different fibers in different situations. For example, a high-threshold unit may use three parameters, but a low-threshold one may use mainly (1) and (3); a unit that discharges only one impulse at the maximum may use only (1) and (2). On the contrary, responses of the ampullary fiber were not clearly demonstrated to electric-organ discharges. It is conceivable, however, that the ampullary fiber makes use of two parameters in order to code the modification of an electric field caused by electric-organ discharges, i.e., "locking" phenomenon and latency of a response.

Phasic and tonic fibers have been found in several types of mechano-receptors (Katsuki and Yoshino, 1952; Wiersma et al., 1953; Eyza-guirre and Kuffler, 1955; Wohlbarsht, 1960). The phasic fiber signals change in a stimulus, while the tonic one codes the presence of a stimulus. In weakly electric fishes, phasic and tonic electroreceptors have been reported (Bullock and Chichibu, 1965; Bennett, 1965). The tuberous and ampullary fibers of *G. carapo* showed tonic and phasic responses to artificial electric pulses of 50 msec, respectively. Discharges of the electric organ which last only 1.5 to 2.0 msec and which are multiphasic are suitable to be processed by the tuberous fiber rather than by the ampullary one. For electric fish, phasic information is a temporary modification of the electric field caused by electric-organ discharges, whereas a tonic one is a sustaining modification. If the general concept derived from the mechanoreceptor is applicable for the electroreceptors, it may be suggested that the tuberous organ is concerned with the reception of a temporary modification of the electric field, and the ampullary one is involved in the reception of a sustaining one. However, this concept would not be applicable to those electroreceptor fibers if one considered the functions of these fibers only in terms of responses to electric-organ discharges, since the tuberous fibers responded tonically to the sustained modification of this a-c field. The ampullary fiber responded to the imposition of a silver plate by changing the rate of spontaneous discharges, regardless of the presence or absence of electric-organ discharges, whereas responses of the tuberous fiber to the silver plate were not found in such a situation when there were no electric-organ discharges. The presence of electric-organ discharges was absolutely necessary for the tuberous fiber in order to code such an imposed object. If there are a-c and d-c components in an electric field, one can legitimately suggest the differentiation of two fibers to different qualities of an electric field. At the present time, it is not clear what causes this d-c component. Although the possible coding mechanism of the ampullary fiber was discussed in the preceding paragraph, the author is of the opinion that it is less concerned with coding the change in an electric field caused by electric-organ discharges. Stimuli of other modalities to the ampullary organ have not yet been examined.

**Electrosensitivity of Ordinary and Specialized Lateral Line Organs.** The sensory cells of the specialized lateral line organs have no ciliary structure, whereas those of the ordinary ones have such an element (Szabo, 1965). Such a change in morphology of sensory cells seemed to be concerned with a change in sensitivity to different modalities of stimuli. The measurement of threshold showed that the tuberous and ampullary fibers were, respectively, 28.3 and 43.2 dB more sensitive to a 50-msec electric pulse than the fibers innervating the ordinary lateral line organs. The ordinary lateral line organs of *G. carapo* are not assigned a function as electroreceptors.

REFERENCES

Bennett, M. V. L. (1965). Electroreceptors in Mormyrids, in sensory receptors. *Cold Spring Harbor Symp. Quant. Biol.* 30, 245-262.

Bullock, T. H., and S. Chichibu (1965). Further analysis of sensory coding in electroreceptors of electric fish. *Proc. Natl. Acad. Sci. U.S.* 54, 422-429.

Dijkgraaf, S. (1963). The functioning and significance of the lateral-line organs. *Biol. Rev.* 38, 51-105.

Eyzaguirre, C., and S. W. Kuffler (1955). Processes of excitation in the dendrites and in the soma of single isolated sensory nerve cells of the lobster and crayfish. *J. Gen. Physiol.* 39, 87-119.

Flock, A. (1965). Transducing mechanisms in the lateral line canal organ receptors, in Sensory receptors. *Cold Spring Harbor Symp. Quant. Biol.* 30, 133-145.

Hagiwara, S., and H. Morita (1963). Coding mechanisms of electroreceptor fibers in some electric fish. *J. Neurophysiol.* 26, 551-567.

————, K. Kusano, and K. Negishi (1962). Physiological properties of electro-receptors of some gymnotids. *J. Neurophysiol.* 25, 430-449.

————, T. Szabo, and P. S. Enger (1965a). Physiological properties of electro-receptors in the electric eel, *Electrophorus electricus. J. Neurophysiol.* 28, 775-783.

————, T. Szabo, and P. S. Enger (1965b). Electroreceptor mechanisms in a high frequency weakly electric fish, *Sternarchus albifrons. J. Neurophysiol.* 28, 784-799.

Katsuki, Y., and S. Yoshino (1952). Response of the single lateral line nerve fiber to the linearly rising current stimulating the endorgan. *Japan. J. Physiol.* 2, 219-231.

Lissmann, H. W. (1958). On the function and evolution of electric organs in fish. *J. Exptl. Biol.* 35, 156-191.

————, and K. E. Machin (1958). The mechanism of object location in *Gymnarchus niloticus* and similar fish. *J. Exptl. Biol.* 35, 451-486.

Machin, K. E., and H. W. Lissmann (1960). The mode of operation of the electric receptors in *Gymnarchus niloticus. J. Exptl. Biol.* 37, 801-811.

Murray, R. W. (1962). The response of the ampullae of Lorenzini of elasmo-branchs to electrical stimulation. *J. Exptl. Biol.* 39, 119-128.

Szabo, T. (1965). Sense organs of the lateral line system in some electric fish of the Gymnotidae, Mormyridae, and Gymnarchidae. *J. Morphol.* 117, 229-250.

Wiersma, C. A. G., E. Furshpan, and E. Florey (1953). Physiological and pharma-cological observations on muscle receptor organs of the crayfish, *Cambarus clarkii* Girard. *J. Exptl. Biol.* 30, 136-150.

Wolbarsht, M. L. (1960). Electrical characteristics of insect mechanoreceptors. *J. Gen. Physiol.* 44, 105-122.

# 22 SOME GENERAL COMMENTS

HANS LISSMANN

Department of Zoology
Cambridge University
Cambridge, England

There is no need, I hope, for me to pay tribute to the high standard of individual contributions during this morning's session. It will not have escaped your notice, however, that about halfway through the proceedings there occurred a rather sudden turn from "ordinary" lateral line receptors to "ampullary" receptors, i.e., from mechano- to electroreceptors.

Earlier the question was raised—and has remained unanswered—of how these two types of receptors may be related and why they should both come under the heading of lateral line detectors. Essentially we base the close morphological relationship between them on a common nerve supply, proximity of brain centers, and a probably similar embryological derivation. Resemblance in the structure of the end organs themselves, as we know it among all other acousticolateral receptors, is not very obvious at first sight. The assumption that the ordinary neuromast is the original form, and the ampullary receptor the secondarily derived, rests simply on the distribution of these organs among the lower vertebrates: the ordinary neuromast is the rule, the ampullary organ the exception.

On the functional side, there are indications of certain similarities between neuromast and ampullary organs: e.g., it has been shown that weak galvanic polarization of lateral line and labyrinthine receptors leads to an alteration in the frequency of the spontaneous discharges in the sensory nerve. However small the effect of a natural electric stimulus on an ordinary neuromast may have been originally, if it represents a significant parameter in the analysis of the outside world, there is every chance that differentiation and elaboration of this property has occurred through natural selection. But in the end product, in the full-fledged electrical receptor of today, there is perhaps no need to postulate absolute stimulus specificity. It has been reported by electrophysiologists that ampullary receptors, if pressed hard enough, can be made to respond to mechanical stimuli. This mechanical sensitivity may perhaps be thought of as a relic of their evolutionary past—provided that one can turn a blind eye to the rich variety of results recorded from these organs in response to many other types of stimuli.

The functional elements we seek in lateral line mechanoreceptors are those of transduction and of amplification of the signal. In the case of ampullary receptors, when the stimulus itself is electric, what is needed is essentially amplification. By comparing the fine structural details of these two receptors, we may be able to guess at the sites where these two functions are carried out. Dr. Flock has suggested, in a passing remark, that the excitable structure of the lateral line neuromast may be associated with the kinocilium, and Dr. Murray has quoted Waltman as having described somewhat atypical kinocilia on the receptor cells in the ampullae of Lorenzini in *Raja*. Now, as far as ampullary receptors are concerned, this condition in *Raja* is as yet the only known exception. No ciliary structures have been revealed by the electron microscope on the receptor cells in the ampullary organs of mormyrids, gymnotids, silurids, or *Torpedo*. Provisionally, it appears therefore that typical ampullary receptor cells lack a kinocilium, just as a kinocilium is characteristically present in all other acoustico-lateral organs. Among these latter, however, there is also one interesting exception: the hair cell of the mammalian cochlea, where the kinocilium seems to have been reduced to a remnant, represented by the basal body. It is tempting, but perhaps frivolous, to suggest that the 80-mV potential across these hair cells creates a condition analogous to that of ampullary electric receptors, and that the disappearance of the kinocilium in both may be a reflection of their mode of operation. It must also be remembered that the acoustic hair cells of lower vertebrates possess normal kinocilia, and that the endolymphatic potential seems low compared with that of mammals. However, comparative data for both acousticolateral and ampullary organs are still incomplete. An investigation of some "intermediate" forms may lead to revision of our views on *how* ampullary organs may have evolved from primitive neuromasts.

There is also, however, the question of *why* ampullary organs should have evolved at all, and this will probably be much more difficult to answer in a definite manner. It is striking that these organs have been found only in relatively few families of fish. There also appears to exist a significant correlation between the presence of ampullary organs and the possession of electric discharge organs. The exceptions here are (1) *Astroscopus,* a fish which has electric discharge organs but in which no ampullary receptors have been described and (2) a number of nonelectric fish (dogfish, many silurids) that possess ampullary receptors. In every case in which an animal with ampullary receptors has been investigated, however, it has been shown to be exceptionally sensitive to electric stimuli. I think it quite reasonable to assume that ampullary organs have arisen by specialization from ordinary neuromasts under the influence of special environmental conditions. There is, I feel, a great need to explore the type of electric stimuli that really occur in the environment of the animal and to examine, as Dr. Dijkgraaf has done, whether the animal accepts these stimuli as biologically adequate. The next logical step would be to investigate, as Dr. Bennett has shown us, the electrical properties of the receptors themselves, by testing the extent to which the values for resistance and capacitance of individual components fit in with our preconceived ideas. Considering how much we have learned in a relatively short time makes one feel optimistic about the prospect that one day we shall know how these receptors operate. It would be unwise, perhaps, to make a similar pronouncement about why and when they evolved.

It is quite possible that ampullary receptors have existed for a very long time. As you may know, the dorsal and lateral cephalic fields of silurian ostracoderms were originally held to be electric discharge organs. When this interpretation was abandoned, paleontologists offered a series of alternative theories. One of these suggested that the "ducts" to the cephalic fields corresponded to the ducts of ampullae of Lorenzini. It would be difficult to accept this view in an unmodified form because (1) ampullae of Lorenzini are typical of marine fish, whereas ostracoderms, according to orthodox theory, were inhabitants of freshwater; and (2) only 4 to 6 such ducts are found on either side of the head of ostracoderms, and these ramify profusely toward the periphery. This is quite unlike the conditions seen in present-day ampullae of Lorenzini. It has also been suggested that these ducts in ostracoderms were in reality cranial nerves, and that their swellings near the hindbrain corresponded to dorsal root ganglia. If this interpretation turns out to be correct, it may offer a way out of all difficulties: between the distal branches of these "nerves" and the peripheral covering, the remaining spaces are only a fraction of a millimeter thick. This may well have accommodated ampullary receptors similar to those of present-day freshwater forms, so that on these grounds alone there would be no need to displace the ostracoderms into a marine environment.

As you can see, there is a wide range of backgrounds against which an organ system such as the lateral line can be considered. To me personally, it has been immensely useful and exciting to hear about the different approaches that have been taken to this common problem.

# V CONJECTURAL ASPECTS AND THE LATERAL LINE

LATERAL LINE DETECTORS (P. Cahn, ed.), 417–435, © 1967 Indiana University Press

# 23 SOME SIMILARITIES IN SENSORY PERCEPTION OF FISH AND MAN

GEORG VON BÉKÉSY

Laboratory of Sensory Science
University of Hawaii
Honolulu, Hawaii

## RESEARCH METHODS

In the anatomy books of the seventeenth and eighteenth centuries, it was quite natural to describe, even for highly specialized cases, the anatomy of all the animals available. For instance, in his book on the anatomy of vocal cords, Casseri (1600) dissected the vocal cords of man, pigs, chickens, roosters, frogs, etc. This broad approach made it possible to separate characteristic data from the more or less unimportant features.

In the nineteenth century, the methods of research were improved by specializing in certain topics. Thus, in our time, results and research methods are distributed throughout a seemingly infinite number of independent articles. Even the best reviews are not of enough help, since they cannot hope to be fully comprehensive. It is essential to integrate what is known, to move ahead to more significant problems. Significant findings are, in general, more basic and thus have a hope of surviving longer. This is one of the reasons why, in attempting to solve problems of hearing in man, it seems necessary to look at the lateral line detectors in fish at the same time.

When I was a student, I was very much impressed by the work of Descartes, who first showed that the position of any point in space can be described by the use of a coordinate system. This was the beginning of the description of the movements of a point in space. An even greater influence, to my way of thinking, was the finding by Lagrange (1867-1892) that any rotation of a body can be described as the combination of three rotations parallel to the axis of a coordinate system (Fig. 1). My impression was that this finding, which provided the basis of modern mechanics, was one of the most significant achieve-

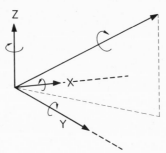

Fɪɢ. 1. Any rotation in space can be represented as a combination of three rotations with three perpendicular coordinates as their axes.

ments of the human mind, and that Lagrange's book on the mechanics of the motions of stars was a turning point in science.

A few years later, during the dissection of a fish head, I was very much surprised to find that the vestibular organ in the fish constituted a natural application of the discovery of Lagrange, since any rotation of the fish head was analyzed by three vestibular canals with axes along three perpendicular coordinates.

As you know, in animal experiments the most difficult question is which animal should be selected for particular research. It is easy to spend a year just finding out which animal should be used for a specific question. When I was first interested in acoustics, I was convinced that the best animal for inquiry in this field was the frog, since it has a large eardrum on the surface of the skull. I was sure that it would best facilitate progress. Peculiarly enough, however, if a frog was exposed to a sudden startling sound, I could not observe any reactions at all. It took me a long time to find out and to prove to myself that submitting a frog to a sound would freeze him in his movements instead of chase him away.

After having had these experiences, I came to the conclusion that the common use of a frog as a standard research animal, as practiced in the last century, perhaps is not the best way to make progress in physiology. For instance, if I were doing research on muscles, I should certainly investigate, besides the frog preparation used by Galvani, a muscle preparation from the grasshopper. It may be a different type of muscle that does the same job, and by combining the two different possibilities, it may be easier to extract the essentials of muscle contraction. For brain research today, the monkey seems to occupy the same dominant position as the frog did a century ago in physiology. For learning and behavior studies, the rat has been the accepted subject. Simply by changing the dose according to the body weight ratio,

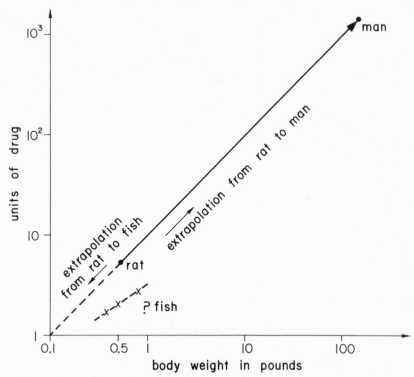

Fig. 2. Extrapolation of optimum doses according to ratio of body weight.

we are almost willing to extrapolate from drug action on the rat to the action of the same drug on man. As can be seen in Fig. 2, this is quite a substantial extrapolation. I think that an extrapolation in the opposite direction—to animals smaller than rats—is quite in order, and since fishes vary so much in size, they seem to be an excellent subject for this type of research.

My specific interest in fish started with a personal experience. When I was working on research concerning the human ear, especially on the cochlea, the main problem was to get fresh preparations. Someone said to me, "Why do you always work on the human cochlea? Why don't you just use a fish? A fish hears just as well as a human being does."

In order to find out something of how the fish hears, I visited an acquaintance who had a tank filled with water, on top of which was mounted a loudspeaker. That was about 1930, when loudspeakers were still quite new. I was impressed by a small fish conditioned so that, upon the presentation of a tone, he went to the surface of the water and

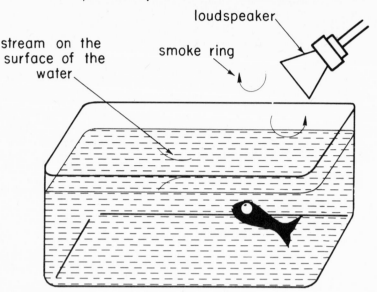

Fɪɢ. 3. Vibrating loudspeaker membrane can produce eddies in the air around the speakers. These can disturb the surface of the water, giving a d-c stimulus to the fish in the tank.

picked up some food. He never failed to do this (Fig. 3), and to my surprise even an extremely weak sound produced a reaction in the fish. The experiment seemed to work almost too well, so I decided to play a trick. I took out my handkerchief and used it to cover the loudspeaker. The handkerchief reduced the transmitted sound about 1 dB or even less at 1000 cps, so this should have had no effect. But to the surprise of my host and myself, the fish did not react at all to this change.

Later on, it was seen with a microscope that the loudspeaker produced a very small displacement of the water surface, in the form of a small eddy, and this is what had produced the stimulation. This movement of the water surface was the consequence of an eddy caused in the air around the loudspeaker membrane. Loudspeakers have several peculiar effects. If we watch the loudspeaker membranes stroboscopically, we can see that at higher frequencies they just do not move the same way as they theoretically should. Some loudspeakers have lateral movements; these introduce an asymmetry, which in turn produces the eddies around the membrane. Later, we replaced the handkerchief with a chicken wire, which produced practically no transmission loss at all; yet again, it canceled all the responses of the fish.

Figure 4 shows how rectification and eddy formation may occur for

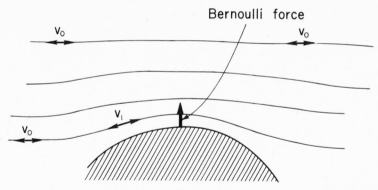

FIG. 4. Vibratory movements of a fluid produce a d-c force on the solid body with a curved surface.

boundary forces. A sound moves the fluid back and forth along the surface, but at the same time the boundary force does not change its direction. Therefore, we have a rectification procedure. Hydrodynamic specialists always say that boundary forces are present only for large amplitudes. That is correct, but in practice, somehow, asymmetrical boundaries may have unexpected effects. A swim bladder that vibrates is quite a complicated system, with possibilities for rectification of the vibrations producing a demodulation of a tone.

Sound propagation in a tank is closely related to questions about room acoustics. It is a serious question when precise measurement must be performed, for there is no inexpensive solution to it. It is interesting to hear that with a tank of water we still have almost exactly the same problems as we had in room acoustics back in 1930. At that time there was current the problem of how to make a studio or a concert hall in an acoustically correct way. It turned out that the low frequencies were very disturbing and difficult to absorb. It was Prof. Ervin Meyer in Göttingen, the editor of the *Akustische Zeitschrift,* the journal in which I published my first papers, who found that a glass window will absorb low frequencies as a membrane but will not absorb high frequencies. He found that some famous concert halls, such as the Gewandhaus in Leipzig, are very good because they have wood paneling that acts like a membrane, absorbing the low frequencies.

I myself had a peculiar experience, for I found that in an ordinary circus tent, with its canvas walls, the acoustics were much better than in some famous concert hall. Therefore, I decided that a good absorbing material for low frequencies would be a membrane. It turns out that we have the same problem in water. In water the problem is greater, however, because the sound speed is much faster and the wavelength is longer; also, very thick absorbing panels are needed. But a membrane can be used to replace very thick absorber panels.

I was told by musicians that the sound we produce through loud-speakers has no energy, and without energy you cannot enjoy an orchestra. The listeners need energy. What they really want is a sort of a swim bladder effect on their chests. The interesting thing was that this low-frequency vibration on the chest seemed just as impor-tant as the low-frequency response in the ear. I agreed with them; for a good reproduction of music, we needed both.

Room acoustics are very important for threshold measurements—I can tell you numerous related stories concerning hospitals. One of my doctor friends told me, "I test my patients, and they hear my whisper 3 to 10 ft away, but after I operate on them, they hear it 30 ft away." If we use the well-known equations, the drop in sound-pressure in-tensity from 3 to 30 ft is quite large. How could he have produced such an improvement?

It turns out that the hearing tests were made in the corridor of the hospital, and this space was about 100 ft long. I used a microphone to find out what happened to sound pressure along the corridor. The sound pressure decreased in going from his mouth to a distance of about 3 m, according to expectations; thereafter it filled the whole width of the corridor, and there was no further loss in sound pressure—creating a sort of tube effect. A fish in a tube would have the same experience as the patient in the corridor.

The doctor's next question was, "All right, how do you measure the threshold of a patient correctly in a free-field situation?" My proposed solution was the use of an earphone. He did not like to resort to this just after surgery. For some tests we used the completely flat roof of a building, recessing the loudspeaker into the floor so that it was flush with it. We then had a half-spherical sound field, which constituted an undisturbed free field. The experiments showed that if the loudspeaker was not perfectly flush with the floor we did not have a really good free field.

We have a similar situation in water if the transmitter is near the surface but is not flush with it. If it is a little below the surface, or a little above it, we immediately have some interference.

### DIFFERENT TYPES OF STIMULATING FORCES

As we all know, there are shearing forces and there are pressures. Figure 5 shows both types, as well as a combination of the two. The question is: Is it shearing force or is it pressure that produces the stimulus? In water, shearing forces are produced by the friction of water during movement, so that the question becomes: Is the movement or the pressure the effective stimulus?

In this connection, Meissner (1853) performed a very famous experiment. First you fill a beaker with mercury (Fig. 6). In a physics laboratory when I was a youngster mercury could be found everywhere. Now no one uses it anymore; I don't know why, but they seem to have replaced it with computers. If you put your finger in the mercury, you have a peculiar feeling; you have no sensation of d-c pressure at the fingertip, so long as you do not move your finger. You feel only the ring where the finger meets the surface of the mercury. This seems to indicate that the skin is completely insensitive to an overall hydrodynamic pressure. It might be said that the skin receptors adapt, and therefore after a while no pressure is felt.

This experiment can be repeated for vibratory pressure, which can be switched on and off to avoid adaptation. The equipment used, as shown in Fig. 7, consists mainly of a big, heavy block of lead to prevent movement. On one side a membrane was attached to a vibrator. The cylindrical opening was filled with parafin oil, in which the finger was immersed. A little screen around the finger impeded the flow of the fluid. A rubber ring tightly fixed the finger in the opening. If the membrane vibrated, no vibrations were felt except where the rubber ring was. It is essentially the same phenomenon as in Meissner's original experiment.

With an even larger lead block, we can insert the whole hand into the fluid with the same effect. This shows that there is no pressure sensitivity in the human skin so long as the stimulus is hydrostatic

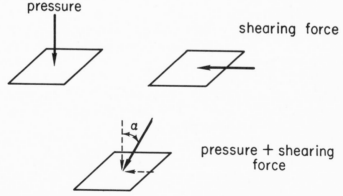

Fɪɢ. 5. Definition of hydrostatic pressure and shearing force.

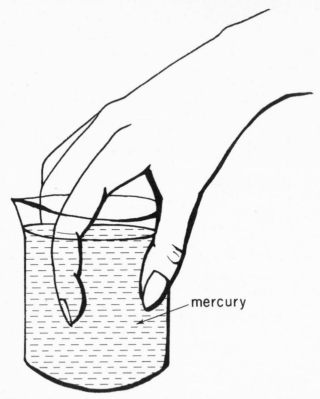

Fᴵɢ. 6. Meissner's experiment showing the lack of sensitivity of human skin for hydrostatic pressure.

pressure. One can repeat this experiment with a little foam rubber with some air bubbles close to the vibrating membrane. Touching an air bubble with the fingertip produced the sensation of strong vibrations. I would like to repeat this experiment, but with a fish on the tip of my finger in order to see how much vibration the swim bladder produces.

On the contrary, the very same skin of the finger is extremely sensitive to shearing forces. Every surgeon knows that, if he wants to pull off his rubber glove, the slightest tug immediately stimulates the whole finger (Fig. 8). This means that the human skin is very sensitive to shearing forces, though insensitive to pressures. Unfortunately, as illustrated in Fig. 9, in general we have a combination of both stimuli. If we have a local pressure, there are shearing forces combined with it. The question then becomes: Which one is the stimulus? A difficult question.

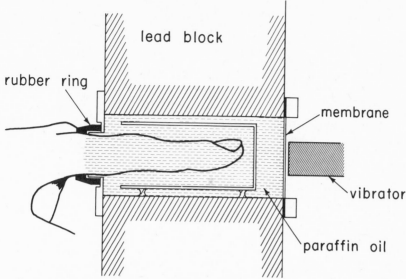

Fig. 7. Meissner's experiment repeated for sinusoidal pressure changes.

In Fig. 10 you see a cross section of skin. If we place a vibrator lightly against the surface, there is little shearing force present; but the moment that we press the vibrator more strongly onto the surface of the skin, we have a large amount of shearing force. If we have a sense organ that is not sensitive to pressure, we get practically no response to a light touch and have therefore a very high threshold. But by pressing the skin a little harder, we produce shearing forces

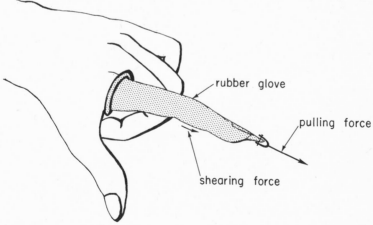

Fig. 8. Experiment showing the high sensitivity of human skin for shearing forces.

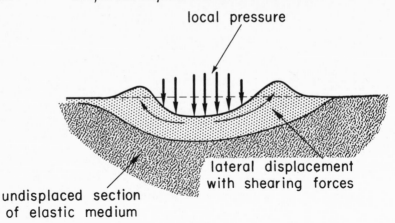

FIG. 9. Any local pressure produces shearing forces.

and a lowering of the threshold. This shows how difficult it is to produce a well-defined stimulus, even under very simple conditions. This in itself is a research problem.

PROJECTION OF A STIMULUS OUTSIDE THE BODY

I have the impression that the fish is a very smart animal. We have a conference on him, but he still keeps most of the solutions to himself.

How can a fish localize the source of a stimulus outside his body and judge its direction and distance correctly? Is a projection of a sensation outside the body possible?

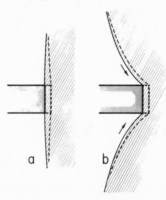

FIG. 10. The magnitude of shearing forces produced by displacement of the skin surface depends to a great extent on the starting point of the deformation.

vibrators

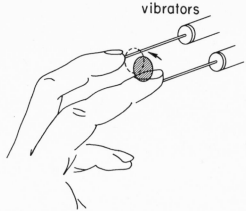

FIG. 11. Two vibrators placed against adjacent fingertips can produce a vibratory sensation between the fingertips that lies outside the skin of the fingers.

If we have the light of an object projected onto the retina, we do not localize the object in the retina. Babies learn in the first 3 to 4 months of life to project the retinal images outside their bodies. Can we project vibratory sensations outside our skin? If a man can do it, then probably a fish can do it also. In Fig. 11, you see our first experiment. We placed two vibrators against the tips of two fingers. The vibrators produced clicks. When the clicks were made equally strong on each finger and were presented simultaneously, and if the fingers were held close together, we felt a sensation between the two fingers. By introducing a time delay of about 1 msec between the two clicks, the sensation seemed to move from one side to the other. The side that gets the click first will always respond first, and that is the finger in which the sensation is localized. In general, the locus of the sensation just jumps from one finger to another; but if one were willing to spend time and repeat the procedure for a few days, the sensation would move from one finger to the other continuously.

If, after a certain training period, we move the two fingers apart, the click sensations between them can be felt in the empty space between the tips. This, then, is a projection of a sensation outside the skin. It takes about 1 to 2 weeks of training, and can be done not only with vibrations but also with heat sensations. We can also place vibrators on the two knees. At first the locus of the vibration will jump from one knee to the other; but after a time, the legs can be placed apart and the sensation will be perceived in the free space.

For any type of masking, this is an important point, because internal

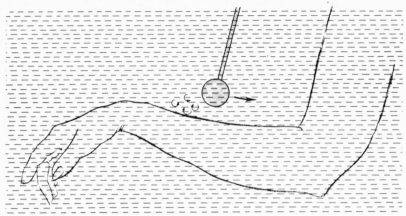

Fig. 12. A moving ball produces mainly direct sensations on the surface of the skin when both are underwater.

noises are localized inside the body but stimuli from outside are localized outside the skin.

The projection of movements of water outside the body is difficult to achieve. We have never really succeeded in doing so. The arm is placed underwater, and a ball is moved back and forth along the skin (Fig. 12). We wanted to train the arm to localize the ball in the correct place. Only movements on the surface of the skin were felt under these conditions, however. To do otherwise, the arm would probably have to be trained for a much longer period, perhaps many days or weeks.

There are situations where localization outside the body is easily learned. In Fig. 13 you see what I call the "screwdriver experiment." For a constant pressure, you localize the pressure in the hand (A). But if you tap on the table with the tip of the screwdriver, you have a combination of your own movements and the shocks on the tip. In this case, you start to localize the shocks to the tip of the screwdriver (B). In general, it takes about 2 hr to localize the vibrations and quick movement to the tip. To project outside the body in any localization phenomenon, the movement of the observer himself is, I think, very important.

If you ask a mechanic where he feels a screw when he screws it in, he will tell you, "I never feel it in my hand; I feel it at the tip of the screwdriver." He has had a long training period. A surgeon feels the edge of the knife when he is cutting. If he does not, he is not a good surgeon.

There are cases where it is possible to project a sensation outside in different ways—a fact that can lead to much confusion. In Fig. 14 I

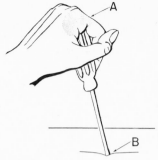

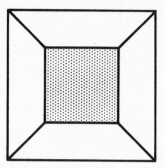

FIG. 13. Pressing a screwdriver against a table, we can localize the sensation in the hand or project it to the tip of the screwdriver.

FIG. 14. There are three possible ways of perceiving this figure.

want to show this situation for a normal optical illusion. You can see the drawing as a pyramidal solid coming toward you, or as a similar but hollow shape receding behind the plane of the paper. You can also see it as simply a flat frame. Every decision-maker should have that figure in his office; it proves that even simple situations can very often be seen in three different ways.

We have an analogy in hearing, as is shown in Fig. 15. If we have two earphones, we can localize the sound inside our head, in front, or in back. In such a situation, reliable and reproducible results can be obtained only if all three different possibilities are described. Unfortunately, I seldom see a description of all these possibilities. In this experiment there is an interesting problem. We can have a sound source in front, in back, or in the middle; but we cannot have it in all

FIG. 15. If we present two earphones to the two ears, the sound source can be localized at three different places.

three places at the same time. This shows that the brain switches from one single thing to another and inhibits the rest of the possibilities at the same time.

It has been said that, in general, inhibition is an unimportant phenomenon. It is certainly not to be regarded as such for lateral inhibition in the sense organs.

We have another experiment, shown in Fig. 16, in which you see 20 loudspeakers from the same company, the same series, and with the same polarity. If someone stands before this long series of loudspeakers, the question is: What does he hear? Does he distinguish a very long sound source, or does he hear only one loudspeaker? We asked several observers, who all reported they could hear only one loudspeaker, and never the whole row. When you walk along the line of speakers, you have the feeling that you only hear one loudspeaker—

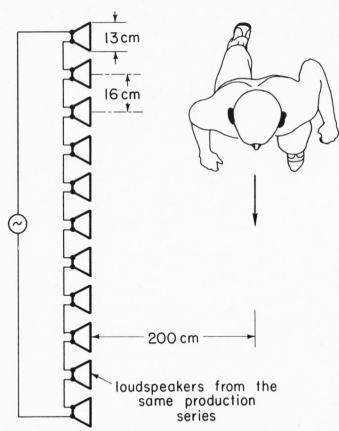

FIG. 16. Inhibitory phenomenon observed along a row of loudspeakers.

and that the same loudspeaker follows you. You can run along the line and have the feeling that someone is running parallel to you, carrying a single loudspeaker.

This type of inhibition is a complicated phenomenon, since it inhibits localization but does not inhibit the loudness. The magnitude of sensation can increase, but the localization is inhibited. In all the research in water tanks, this phenomenon plays an important role because of the sounds reflected from the walls.

Incidentally, lateral inhibition is easy to observe at a cocktail party. In order to hear the man with whom we would like to talk, we inhibit the speakers behind us and on both sides. When someone has nerve deafness, his inhibition does not seem to work, and in that condition he does not understand the speaker in front of him. A very simple method of testing whether or not someone has nerve deafness is to ask him a question at a noisy cocktail party. If he has difficulty understanding the speaker when surrounded by noise, then he probably has nerve deafness.

In Fig. 17, we have a wave that travels along the surface of the skin when it is touched by a vibrator. It was stroboscopically observed. If we touch the fingertip with the vibrator, the wave runs along the whole arm. Where do you feel the vibration? The answer is, "I feel the vibration only directly under the vibrator." Everything else is completely inhibited and disappears. With higher frequencies, vibrations are felt

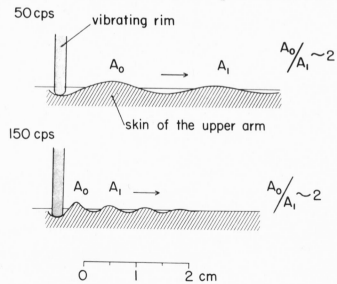

FIG. 17. Waves traveling along the skin surface.

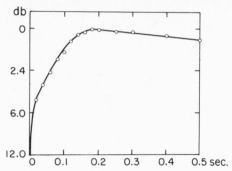

FIG. 18. Increase in loudness of a suddenly started tone plotted with time.

for only about a few millimeters. This type of lateral inhibition can be so strong that, under certain conditions, we misjudge the location of the vibrator. We can have a section along the skin surface where the sensitivity changes, and we will tend to localize the vibrator on the place where amplitude and sensitivity reaches its maximum. If we go on with this line of thinking, we meet with a very interesting phenomenon. Since a flat vibration that extends along the whole arm is inhibited except in a small area, we have a sharpening effect for widespread stimuli. I am sure exactly the same phenomenon occurs along the lateral line in fish. It may help very much in localizing. I have a feeling that inhibition along the lateral line in fish is similar to this phenomenon on the human skin.

I would like to talk about one more problem, namely, the speed of some reactions. In all localizations and movements in fish we see that quickness is a very important factor. From investigations of hearing in man we know, as seen in Fig. 18, that it takes about 0.2 sec until the loudness of a tone reaches its full magnitude. For vibrations, it takes about 1.2 sec. Thus we have in the nervous system a very slow process, ranging between 0.2 and more than 1 sec.

On the other hand, we know from directional hearing studies that we make use of 1-msec time delays between the two ears to localize sound (von Békésy, 1960). From this we can conclude that in the sense organs we have two absolutely different nervous processes. We have a fast one in the range of about 1 msec or even less, and we have a much slower one, such as loudness sensation, which is on the order of 1 sec. For other sense organs such as taste and smell, we have the same situation.

Looking at an actual situation, we realize how important it is to localize a stimulus very quickly. When we move a foreign object along the surface of the water, as shown in Fig. 19, the waves and eddies

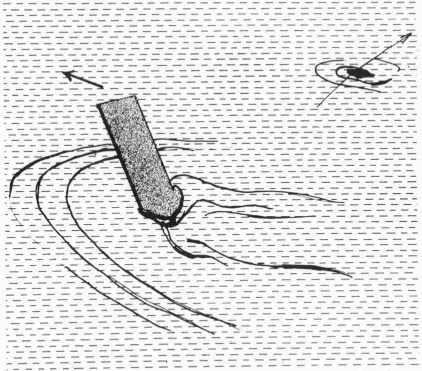

Fɪɢ. 19. Wave and eddy formation produced by movement of a solid body on the surface of a fluid.

which are produced move much faster over the water surface than does the object. It is quite clear that these waves disturb the localization of the moving object. To localize the object, every small change in speed produced by a wave must be localized immediately, and later ones must be inhibited since they do not help in the localization. This requirement seems almost impossible to fulfill. But it is well known that in interior acoustics, we have exactly the same problems, as can be seen from Fig. 20. Sound waves from the source S can reach listeners $O_1$ and $O_2$ either directly or after reflection from the ceiling of the concert hall. The balance between the direct sound and the reflected sound determines the tonal quality of the concert hall. If, for instance, the direct sound is much weaker than the reflected sound, we would tend to localize the orchestra somewhere behind the ceiling—that is, according to the direction from which the reflected sound reaches the listener. This would be a very disturbing mistake in localization. The

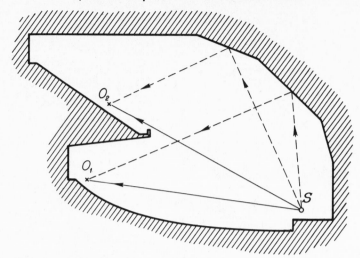

Fɪɢ. 20. Direct and reflected sound in a concert hall.

reason why this seldom happens is that ideally the direct sound reaches the listener first, and satisfactory localization is completed within a millisecond. Therefore, the later-arriving reflected sound no longer disturbs the localization, since it is inhibited. Nevertheless, it contributes to the loudness to a certain degree.

## THE ROLE OF FREQUENCY RANGE OF VIBRATIONS

Since we found so many similarities between human sense organs and the sense organs in fish, some of the observations that have been made for man can help us to decide the important points to settle before trying to make final measurements. One of these important points in the field of vibratory sense organs is the frequency range of vibrations.

In practically all textbooks of physiology, it is said that for the human ear the lowest frequency heard is about 35 cps. It is easy to show by directional hearing experiments that we can hear much lower frequencies, as indicated in Fig. 21. We can produce sinusoidal sound without any disturbing overtones down to 1 cps, and it gives us a very peculiar sensation. But this seems to stimulate the cochlea, since it exhibits all the phenomena of directional hearing observed at higher frequencies. This indicates that the human cochlea can respond to low frequencies that come close to the low-frequency response of the lateral line.

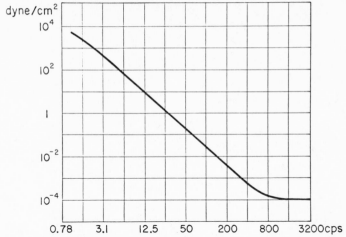

Fɪɢ. 21. Threshold of the hearing of sinusoidal pressure changes on the eardrum as a function of frequency.

For the human being, this low-frequency sound is physiologically unimportant. It is well known that for speech communication we can eliminate all the frequencies below 300 cps and no reduction of intelligibility will result. We could also ignore the frequencies above 2500 cps without disturbing the intelligibility of speech transmission, but we would have difficulty recognizing who was talking. It is this higher-frequency range which becomes so important in differentiating, for instance, between a friend and an enemy. From this we might conclude that, in the case of a fish, there are also characteristic frequency ranges for the different phenomena. It would be most important to determine these frequency ranges, because it would facilitate the construction of appropriate experimental tanks.

REFERENCES

Békésy, G. von (1960). *Experiments in Hearing* (E. G. Wever, ed.). McGraw-Hill, New York.
Casseri, G. (1600). De vocis auditusque organis. Ferrara-Venice.
Lagrange, J. L. (1867-1892). Œuvres de Lagrange, Serret and Darboux (eds.).
Meissner, G. (1853). Beiträge zur Anatomie und Physiologie der Haut. Leipzig.

LATERAL LINE DETECTORS (P. Cahn, ed.), 437–446, © 1967 Indiana University Press

# 24 HYDRODYNAMICS OF NAVIGATION BY FISHES IN TERMS OF THE MUCUS-WATER "INTERFACE" †

VLADIMIR WALTERS AND ROBERT K. LIU

Department of Zoology
University of California
Los Angeles, California

If a nonvisual navigator such as the blind cave characin (*Astyanax mexicanus jordani*) is allowed to swim among upright glass vials in a bentonite polariscope, the fish will be seen to initiate a navigational maneuver whenever the birefringence pattern surrounding its head becomes deformed by a nearby vial (Walters, unpublished observations). The fish seems to navigate in response to changes in the fluid flow pattern about its head, changes induced by nearby objects. A number of aquatic vertebrates do not appear to require visual cues in order to navigate; that is, the eye does not seem to be required to locate prey, predators, obstacles, and fellow members of the species. Some fish species appear to be echo-, electro-, olfactory, or gustatory navigators. The other nonvisual navigators appear to obtain information concerning the environment from mechanical stimuli acting on the neuromast cupulae of their lateral line systems. The cephalic portion of the lateral line system seems to be more important than the trunk portion, in this respect. For example, Eigenmann (1909) described experiments which demonstrated that the amblyopsid cave fishes responded to prey organisms only when the prey were in front of or to one side of the head of the fish. The mechanosensory basis for this type of nonvisual navigation is termed *Ferntastsinn*, or distant perception (Dijkgraaf, 1934, 1963). Distant perception is particularly well developed in cavernicolous fishes. For the remainder of this paper, nonvisual navigation will be restricted to those swimming movements

† This publication is based on work supported by contracts between the Biology Branch of the U.S. Office of Naval Research and The American Museum of Natural History (NR-301-257) and the University of California (NR-104-669), and also by University of California Faculty Research Grant No. 1780 to the senior author.

made by a fish in response to stimuli detected by its distant perceptive structures (i.e., the neuromasts of the cephalic lateral line system).

In general, cavernicolous fishes swim more slowly and have broader heads than do their epigean relatives (Eigenmann, 1909; Heuts, 1951; Hubbs, 1938; Pavan, 1946; Poulson, 1963; Walters and Walters, 1965; Woods and Inger, 1957). Neither the swordfish nor the tuna body form appears in caves, and very high-speed locomotion is absent from cave fishes. Thus, nonvisual navigation is possibly dependent upon body shape and swimming speed as well as upon the cephalic neuromasts of the lateral line system. To the best of our knowledge, water movements about the swimming navigator have not been studied by anyone other than Rosen (1959), who was concerned with fish locomotion and propulsion energetics.

The present investigation was undertaken to evaluate the influences of head shape and swimming speed on the fluid movements about the head of a fish, and to relate the fluid behavior to the structure of the cephalic lateral line system and the navigational method used by the fish.

## THEORETICAL BACKGROUND

The literature on the physiology of the cephalic lateral line neuromasts expresses a number of views concerned with how these organs are stimulated. At present, two views predominate. One school of thought envisions the neuromasts as being stimulated by variations in fluid flow; the other school maintains that the neuromasts respond to changes in acoustic pressure. It is possible that both views are correct, for the neuromast cupula is deflected by the dynamic pressure that develops on its surface when the ambient fluid moves. It is not possible to distinguish between dynamic pressure phenomena and flow phenomena acting on the cupula. However, for reasons presented below, it is our opinion that neither school of thought correctly interprets the role of the neuromast in navigation; previous studies have not considered the fish's mucous film.

## PHOTOVISCOSITY STUDIES: MATERIALS AND METHODS

Fluid movements were made visible in this phase of our study by means of a stream-birefringent bentonite sol and polarized light.

**Preparation of Birefringent Sol.**[†] A 2.5% suspension of White Hector

[†] Andrew Fejer, of the Illinois Institute of Technology, gave us advice on preparation of the birefringent sol.

bentonite clay (aluminum silicate) in distilled water was thoroughly mixed and then allowed to settle overnight. The bentonite was obtained from the Baroid Division of the National Lead Company, Houston, Texas (one of the relatively few sources for a bentonite having high optical activity). The supernatant was clarified with a constant-feed Sharples supercentrifuge, at a rate of 2 ml per sec and a bowl speed of 23,000 rpm; under these conditions the clarified sol's particles were in the desired size range for stream-birefringence phenomena. The sol's pH was 9.6, however, and this was quickly toxic to most freshwater fishes. The sol pH was adjusted to 7.0 to 7.5 with a cation-exchange resin: Dowex 50W-X4, hydrogen form, analytical grade, finely ground. The resin was added at the rate of 2.5 to 5.0 gm per liter; the mixture was allowed to stand for several days with occasional stirring. Attempts to lower the pH by other means, such as titration with dilute acids and addition of chelating agents, either increased the sol's viscosity, caused gelation, or brought about coagulation. The resin was removed by centrifugation, and the sol's pH was checked for several more days. If insufficient ion exchange had taken place, the pH gradually rose and toxicity returned, necessitating further treatment with the resin. The sol finally was stabilized by addition of 0.1 gm tetrasodium pyrophosphate per liter. The resulting emulsion, which looked like clam juice, was a stable sol with a concentration of about 1.25% and a viscosity of about 2.2 cP. In practice, it was often diluted further to permit using greater depths of emulsion fluid without excessive loss of light.

During tests involving live fish, the animals secreted mucus and released wastes into the sol, which caused its viscosity and relaxation time to increase. When this happened, it was necessary to recentrifuge the sol and, in some cases, to re-treat it with resin.

**Polariscope Assembly** (Fig. 1). *Light source.* An iodine-vapor incandescent tungsten lamp, such as the type now in use for filming motion pictures indoors, was found to be satisfactory for our qualitative studies. Monochromatic light would have been more desirable, but filtered mercury-vapor light was found to have considerable ripple in our laboratory, which made it impossible to obtain the proper exposure values for cinematographic recording. The light source was positioned above the optical assembly. A water bath containing copper sulfate (basic potassium chromate for mercury-vapor light, to absorb the ultraviolet) acted as a heat absorber. A sheet of translucent plastic beneath the water bath served as a diffuser. A 32-cm, f/0.8 Fresnel lens placed beneath the diffuser projected a parallel beam of light through

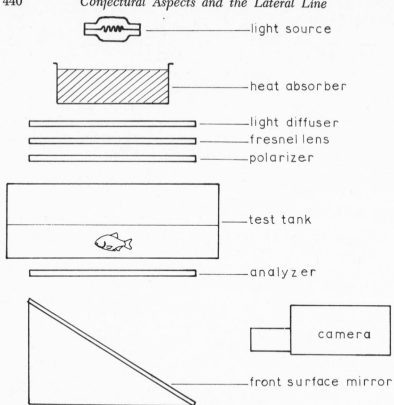

FIG. 1. Polariscope assembly.

the optical assembly. The proper distance between light source and lens was adjusted later.

*Polarizer.* The polarizer consisted of a 30-cm square of laminated-plastic HN-38 polarizing filter sandwiched between two sheets of glass, mounted directly beneath the Fresnel lens.

*Test chamber.* The bentonite sol was contained in a test chamber between the polarizer and the analyzer. The test chamber was a glass-bottomed aquarium measuring 30 × 60 × 20 cm; its top was fitted with an opaque lid having a central opening 28 cm square to accommodate the polarizer, and a small access door near either end. The test chamber was mounted on a wooden stand, which was slotted to hold the analyzer in line with the polarizer.

*Analyzer.* The analyzer consisted of the same materials as the polarizer and was mounted beneath the test chamber. During a test the analyzer axis was oriented 90° to the polarizer axis; this resulted in extinction of the field.

*Mirror.* A front-surface mirror was positioned beneath the analyzer, in order to record the events taking place in the test chamber. With the mirror in place, the light source was positioned at the focal point of the lens to give as uniform and as bright a field of illumination as possible. This adjustment was made with crossed polaroids.

*Recording.* Exposure-meter readings were taken with a bright field; polaroid axes were made parallel for light readings and recrossed for recording. The tests were recorded with a calibrated d-c-powered Wollensak Fastair 16-mm camera, taking 100 pictures per sec. Negative film was used because it is finer-grained and has a higher emulsion speed than does reversal film, and selected sequences could be enlarged and printed in a single step. Tri-X or Royal-X Pan negative films were used.

**Testing Procedures.** Three groups of photoviscosity studies were carried out:

1. Recordings were made of the fluid movements past Plexiglas models of fish heads.

2. Recordings were made of live animals swimming through the bentonite.

3. Recordings were made of fluid movements past preserved specimens and clay models that were moved through the bentonite by means of rigid wires.

*Plexiglas head models.* Seven different head shapes were constructed from 12.7-mm Plexiglas rod. These shapes included a flat-ended cylinder, a convex cone, a straight-sided cone, and a concave-convex cone. The last-named shape was modeled after the head of an adult swordfish (*Xiphias gladius*) as seen in dorsal aspect, based on a photograph taken by Walters of a mounted specimen at The American Museum of Natural History. The head models were turned on a lathe, so that each model was a perfectly symmetrical body of revolution, and lacked the dorsoventral and lateral deviations which characterize the real fish head. The models were sprayed with flat black enamel. Each was then affixed to the tip of a Plexiglas cannon powered by a rubber band. An ordinary glass microscope slide ($25 \times 75 \times 0.8$ mm) was propelled on edge along its major axis to obtain the flow past a flat plate for comparison with the head-shape data.

*Live animals.* Adult specimens of the blind cave characin (*A. m. jordani*) were introduced into the test chamber, which contained one to four randomly placed upright glass cylinders, each 25 mm in diameter. The fish were approximately 75 mm in total length. Recordings were made of their swimming behavior and the flow characteristics of the sol as the fish swam among the glass cylinders.

*Preserved specimens and clay models.* Adult specimens of *A. m. jordani* and the amblyopsid *Typhlichthys subterraneus* were killed and fixed in formalin, then rinsed in tap water. Their rigid bodies were then affixed to stiff wires and moved headfirst through the emulsion, toward and past an upright glass cylinder 25 mm in diameter. The flow picture was recorded for these simulations of nonvisual navigation. We had intended to use *T. subterraneus* and another amblyopsid, *Amblyopsis rosae,* for live recordings, but the colony became sickly with a fungus infection and died off before the photoviscosity equipment was in working order.

Replicas of amblyopsid heads were modeled of plasticene, using as guides the figures published by Eigenmann (1909) and by Woods and Inger (1957), as well as the preserved specimens of *T. subterraneus* and *A. rosae.* The clay models were pushed through the bentonite on stiff wires, and birefringence recordings were made.

**Interpretation of Birefringence Patterns.** Although it is possible to obtain quantitative information from birefringence studies of nonliving systems, the mucus and wastes produced by a live fish so alter the physical characteristics of the bentonite sol that a quantitative analysis cannot be accomplished. Bentonite, being an aluminum compound, reacts with mucus. The birefringence recordings of fishes can only be interpreted in qualitative terms. Furthermore, it is not possible to apply the birefringence recordings of inert models to the quantitative interpretation of fish hydrodynamics because the models lack mucus and, as pointed out elsewhere in this paper, the nonnewtonian (thixotropic) properties of mucus should significantly affect the mechanics of the fish's boundary layer.

The birefringence pattern that is seen to surround a body moving through the bentonite sol results from hydrodynamic forces which orient the clay particles in certain planes, and the disappearance of birefringence (relaxation of the sol) is due to Brownian movement, which causes the particles to become randomly oriented. The phenomenon of stream birefringence makes it possible to observe instantly the flow characteristics of the entire system—which is to say, a photograph will give the steady flow information concerning the system at the moment the picture is taken.

Plane-polarized light, which was used in our studies, reveals two forms of birefringence when the flow is laminar:

1. A well-defined bright fringe that tends to follow changes in the body profile, regardless of the orientation of the fish with respect to the plane of light polarization, indicates the direction of the streamlines. Occasionally two or more fringes are seen. According to Rosen-

berg (1952), a fringe occupies a zone of equal velocity gradients (i.e., a shear plane). For convenience, we term the fringe nearest the body the "boundary layer," although the real boundary layer may be thicker than this. However, the real boundary layer will vary in the same manner as the inner fringe. Since the outer limit of the mathematically defined boundary layer (Schlichting, 1960) has a velocity only 1% less than full stream velocity, there is very little shear at the edge of the mathematical boundary layer. It is entirely possible that, in the case of the live fish, the inner fringe lies in the shear plane internal to the mucus-water "interface" (see below); whereas in the case of an inanimate object, the inner fringe may occupy part of the lower limb of the boundary layer's velocity profile.

2. Diffuse birefringent lobes which are oriented at 45°, 135°, 225°, and 315° to the plane of polarization and which usually originate on an advancing surface are interpreted by us to be indicative of dynamic pressure gradients resulting from the convergence of streamlines. On a fish, the diffuse birefringent lobes are associated with the head and the outer surfaces of the crests of backward-traveling waves of body undulations. When there is no nearby submerged obstacle, the diffuse lobes intensify and become enlarged between the fish and a nearby submerged object.

When the flow is turbulent rather than laminar, the same interpretations are given to the birefringence patterns, although the picture is considerably more complicated than it is when the flow is laminar.

PHOTOVISCOSITY STUDIES: PRELIMINARY RESULTS

The various head shapes were propelled through the bentonite solution at speeds of 1 to 2.3 m per sec. The concave-cone model head showed no noticeable birefringence near the anterior two-thirds of the head. This head shape developed no boundary layer to speak of and generated no dynamic pressure gradient by itself.

The flat-sided cone, which is the head shape of tunas, eels, and other fish, formed a thin boundary layer at 2.3 m per sec, with a faint indication of a dynamic pressure.

The convex cone, which is the head shape characteristic of most fishes, developed a thicker boundary layer than was seen in the above-described head shapes. This pattern showed up at a speed of 2.1 m per sec.

The bluntly rounded cylinder, which is the head shape seen in the highly specialized cave fish and in the deep-sea fish, resulted in a thicker boundary layer than the convex cone.

The flat-ended cylinder generated the thickest boundary layer and the greatest dynamic pressure gradient when the model was propelled through the bentonite at a speed of 1.6 m per sec.

Thus the fish that operate at the thinnest boundary layers, such as the tunas, swordfish, and marlin, have flat or concave head shapes and generate little pressure when they move through the water. The fish with thicker boundary layers and a more convex head shape generate greater dynamic pressure changes.

DISCUSSION OF RESULTS

It is well known that the cephalic lateral line system is very well developed in cave fish and in deep-sea fish, and these fish possess head shapes that generate the thickest boundary layers and the greatest dynamic pressure gradients. It therefore appears that an extremely well-developed cephalic lateral line system seems to be associated with the ability to navigate in the absence of light. Tunas have almost imperceptible cephalic lateral line pores; in fact, we have not found them in most of the species we examined. Iversen (personal communication), who has observed cephalic lateral line pores in all the tuna species he examined in Hawaii, emphasizes the importance of studying fresh material. The pores, which are very small, were found in the typical locations as described for most other fish. Iversen did not study the internal structure of the cephalic lateral line system in scombrids, so that there is need for research on the neuromast and canal size in these fishes.

Although Gero (1952) stated that fish mucus cannot reduce drag, we now know that long-chain molecules can effectively reduce surface-drag coefficients (Rosen, 1959). At a low Reynolds number, the boundary layer is much thicker than the mucous layer. At a high Reynolds number, on the other hand, the boundary layer is thin. Despite the fact that we do not know the thickness of the mucous layer on a living fish, it is safe to assume that at a low Reynolds number, where the boundary layer will be very thick, it will be considerably thicker than the mucous layer. At a high Reynolds number, on the other hand, where the boundary layer is comparatively thin, the mucous layer and boundary layer are about the same. In the former case, where the boundary layer is much thicker than the mucous layer, water flows at stream velocity at some distance away from the mucous layer. But when the boundary layer is thin, water at stream velocity flows close to the mucus-water interface.

Where the boundary layer thickness greatly exceeds the mucous layer thickness, it is obvious that a shear plane exists in the mucous film deep inside the boundary layer. This shear plane results in the absorption of boundary layer energy by the mucus. The boundary layer seen in the bentonite photoviscosity studies may be this shear plane. This immediately suggests a function of the lateral line neuromasts in the nonvisual navigators. At the low Reynolds numbers, such as we have for the nonvisual navigators, the boundary layer is so thick that the neuromasts must lie in nearly stagnant water. However, the neuromasts do have cupulae, and in nonvisual navigators such as the cave fish and the deep-sea fish these cupulae are believed to project considerably beyond the body surface. Therefore the cupulae may lie in or near this shear plane. This is in accordance with the low swimming speed recorded for the cave fish and the very thick boundary layer.

The boundary layer displaces the streamline surrounding the fish to an extent that is approximately one-third the thickness of the boundary layer. It seems to me that, if a streamline can be displaced by a boundary layer, then any change in the streamline will alter the thickness of the boundary layer. If nonvisual navigators come in contact with a nearby obstacle, their boundary layer thickness will change by a factor approximately three times the externally produced streamline displacement. This effect was seen in a sequence of films made of the blind cave characin in bentonite.

In other words, we postulate that the boundary layer acts as a hydrodynamic amplifier by tripling the disturbance to the navigator's streamline pattern. The disturbances are produced by obstacles, prey, predators, and other fish of the same species. According to this hypothesis, externally produced water movements that approach the fish head from any direction, when the fish is swimming, are all translated into one continuous traveling stimulus, which then impinges on the cupulae. The degree of cupular deflection will be proportional to the change in boundary layer thickness, and this will be transmitted to the navigator's central nervous system.

## REFERENCES

Dijkgraaf, S. (1934). Untersuchungen über die Funktion der Seitenorgane an Fischen. Z. *Vergleich. Physiol.* 20, 162.

——— (1963). The functioning and significance of the lateral line organs. *Biol. Rev. Cambridge Phil. Soc.* 38, 51.

Eigenmann, C. H. (1909). Cave vertebrates of America. A study in degenerative evolution. Carnegie Institute, Washington, D.C.

Gero, D. R. (1952). The hydrodynamic aspects of fish propulsion. *Am. Museum Novitates* 1601, 11.

Heuts, M. J. (1951). Ecology, variation and adaptation of the blind African cave fish, *Caecobarbus geertsi. Ann. Soc. Roy. Zool. Belg.* 82, 155.

Hubbs, C. L. (1938). Fishes from the caves of Yucatan. *Carnegie Inst. Publ.* 491, 261.

Pavan, C. (1946). Observations and experiments on the cave fish *Pimelodella kronei* and its relatives. *Am. Naturalist* 80, 343.

Poulson, T. (1963). Cave adaptation in amblyopsid fishes. *Am. Midland Naturalist* 70, 257.

Rosen, M. (1959). Water flow about a swimming fish. U.S. Naval Ordnance Test Station, China Lake, Calif.

Rosenberg, B. (1952). The use of doubly refracting solutions in the investigation of fluid flow phenomena. Dept. of the Navy, Rept. 617. David Taylor Model Basin, Washington, D.C.

Schlichting, H. (1960). *Boundary Layer Theory.* McGraw-Hill, New York.

Walters, L. H., and V. Walters (1965). Laboratory observations on a caverniculous poeciliid from Tabasco, Mexico. *Copeia* 2, 214.

Woods, L. P., and R. F. Inger (1957). The cave, spring and swamp fishes of the family Amblyopsidae of central and eastern United States. *Am. Midland Naturalist* 58, 232.

## COMMENTS

MARSHALL: I work in a museum in London, and I've never worked on a living lateral line neuromast in a laboratory. I'm going to make certain generalizations concerning the structure of the lateral line system. There are two different patterns of lateral line design that I will talk about. One design is found in a good many deep-sea fishes, for instance, the macrourids, halosaurs, and the brotulids. It's also found in certain freshwater fishes, for example, the notopterids and *Acerina*. In all these fish the head canals are very wide, and the main plane of each cupula runs across the canals. In many macrourids, the head-canal volume is practically a third to one-quarter of the total head volume. The head canals are filled and distended with mucus, and they either are closed or are open to the water through pores. When the tubes are present, they are very short.

In a second kind of system, found in many other fish, for example, in codfish and in *Fundulus,* the orientation of the main plane of the cupula is along the canal. The canals are narrow and have outlets in the form of relatively long tubes, which may be extremely elaborate. There are fluid movements in the canals, and we ought to know more about these, particularly in the two kinds of lateral line designs just described.

It was interesting to hear that a good many broad-headed, roundnosed fish feed on the surface, such as many killifishes and flying fishes. In many broad-snouted fishes, particularly the deep-sea varieties, there are very large neuromasts on the head. This is true of macrourids, myctophids, melamphoids, and others. Besides the wide canals on the head, macrourids also possess freestanding organs.

LATERAL LINE DETECTORS (P. Cahn, ed.), 447–451, © 1967 Indiana University Press

# 25 SPECULATIVE COMMENTS FROM PANELISTS

### a. J. FITZGERALD: THE LATERAL LINE AS A HYDROACOUSTIC SENSOR †

It is considered that the fish has adapted its basic transducing mechanism, the neuron, to sense the various aspects of its ocean environment which are important to its adaptation and survival. Through ingenious use of coupling elements, the fish has developed sensory systems for signal detection in the hydrodynamic field, the acoustic field, and the interacting hydroacoustic field.

It appears that fish in the hydrodynamic field may use Meissner and Pacinian type corpuscles, which may be well distributed over the body surface. These "skin type" corpuscles are presumed to respond mainly to the gross hydrodynamic forces of fluid flow across the body: namely, drag, lift, and large-scale turbulence. Their principal use to the fish is probably, with the aid of feedback loops, that of propulsion control. As a secondary function, they would appear capable of obstacle avoidance by sensing the Bernoulli flow around an obstacle.

Fish ears, like most vertebrate ears, possess three semicircular canals that serve an equilibrium function. The hearing organ of the inner ear, is a fluid-filled structure made up of hair cells. In the Ostariophysi fishes, such as the catfish, there is found a specially designed method of coupling to the acoustic field. The swim bladder is connected to the inner ear by a series of four small bones. These structures serve as an impedance-matching device. Water-borne sound, incident on the fish, traverses the sound-transparent fish body readily and excites the swim bladder in one or more of its normal vibrational modes. The complex vibrations are then transmitted to the inner ear.

The third fluid-dynamic receptor system, the lateral line, is considered to be intermediate between the hydrodynamic and acoustic sensors. The lateral line may be characterized as a directional, bilateral, spatial sensor array that is intermediate, both in sensitivity and frequency response, between the tactile hydrodynamic sensor system and the labyrinth sensor systems which operate in the acoustic field.

Our conjecture is that the lateral line responds basically to the

† James Fitzgerald, Fitzgerald and Associates, Annapolis, Maryland.

447

*gradient* of the *pressure field* and is, therefore, capable of sensing: (1) the "near field" from hydroacoustic sources, such as acoustic radiation from other fish and turbulent eddies generated by other fish; (2) small-scale lower-intensity hydrodynamic turbulence impinging on the fish's body. It should be pointed out that the two near-field effects are field disturbances which are propagated from their sources and which are essentially acoustic velocities. By contrast, hydrodynamic turbulence is a mass-transport phenomenon moving at the much-lower average stream velocities. To be detected by the lateral line, the turbulent stream must pass over the fish or, alternatively, the fish must swim to the turbulent field.

Another reason for the three separate systems arises from the fact that useful information of the two mechanical fields exists in basically different forms. To extract this information from the noise background requires basically different senses, different spatial assembling, and different data processing.

### b. E. R. LINDGREN: THE LATERAL LINE FROM THE POINT OF VIEW OF A FLUID DYNAMICIST †

In a Karman vortex street that trails behind a cylinder moving in a fluid, the wake vortices do not move with the cylinder but seem to be at rest in the fluid. This state of affairs does not necessarily mean that there is no net flow backward. In the specific case of a cylinder moving in a fluid, it so happens that there is practically no net backward flow across the vortex wake.

The conditions are a little different for a fish that propels itself through the water. There must be a net backward flow in the fish wake for the creation of propulsive power. If we apply the momentum theorem to the matter inside a control volume $V$ that contains a fish, we can reason as follows: instead of letting the fish move with constant velocity in some direction, keep the fish and the control volume at rest and move the fluid (with the same constant velocity), undisturbed by the fish, in the opposite direction. Since there are stationary conditions, the momentum theorem for the mechanical system inside the control surface $S$ of the control volume $V$ gives

$$\mathfrak{F} = \Sigma q_e \mathfrak{V}_e - \Sigma q_c \mathfrak{V}_c$$

where $\mathfrak{F}$ is the resultant (vector) force acting upon the matter inside

---

† E. Rune Lindgren, Department of Engineering Science and Mechanics, University of Florida, Gainesville, Florida. [Some of these comments were made in reference to the papers of Walters and Liu (Chap. 24) and Kuiper (Chap. 9).]

$S$; $q_e$ is the outflux of mass per time unit from $V$ with (vector) velocity $\mathcal{V}_e$; and $q_c$ equals the influx of mass per time unit into $V$ with (vector) velocity $\mathcal{V}_c$. Since there is no acceleration of the system, the resultant force $\mathfrak{F} = 0$, and we have

$$\Sigma q_e \mathcal{V}_e = \Sigma q_c \mathcal{V}_c$$

which means that the influx of momentum into $V$ must equal the outflux of momentum from the same volume. There will thus be a rather narrow "jet wake" with high velocities backward, caused by the fish's propulsion mechanism, circumferenced by a wider belt of lower velocities forward, representing the boundary layer effects from the fish's body. It is then quite clear that there will be a row of horseshoe or perhaps spiral vortices which will not move with noticeable velocity relative to the fluid space, since their core centers will be located in the "neutral layer" of zero velocity between the flow regions of backward and forward velocities.

Thus, if experiments seem to indicate stationary vortices with no translational motion, this does not mean that there is no resultant backward wake velocity due to fish propulsion. As has been shown, there must be a region of backward jet-wake velocity relative to the fish when it swims.

The following considerations are also of interest in connection with fish propulsion. We know that, in general, fluid flow changes from laminar to turbulent for flows along flat plates at Reynolds numbers of about 300,000, which equals the flow velocity ($U$) times the distance from the front edge of the plate ($x$), over the kinematic viscosity of the fluid ($v$). This results in quite an increase of the frictional flow resistance as compared with the laminar flow condition. The fish is not a plane surface, nor is it rigid, so that it should produce transition to turbulence at Reynolds numbers even lower than 300,000. This is especially true since sea or river waters are always disturbed by eddies and thermal currents.

Thus, if we consider an ordinary fish of a length of $\frac{1}{3}$ of a meter, and with the requirement that turbulence must be established over at least $\frac{3}{4}$ of its length before an increase of the frictional drag will occur, we get:

$$x = \frac{1}{4} \times \frac{1}{3} = \frac{1}{12} \text{ m}$$

Further, the kinematic viscosity of water at room temperature is approximately $10^{-6}$ sq m per sec, giving

$$U = \frac{300,000 \times 10^{-6}}{1/12}$$

so that turbulent frictional drag should occur at a velocity of $U = 12.0 \times 0.3 = 3.6$ m per sec. This means that for a fish moving at a speed of 3.6 m per sec (about 6.2 knots), the flow drag would increase to values too high for the fish to overcome. If I am correct, the discrepancy between available power of a fish and the power required for the fish to swim at high velocities amounts to more than one order of magnitude. In consideration of the known facts about transition along plane and curved surfaces, I must conclude that boundary layers about fish swimming at velocities so high that the critical Reynolds number is exceeded should be turbulent.

In recent years more and more knowledge has been gained about artificial and natural substances of giant chain molecules that have a profound frictional-reduction effect on turbulent flows, even in very weak concentrations. I myself have made such experiments on flows of solutions of polyethylene oxide with remarkable frictional-reduction effects even in the presence of very rough surfaces at such low concentrations as 0.006%. Such effects, perhaps, may lead toward an explanation of the fish's swimming abilities.

### c. R. S. MACKAY: ON THE POSSIBILITY OF FISH SENSING 50-KC SOUND [†]

If we were to insert into a fish a transmitter from which information was carried acoustically at a frequency of 50 kc, we would expect that the fish would not hear the transmitter and would be unaware of its functioning. There are actually several mechanisms by which a fish might sense a high-frequency signal, if it is modulated. There is an effect called acoustic pressure, in which a sound wave always exerts a net push upon a surface. The compression half-cycle pushes an object away more effectively than the other half-cycle pulls it back. Thus an amplitude-modulated signal cyclically varying in intensity at 100 cps will exert a 100-cps variable push on the fish. Even if the signal is steady, this mechanism leads to the possibility of the animal's sensing the turning on and off of the transmitter.

In any nonlinear system, a rectifying-like action can allow the organism to sense the turning on and off or the modulation envelope of an a-c signal that supposedly was of a frequency too high to hear at all. Quite a separate effect from the previous two is the possibility of the generation of subharmonics. Thus certain systems, including two-dimensional surfaces, can vibrate at a frequency lower than that of the

[†] R. Stuart Mackay, Division of Medical Physics, University of California, Berkeley, California; and Boston University Medical School, Boston, Massachusetts.

sound signal acting upon them. (We usually think of harmonics as being of a frequency higher than the driving signal, but this is not necessarily the case.) Such subharmonics can in some cases fall within the range of hearing.

It might be mentioned that if a 50-kc sound, or other higher-than-audible frequency, is applied to the jawbone of a human subject, he will hear a tone which is actually the threshold of hearing for that particular subject. This is apparently because of the direct stimulation of the sensors in the cochlea, and similar mechanisms might allow fish to perceive sound fields of unexpectedly high frequency if these were of sufficient intensity.

# VI INSTRUMENTATION PROBLEMS IN LATERAL LINE RESEARCH AND SOME SUGGESTED SOLUTIONS

LATERAL LINE DETECTORS (P. Cahn, ed.), 455–457, © 1967 Indiana University Press

# 26 PANEL COMMENTS
# ON UNDERWATER ACOUSTICS

J. STEINBERG †: As a physicist, one of the things I'd like to see is a better description of the sound field in experiments on fish. This problem is primarily related to that of getting instrumentation small enough to work at low frequencies, to measure displacement, velocity, or acceleration. These are vector quantities, and it is almost imperative to measure their direction if they are to be studied in relation to the organ systems of the fishes.

V. ALBERS ‡: I feel like a fish out of water at a meeting like this, since I know very little if anything about the biological problems. I also have much admiration for the biologist, because his problems are much more difficult than those of the physicist or the engineer. The latter can read a meter or an oscilloscope to get his answers. When the answer to a problem depends on the behavior of an animal, another dimension is introduced that makes the problem much more difficult.

In dealing with a moving animal such as a fish, the possibility of flow noise being generated must be considered. When we deal with something like an oceanographic probe or a torpedo, it may require a power plant of several hundred horsepower and much auxiliary machinery. It is not too difficult, however, to design such a vehicle so that the noise generated by all the machinery is lower in level than the noise due to the flow of water over the body of the vehicle, provided that the speed of the vehicle is relatively high. In the case of the fish, we know nothing about the problem of flow noise. In our laboratory we have done some work using a coating of vaseline over an inanimate vehicle and have found considerable reduction of flow noise. It may be that the mucus on the outside of the body of the fish is a factor in reducing the flow noise of the animal.

We do know that, if we have a streamlined body traveling through the water, there will be more nearly laminar flow at the front end, where the boundary layer will be very thin. A hydrophone placed anywhere in that region will record a higher level of flow noise than one

† John Steinberg, Institute of Marine Science, University of Miami, Miami, Florida.

‡ Vernon Albers, Ordnance Research Laboratory, Pennsylvania State University, University Station, Pennsylvania.

placed farther back on the body. This is because, as the boundary layer thickens, the smaller roughnesses do not project into the flow to generate eddies.

Two types of flow noise can be recognized: far-field noise, which can be radiated to a great distance, and near-field noise, which is not radiated very far. The near-field noise may be as much as a thousand times greater than the radiated far-field noise. The area of the hydrophone used to measure near-field flow noise has a significant effect on the values obtained. This is because there are pressure components which cancel each other over the surface of the hydrophone. It seems to me that flow noise is something to be concerned with in studies of acoustic response of fish. It may be that, in measuring thresholds in any of these animals which are traveling through water, you may not be measuring the threshold of the sensory mechanism but rather the signal-to-noise ratio.

It would be desirable for someone to design an experiment in which a hydrophone is planted on the surface of a fish to measure the flow noise. We should like to see the results of such an experiment to find out whether the flow noise is lower than that which we would expect by extrapolating from the kind of test vehicles we have run. This would indicate whether the mucus on the surface of the fish is a factor in reducing the flow noise.

A. PARVULESCU †: During the past few years I have maintained an "answering service" for biologists concerned with ear and lateral line instrumentation problems. In the main, the questions have dealt with the following two matters: (1) When subjected to an underwater sound source, are the fish actually receiving acoustic pressure, or is it a different kind of pressure, such that it cannot be considered sound at all? (2) How can we design a well-controlled underwater bioacoustics experiment?

These questions, which have created much confusion in the minds of biologists, are somewhat disconcerting even to the underwater-acoustics specialist.

When we talk about sound waves, we are dealing with complex vibratory phenomena. These vibrations may be traveling or stationary, plane waves or spherical, and they may involve near- and far-field components. All these phenomena can be defined mathematically and can be described in terms of X, Y, and Z components for idealized infinitesimal pieces of ocean, and the relationships among these components can be examined (Parvulescu, 1964).

---

† Antares Parvulescu, Hudson Laboratories, Columbia University, Dobbs Ferry, New York.

When we try to apply these idealized parameters to conditions existing in an experimental tank or in the open ocean, or to the forces exerted on a swimming fish, it is necessary to make extensive measurements for each different situation. This is important in order to be certain that our experimental conditions have not altered the theoretical phenomena. All these measurements are difficult to make, for expensive gadgetry is needed and must be specially constructed for each specific problem.

It is very important for biologists to think carefully about the kinds of experimental controls that they require to obtain precise answers to their questions of sense-organ function.

R. RASMUSSEN[†]: In regard to the sound field around a fish, the resultant field is, of course, affected by the presence of the fish. Regardless of the location of the source, a pressure gradient will exist and will cause the fish to "move." The fish will oscillate and produce a field of its own. The resultant sound field is, then, the composite of those due to the source and to the fish. The field is not simply dependent on the density or compressibility of the fish. However, a fish with a swim bladder would be very poorly matched to the water from a compressibility standpoint, and the field produced by such a fish would be different from that produced by a fish without a swim bladder.

REFERENCES

Parvulescu, A. (1964). Problems of propagation and processing, in W. N. Tavolga (ed.), Marine Bio-Acoustics. Pergamon Press, New York.
Skudrzyk, E. J. (1963). Flow noise, theory and experiment, in V. M. Albers (ed.), Underwater Acoustics. Plenum Press, New York.

† Robert Rasmussen, Department of Physics, Scripps Institution of Oceanography, San Diego, California.

LATERAL LINE DETECTORS (P. Cahn, ed.), 459–465, © 1967 Indiana University Press

# 27 MEASUREMENT OF PARTICLE VELOCITY IN UNDERWATER SOUND

BENJAMIN B. BAUER

Acoustics and Magnetics Department
CBS Laboratories
Stamford, Connecticut

I was asked to speak about particle velocity in underwater sound and about its measurement. Thus, I will deal with four questions:

1. What is particle velocity?

2. What is a pressure-gradient, or "velocity," hydrophone?

3. How can one best use gradient hydrophones to measure particle velocity?

4. How are pressure-gradient hydrophones calibrated?

The answer to the last question may also suggest methods for setting up experimental particle-velocity fields for lateral line research.

## PARTICLE VELOCITY

I ask your indulgence if I am about to describe particle velocity in a manner too elementary for the physicists. However, the zoologists may not have the concept so clearly in mind, and a very brief review is in order. In Fig. 1 is shown a sinusoidal sound-pressure wave of frequency $f$, traveling from left to right in an unbounded body of water, with a velocity $c$. The pressure distribution in space at time 0 is shown by the solid line. An instant later, at time $t$, the wave has moved to the right, as shown by the dashed line. Thus, at any point $P$, the instantaneous excess pressure $p_i$ varies as a sinusoidal function of time such that

$$p_i = p_m \sin \omega t \qquad \text{dynes per sq cm} \qquad (1)$$

where $\omega$ is $2\pi f$.

The velocity of propagation $c$ is relatively large, that is, approximately 150,000 cm (almost 1 mile) per sec; but this is not to be confused with the velocity of the water particles, which *on the average* are stationary and merely oscillate to-and-fro in the direction of wave

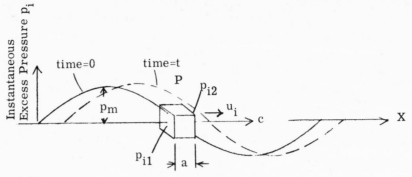

FIG. 1. Pressure relationships at an elementary cube that oscillates with particle velocity $u_i$.

travel, as successive crests and troughs of sound pressure pass the point $P$. Let each particle of water be represented by a little cube, having dimensions $a$ on a side, which moves to-and-fro with an instantaneous velocity $u_i$. Since the cube is $a$ cm long and the velocity of the wave is $c$ cm per sec, it is evident that the pressure reaches the front of the cube $a/2c$ sec prior to, and the back of the cube $a/2c$ sec after, arriving at the center. Thus, the instantaneous pressures $p_{i1}$ and $p_{i2}$ at the front and back of the cube, respectively, are

$$p_{i1} = p_m \sin (\omega t + \omega a/2c) \tag{2}$$

and
$$p_{i2} = p_m \sin (\omega t - \omega a/2c) \tag{3}$$

The force $F_i$ upon the cube is caused by the difference of pressures at both sides of the cube $(p_{i1} - p_{i2})$. This difference is readily obtained by expanding the right-hand sides of Eqs. (2) and (3) and subtracting:

$$p_{i1} - p_{i2} = 2(\sin \omega a/2c)p_m \cos \omega t \tag{4}$$

or, since $a$ can be chosen to be infinitesimally small (whereupon the sine equals the angle),

$$p_{i1} - p_{i2} = (\omega a/c)p_m \cos \omega t \tag{5}$$

$F_i$ is equal to the pressure difference times the area $a^2$; thus,

$$F_i = (\omega a^3/c)p_m \cos \omega t \tag{6}$$

The instantaneous velocity of the cube $u_i$ is opposed by its inertia reaction, $M\, du_i/dt$, where $M$ is the mass of the cube, $a^3\rho$. ($\rho$, the density of water, is under most circumstances close to 1 g per cc.) Assuming that the velocity has the form $u_i = u_m \sin \omega t$, where $u_m$ is the maximum particle velocity, $du_1/dt = \omega u_m \cos \omega t$, we find $u_m$ as follows. Equating the inertia reaction to the instantaneous force $F_i$, from Eq. (6),

$$(\omega a^3/c)p_m \cos \omega t = a^3 \rho \omega u_m \cos \omega t \qquad (7)$$

or
$$u_m = p_m/\rho c \qquad (8)$$

And finally, keeping in mind that pressures and velocities are generally denoted by their root-mean-square values ($p$ and $u$, respectively), which are obtained by dividing the maximum values by $\sqrt{2}$, we can rewrite Eq. (8) in its usual form,

$$u = p/\rho c \qquad (9)$$

Thus, it is seen that in a plane-progressive wave, the velocity is directly proportional to the pressure and inversely proportional to $\rho c$, which is known as the surge impedance of the medium. Since density $\rho = 1$, $\rho c$ underwater is approximately 150,000 in cgs units.

Whereas the velocity of propagation is very large, the particle velocity is very small indeed. For example, assuming a sound-presure wave of 100 dynes per sq cm, which corresponds to a rather intense sound, $u = 100/150,000 = 0.667 \times 10^{-3}$ cm per sec. The displacement amplitude corresponding to this velocity is equally minute. It is obtained by dividing the velocity amplitude by $2\pi f$. If the aforementioned wave has a frequency of 1000 Hz,† the displacement amplitude is $0.667 \times 10^{-3}/6280 = 0.106 \times 10^{-6}$ cm $= 10.6$ Å, or approximately 1/500 wavelength of green light. In the study of lateral line phenomena, we should keep in mind these extremely tiny displacement amplitudes.

It would seem, at first glance, that particle velocity can be measured by the simple expedient of measuring sound pressure with a conventional hydrophone and then dividing by the constant $\rho c$. This assumption is true only under the very special condition of a plane-progressive sound wave, which is seldom realized in practice. In experimental work we are most often dealing with nearby sound projectors, which produce a spreading sound wave, and with reflections from the surface of the water and the walls of the container. Therefore, the sound wave is neither plane nor progressive, and Eq. (9) is not applicable. If lateral line phenomena are dependent on particle velocity, then to study them in a meaningful manner we must find some way of measuring particle velocity directly.

† The newly adopted unit Hz (hertz) denotes frequency in cycles per second.

PRESSURE-GRADIENT HYDROPHONE

This brings us to the following quesions: what is a pressure-gradient hydrophone, and how does it measure particle velocity? These questions will be answered in connection with Fig. 2, where such a hydrophone is shown in schematic cross section.

At (1) is situated a piece of circular inner magnetic pole, and at (2) is a piece of circular outer magnetic pole. These are magnetized—for example, north and south, respectively—by means of an external magnet structure (not shown on the sketch), whereby a strong magnetic field $B$ is established. Between the pole pieces, in the air gap, is arranged a circular coil (3) that is free to move, with a winding of many turns of thin aluminum wire, having a total length of approximately 3000 cm. It will be recognized that the outer pole piece (2) forms a rigid circular baffle which the sound wave cannot penetrate but must go around, as indicated by the arrow (4). This defines a distance $d$ around the baffle, which is about equal to the hydrophone diameter. The corresponding pressure difference $(p_{i1} - p_{i2})$ can be derived approximately, by use of Eq. (5), but with $d$ in place of $a$. Thus,

$$p_{i1} - p_{i2} = (\omega d/c)p_m \cos \omega t \tag{10}$$

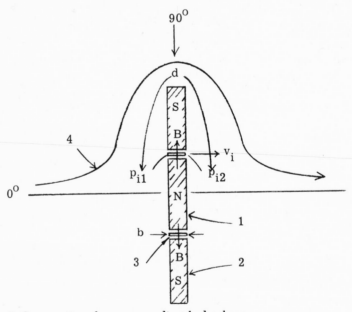

Fig. 2. Cross section of pressure-gradient hydrophone.

The force $F_i$ is found by multiplying the pressure difference by the projected coil area, $A$ sq cm; therefore,

$$F_i = (p_{i1} - p_{i2})A = (\omega d/c)p_m \cos \omega t \qquad (11)$$

To find the instantaneous velocity of the coil $v_i$, we proceed in a manner entirely analogous to that followed with the particle velocity. The instantaneous coil velocity $v_i$ is opposed by its inertia reaction $M \, dv_i/dt$, where $M$ is the mass of the coil.† If the coil is $b$ cm wide, then $M = Ab\rho_a$, where $\rho_a$ is the average density of the coil material. Assuming that the velocity of the coil is $v_m \sin \omega t$, where $v_m$ is the maximum velocity, $dv_i/dt = \omega v_m \cos \omega t$. Equating the inertia reaction to the instantaneous force from Eq. (11),

$$(\omega \, dA/c)p_m \cos \omega t = Ab\rho_a \omega v_m \cos \omega t \qquad (12)$$

or, solving for $v_m$:

$$v_m = (d/cb\rho_a)p_m \qquad (13)$$

To convert to rms velocity and pressure amplitudes, divide both sides by $\sqrt{2}$:

$$v = (d/cb\rho_a)p \qquad (14)$$

The voltage generated in a coil of wire with length $l$ cutting the lines of flux of density $B$ is known to be $Blv \times 10^{-8}$ V, where $l$ is the length of wire. Thus, the theoretical output voltage of the pressure-gradient hydrophone is

$$e = (Bld/cb\rho_a)p \times 10^{-8} \quad \text{V} \qquad (15)$$

Thus, high sensitivity is achieved by using high flux density, great wire length, and large baffle diameter and by designing the coil as light as practicable. There is a limit to the diameter, because the conditions for which Eq. (15) was derived no longer hold when the hydrophone dimensions approach the wavelength of sound. A practical hydrophone of this type has a 3-in. diameter and covers a frequency range extending to some 10,000 cps.

USE OF GRADIENT HYDROPHONES FOR MEASUREMENT
OF PARTICLE VELOCITY

Velocity is a vector quantity that has direction as well as amplitude, and the pressure-gradient hydrophone measures only that component of velocity which is parallel to its axis. This is clarified by the following considerations: Suppose that a sound wave travels in the direction of

† In reality there is an added term due to the reaction of the medium, which we neglect for the sake of simplicity.

the 90° arrow in Fig. 2. It is obvious that the pressures at both sides of the coil would be equal and opposite, whereupon the motion of the coil would be zero. It is readilly shown that the output of a gradient hydrophone varies as the cosine of the angle of incidence.

In measuring particle velocity in lateral line research, the investigator may not be sure in which direction the sound travels. One could, of course, arrange the hydrophone on a movable platform whereby it would be adjusted in two planes to maximize the output voltage. The magnitude and direction of particle velocity would then be determined. Such an arrangement is cumbersome to make and slow to use, but fortunately we can use the cosine-law directional property of pressure-gradient hydrophones to overcome this problem.

Since the component of particle velocity projected on the axis of the hydrophone follows the cosine law, we can arrange three hydrophones in orthogonal (or X, Y, and Z) directions, connecting each to a separate amplifier and meter and reading thereby the direction cosines of the particle velocity. Let the three output voltages from these hydrophones be $e_x$, $e_y$, and $e_z$, respectively. The three components of velocity are then $v_x = ke_x$, $v_y = ke_y$, and $v_z = ke_z$, respectively. The total velocity amplitude is

$$v = (v_x^2 + v_y^2 + v_z^2)^{1/2} = k(e_x^2 + e_y^2 + e_z^2)^{1/2} \tag{16}$$

The angle of the velocity vector is specified in terms of spherical coordinate angles $\theta$ and $\phi$, as follows:

$$\theta = \arctan (e_y/e_x) \tag{17}$$

and

$$\phi = \arctan (e_x^2 + e_y^2)^{1/2}/e_z \tag{18}$$

### CALIBRATION OF PRESSURE-GRADIENT HYDROPHONES

The method of calibrating pressure-gradient hydrophones is of interest for possible insight on how to generate waves of known particle velocity for lateral line research. The method used at CBS laboratories is to hang an extremely rigid tank with openings at the top on springs (Fig. 3). The tank is set into oscillation with a known velocity. The hydrophone to be calibrated is immersed in the tank, and its output voltage is measured with a voltmeter. The velocity is measured by means of an accelerometer and an integrating amplifier. It may be shown that, when the wavelengths are long compared with the dimensions of the tank, a plane standing wave is produced with a velocity related to the velocity of tank motion. However, the tank must be very rigid (our 1-cu-ft tank weighs 400 lb), very freely mounted,

F‌ɪɢ. 3. CBS Laboratories' pressure-gradient hydrophone calibrator.

and symmetrically driven. Because the motion is very small, a moderate driving power is required to produce respectable values of particle velocity. A description of the calibrator is given in Bauer and Torick (1966). This type of construction obviously is applicable only to small tanks.

REFERENCE

Bauer, B. B., and E. L. Torick (1966). Experimental studies in underwater directional communication. *J. Am. Acoust. Soc.* 39, 25-34.

LATERAL LINE DETECTORS (P. Cahn, ed.), 467–469, © 1967 Indiana University Press

# 28 UNDERWATER TELEMETRY †

R. Stuart Mackay

Division of Medical Physics
University of California
Berkeley, California
    and
Boston University and Boston University Medical School
Boston, Massachusetts

AND

Howard Baldwin

Sensory Systems Laboratory
Tucson, Arizona

Mackay: Telemetry methods are important because they allow the subject to be monitored in considerable detail without interfering with his normal pattern of activities. That is, they leave him in a relatively normal psychological and physiological state. For example, such techniques allow separate sensing of the motion and the pressure around a fish schooling in a normal fashion with his fellows. If the tail of the fish moves forward into a previous compression reflected from an adjacent fish, obviously the animal will feel a different sensation (in the lateral line or elsewhere) than if the motion is into a rarefaction. This may be the basis for the spacing of fish while schooling. To date, most of the experiments both on fish and on aquatic mammals have had to do either with temperature or with heart rate.

Telemetry under water can utilize either radio signals or acoustic signals to carry the information. I have described many of the details of both approaches elsewhere (1965, 1967a, 1967b).

In the case of aquatic mammals, I prefer to use radio transmission because of the wide frequency range of hearing in many of these ani-

† This short chapter is included to introduce the field of marine biotelemetry to those who may be unfamiliar with its enormous potential for studies in marine behavior and physiology. The two authors served on one of the panels at this conference, where more details, in discussion form, were presented. Much of this information can be obtained from the authors' publications.—*Editor*

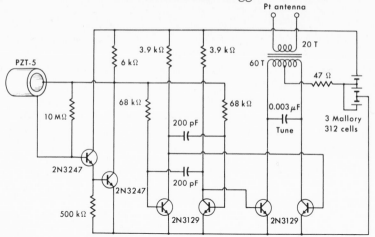

Fig. 1. Schematic diagram of circuit used for sensing relatively low-frequency sounds and converting them into a frequency-modulated radio signal.

mals. In a typical experiment a small radio transmitter, about half the size of one's finger, is swallowed by the animal. The radio signal is propagated out through the body of the animal and through the ocean water for a distance of about a dozen "skin depths." This latter quantity is the distance a signal goes while being attenuated to approximately one-third of its original value by shielding action; for ocean water, this is about 240 over the square root of the frequency, in meters. In shallow water, some signals may be picked up farther away because part of the transmitted signal will go straight up to the surface, where it will be refracted parallel to the surface and propagated a relatively long distance through the air. Various loop antennas or electrodes in the water can be used to pick up the signal and communicate it to a standard receiver. In general, my experiments of this type have been done with porpoises at frequencies in the range of 50 kc per sec, in a 7-ft-deep tank approximately 2500 sq ft in area.

Acoustic signals of this same frequency travel considerably farther, being detectable at ranges of anywhere from 500 ft to a mile. I have used this type of transmission in experiments on fish in large lakes. Acoustic transmission of information seems more appropriate in the case of fish because of their restricted frequency range of hearing.

In Fig. 1 is seen a diagram of a circuit used for sensing relatively low-frequency sounds and then converting them into a frequency-modulated radio signal radiated from the electrode pair. This unit has been tested in sensing the sound of the heartbeat of a freely swimming dolphin. With a slightly different output-transformer arrangement, the two electrodes could apply their signal to a piezoelectric cylinder, similar to the one shown for sensing the sounds, to transmit the signal acoustically rather than by radio. Such a unit could be considered for many other experiments: for example, it could be implanted in the skin of a fish to monitor the turbulent noise produced by a freely swimming animal. The size of such a unit typically is less than that of one's little finger.

Until shown otherwise, it appears desirable that the transmission of the information from the animal subject be undetectable by him, in order to be certain that the disturbance does not produce an abnormal situation. In this connection, my earlier comments on the possibility of a fish sensing a modulated 50-kc sound signal should be kept in mind.

BALDWIN: I am of the firm opinion that open ocean studies should be encouraged to learn more about fish physiology. I have designed several devices that have been found very useful for studying marine animal electrocardiograms and various other kinds of surface voltages. These devices have a range of about 1 mile and send either analog or digital signals that can be picked up very easily. References to some of this work can be found in Baldwin (1965).

REFERENCES

Baldwin, H. (1965). Marine biotelemetry, *BioScience* 15, 95.
Mackay, R. S. (1965). Telemetering from within the body of animals and man: endoradiosondes, in *Biomedical Telemetry* (C. Caceras, ed.). Academic Press, New York, pp. 147-235.
────── (1967a). *Bio-Medical Telemetry.* Wiley, New York.
────── (1967b). Telemetry and telestimulation, in *Methods in Psychophysiology* (C. Brown, ed.). Williams & Wilkins Co., Baltimore, Chap. 14.

# VII PANEL ON THE LATERAL LINE AND FISH BEHAVIOR

# 29 SUMMARY OF DISCUSSIONS

Phyllis H. Cahn

Department of Biology
Stern College
Yeshiva University
New York, New York
and
Graduate Department of Marine Science
Long Island University
Greenvale, New York

This panel was planned to enable the behavioral biologists to evaluate lateral line structure and function in relationship to fish behavior. The participants were, by design, those who had no direct experience with the lateral line system. It was not possible, nor was it rational, to include in the published version all the material of the discussions, since great candidness was encouraged. Special thanks are extended to all the people who served on this panel.

**Points of Agreement.** The behavior of an organism requires the integrated action of many sensory systems. Since the lateral line is present only in fishes and in the aquatic stages of amphibians, its function is presumably related to the aquatic environment. Many of the conference participants considered the lateral line to be biologically significant in current detection and in the reception of water movements produced by prey, predators, and other members of the species. There was general agreement on the dearth of conclusive behavioral studies on the lateral line. The difficulties involved in total extirpation of the ubiquitous series of neuromasts and nerve components contributed to this lack.

**Points of Disagreement.** There was major disagreement on the role of the lateral line in fish schooling behavior. Some of the panelists considered that the lateral line is needed as a significant accessory to vision in schooling orientation, especially under conditions of poor visibility. Others offered the opinion that the lateral line probably is not of direct importance in schooling behavior, but rather that acoustic and cutaneous cues predominate when darkness ensues. Resolution of this disagreement will depend on new and inventive approaches to this problem.

# 30 COMMENTS FROM PANELISTS

K. JOHN†: Some time ago I studied obstacle avoidance in characin blind cave fishes. It was determined that fish about 8 cm long could avoid obstacles at a mean distance of 3 mm (John, 1957). It appears thus that no stimulation of the specific sense organs involved in obstacle avoidance occurred until the obstacle was within very close range. What this means in terms of the sensory system involved is not very clear.

D. NELSON‡: It is very important to remember that the lateral line does not act alone in the natural response of a fish. The other sensory systems must be taken into consideration. In the underwater environment, visual cues may be difficult to detect at a distance. In the absence of a current, olfactory stimuli may diffuse at a very slow rate. Therefore a mechanoreceptor may be a more effective distance detector. Also, a detector that is directionally sensitive will be more useful to the organism than one that is not.

Directional hearing has not been definitively demonstrated in teleosts, except when they are very close to the sound source. In elasmobranchs, however, we have found evidence for directional hearing in both the near and far field (Nelson, 1966)—that is, at low frequencies in the far field. The major structural difference of importance in this regard is the absence of a gas bladder in elasmobranchs, although there are some teleosts that also lack this structure.

Let us consider what happens when a sound of 100 cps and 1 $\mu$bar of acoustic pressure reaches the fish. In addition to the 1 $\mu$bar of pressure, 1 Å of far-field displacement also gets to the fish. The gas bladder of the fish responds in such a way that its radius is changed, so that if we are dealing with a gas bladder of 1 cm radius, under a pressure of 1 $\mu$bar it will change by about 30 Å. These swim-bladder vibrations of 30 Å displacement will probably mask the 1-Å displacements arriving directly from the source, at any of the fishes mechanoreceptors, thereby denying the fish directional information. Thus it appears that, for fish with swim bladders, the only way they will be able to detect direction-

† Kenneth John, Department of Biology, Franklin and Marshall College, Lancaster, Pennsylvania.

‡ Donald Nelson, Department of Biology, California State College, Long Beach, California.

ally is when they are very close to the source of vibration, so that the displacements coming directly from the source are greater than those coming from the swim bladder. This condition will probably occur only when the fish are well within the near field.

In an elasmobranch, without the swim bladder, pressure does not seem to cause any kind of conversion to displacement. Whatever the animal detects as displacement must be coming straight from the source. The displacements will arrive at one point on the body ahead of their arrival at another point. If there is present a suitable array of mechanoreceptors, then these may function for directional detection.

In our studies on sharks in an open-water environment, we have found that they are directionally sensitive to a frequency of 20 to 60 cps at a distance of about 200 m when they are at a depth of about 25 ft. Although the sharks were well within the far field at this frequency (according to the formulas of Harris and van Bergeijk), the displacement was of considerable magnitude, such as about 15 Å.

In regard to the lateral line, in a teleost with a swim bladder you might expect that, as the animal went deeper into the ocean, this sensory system would assume increased importance in directional detection. That is, at increased depths, where the hydrostatic pressure causes an increase in density of swim-bladder gas, the swim-bladder displacement would be reduced, so that the lateral line neuromasts would be subject to less masking.

J. MOULTON[†]: Recent studies of mine have given evidence of a directional hearing mechanism in teleosts (Moulton, 1967). This mechanism is related to the function of the Mauthner's neurons in the fish medulla. The familiar tail-flip response of fish to acoustic stimuli can be extinguished by cutting the saccular branch of the auditory nerve.

One of the places that the lateral line system seems to operate with a good deal of significance at the behavioral level is that of schooling. This has not been directly demonstrated, chiefly because it has not been possible to eliminate the lateral line on the head of any schooling fishes. Many of us have made extensive field observations that have suggested the importance of the lateral line in schooling. For example, we have observed that during the day anchovies may break up into smaller schools but that at night these smaller schools again come together into larger groups.

G. WILLIAMS[‡]: I do not believe that the lateral line is important in

[†] James Moulton, Department of Biology, Bowdoin College, Brunswick, Maine.

[‡] George Williams, Department of Biology, State University of New York, Stony Brook, New York.

schooling behavior. A number of people, including myself, have advanced the theory (Williams, 1964) that schooling behavior represents an aspect of predator avoidance. If there is a small fish out in the middle of the ocean, and there exists the possibility that a large predatory fish will appear, a good place for the small fish to be is nearby other small fish. I look upon schooling as the fish's means of ensuring that there is always at least one other fish between himself and the source of danger. Schooling disappears at night because it's no longer adaptive at night. The kind of predation that occurs during the day, when big fish chase small fish and when the prey are visually localized, disappears at night.

H. WINN†: We know from our experiments on fish sound production and hearing (Winn, 1964) that toadfish, for example, will respond when they are 20 ft or more away from the sound source, and for the frequencies we are concerned with this is considered the far field. This type of reaction does not involve the lateral line. Toadfish, in fact, appear to space themselves from each other on the basis of the maintenance of a certain distance from the other sound-emitting toadfish. Sound production thus becomes a force involved in the regulation of fish-fish spacing.

REFERENCES

John, K. (1957). Observations on the behavior of blind and blinded fishes. *Copeia* 2, 123-132.
Moulton, J. (1967). *Marine Bio-Acoustics* II (W. N. Tavolga, ed.). Pergamon Press, Oxford.
Nelson, D. (1966). Hearing and acoustic orientation in the lemon shark, *Negaprion brevirostris* (Poey), and other large sharks. Ph.D. Thesis, Univ. Miami. *Dissertation Abstr.* 27(1), 333B.
Williams, G. (1964). Measurement of consociation among fishes and comments on the evolution of schooling. *Publ. Museum Michigan State Univ. Biol. Ser.* 2, 349-384.
Winn, H. (1964). The biological significance of fish sounds, in *Marine Bio-Acoustics* (W. N. Tavolga, ed.). Pergamon Press, Oxford, pp. 213-231.

† Howard Winn, Narragansett Marine Laboratory and Graduate School of Oceanography, University of Rhode Island, Kingston, Rhode Island.

LATERAL LINE DETECTORS (P. Cahn, ed.), 479–480, © 1967 Indiana University Press

# 31 COMMENTS
# FROM PANEL CHAIRMAN

EVELYN SHAW

Department of Animal Behavior
American Museum of Natural History
New York, New York

We have studied the lateral line in detail, from its gross anatomy, to its submicroscopic parts, to its neurophysiology. We know much about the anatomy of the nerves, their sensitivity thresholds, the anatomy of the neuromasts and their associated hair cells, and their possible functional capacity. Yet, on a behavioral basis, we have little conclusive evidence on how the lateral line functions to inform the animal that some change has occurred in the water environment. In fact, to precisely what aspects in the environment is it sensitive? Some experiments indicate that the sense organs are sensitive to small water displacements and/or low-frequency vibrations. This may well be the principal function; but once the fish has been stimulated, how does the information affect its behavior?

A fish can do three things when it receives a stimulus. It can approach, or swim toward, the stimulus; it can move away from the stimulus; or it can show no motor activity at all. The generalization that the lateral line is sensitive to small water displacements is broad, and should not be used to infer what the sensitivity means in terms of motor activity. For example, one kind or volume of displacement can be considered a stimulus of moderate or low intensity, with the result that the fish approaches in the direction of the stimulus, whereas another volume of displacement can be considered a stimulus of high intensity, with a resultant withdrawal of the fish. In addition, responses to the stimuli may be determined by many factors, such as early previous and immediately previous experiences, plus biological propensities. Dependent upon these experiential, environmental, and biological influences, the magnitude of the displacement changes may be the critical aspects of the fish's response to water displacement.

Another problem yet to be solved is how the information from the lateral line system operates in conjunction with the visual system. One of the dangers is in the assumption that sensitivity to water displacement is the only way that fish find prey and escape from predators. But fish are equipped with good visual systems and can find prey and see predators when they are sufficiently close to be a threat. Perhaps, then, the lateral line system is used along with the visual system to provide the fine details of pinpointing a morsel of food when it is too close to be seen, acutely, with the eyes.

LATERAL LINE DETECTORS (P. Cahn, ed.), 481–483, © 1967 Indiana University Press

# 32 RELATION OF THE LATERAL LINE TO COMMUNICATION IN FISHES AND THE GENERAL PROBLEM OF ANIMAL COMMUNICATION

WILLIAM TAVOLGA

Department of Animal Behavior
American Museum of Natural History
New York, New York

When considering the function of the lateral line in fish behavior, it is important to distinguish between the lateral line neuromast organs and the lateral line system as a whole. It must be remembered that we are dealing with two different levels of organization. We can study how the neuromast organ itself functions, how the cupula is displaced, and can measure the resultant microphonic potentials. We can try to determine what is the most adequate stimulus for the particular organ. This tells us very little, however, about how the lateral line system as an integrated unit functions, or how the sensory information is integrated in order to result in an adaptive response on the part of the organism.

When we talk about the various kinds of thresholds of the lateral line, we must keep in mind the different threshold levels for the separate organs and for the total system. Then we must consider the threshold of the system in relation to the other sensory systems of the animal and examine the relative importance of each system in the total behavior of the organism.

Most animals influence each other's behavior by visual, acoustic, olfactory, chemical, or other means. Some of these interactions have been called "communication." It is difficult to define what is meant by communication. In a recent book on animal communication (Frings and Frings, 1964), the authors stated: "Communication between animals involves the giving off by one individual of some chemical or physical signal that, on being received by another, influences behavior." Setting certain limits on this definition, they stated further:

"The sender must utilize some specialized structure in the production of the stimulus, and both the sender and the receiver must be members of the same species." It is easy to see how one can stray from these limits and still fall within the framework of communication. For example, how do we define a specialized structure? There exists thus a vast variety of animal interactions, and there is no real theoretical framework within which we can place and relate them.

We can try to group the stimuli that impinge on an organism in the following way, depending on their source: the stimuli from the physical environment, such as light, temperature, and salinity; and the biological stimuli from other organisms, both plants and animals, and from individuals of the same and of other species. This brings up the question of whether the effect of an organism on its physical environment is communicated to other organisms. If it is, this greatly broadens the definition of communication.

It is my opinion that communication does not exist as a single phenomenon but involves many different levels of interactions on the part of the organisms. Three fundamental elements must be present: the emitting organism, giving out some form of energy into the environment; the stimulus, which is essentially the energy output of the emitter; and the receiving organism, which consists of any organism capable, by virtue of its sensory equipment, to receive the energy change.

The stimulus involved in the communication can be photic, thermal, mechanical, chemical, or electrical. Thus the receiving sense organs can be visual, tactile, acoustic, and other mechanoreceptors, and chemo- and electroreceptors. In many instances, it is probable that the stimulus or signal involves more than one form of energy. The energy output, of course, must be sufficiently intense in relation to the background noise and the self-noise for a communicatory event to take place.

When referring to signals or signs, however, we usually imply a more specialized form of emitter output, in which there is usually a single form of energy, and only a narrow portion of its spectrum is involved. This is true in the production of a specific chemical odor or of a sound of specific frequency and duration. At higher levels of communication, signals can often be patterned, such as in the songs of birds.

I'd like to offer a tentative scheme for the classification of levels of interaction in organisms. These levels are not clearly and irrevocably separable, but nor are they artificial. We can call the simplest level "vegetative." That is, an organism is an emitter simply by its very being, so that its physical presence can affect the behavior of other organisms. The next level can be called "tonic"—an expanded form of

Schneirla's (1965) use of the term—to include such energy outputs that result from the regular physiological and behavioral activities of organisms. For example, this can include chemical exudates or loco-motor patterns; among protozoa and primitive metazoa, virtually all interactions are on this level. Finally, there are the so-called "phasic" levels (Schneirla, 1965), those which involve some specialization on the part of the emitter and which can thus be considered higher levels of interaction. We can include echo- and electrolocation in this category.

Getting back to the lateral line, it appears that structurally and functionally it is mostly concerned with what goes on at the tonic level, with some involvement at the phasic level. The lateral line system, as a more primitive system than the acoustic, is one that seems to be involved with such basic activities of the fish as swimming and with the gross detection of obstacles. We can thus say that, on a primi-tive level of integration, the lateral line is involved in communication in fishes.

REFERENCES

Frings, H., and M. Frings (1964). *Animal Communication*. The Blaisdell Company, Philadelphia.
Schneirla, T. (1965). Aspects of stimulation and organization in approach-with-drawal processes underlying vertebrate behavior development, in *Advances in the Study of Behavior* (D. Lehrman, R. Hinde, and E. Shaw, eds.). Academic Press, New York, pp. 1-74.

LATERAL LINE DETECTORS (P. Cahn, ed.), 485, © 1967 Indiana University Press

# CONCLUDING REMARKS

PHYLLIS H. CAHN

When I first became interested in this sensory system, and was confronted by the vast literature on the various aspects of lateral line function, my thoughts were that the performance of the system must be well known. When it then became apparent that study of the lateral line remained a great challenge, I entered the field and was faced with one unanswered question after another. I discovered that many others who were working on this system were equally perplexed. This led to the organization of this conference.

Now that the conference and this publication are completed, we can earnestly conclude that it performed a valuable purpose. Primarily, it showed how little we know and how much work is left in order to unravel the role of the lateral line in the integrated, adapting, dynamic organism. The questions that have been partly answered are mainly those concerning the structure and action of the neuromast end organ and its associated ultrastructural components. How the lateral line system, as a member of a hierarchy of sensory systems, transmits, masks, is inhibited by, or augments the other body senses has yet to be determined.

# INDEX